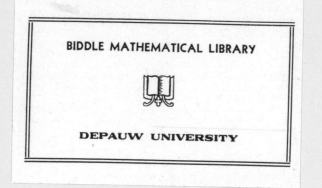

METHODS OF
STATISTICAL ANALYSIS

METHODS OF
STATISTICAL ANALYSIS

BY

C. H. GOULDEN

Senior Agricultural Scientist, Dominion Rust Research Laboratory
Honorary Lecturer in Statistics, University of Manitoba
Winnipeg, Manitoba

NEW YORK

JOHN WILEY & SONS, Inc.

London: CHAPMAN & HALL, Limited

1939

A 20 my 41 2-68 Biddle Ed

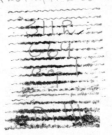

PRINTED IN U. S. A.

PRESS OF
BRAUNWORTH & CO., INC.
BUILDERS OF BOOKS
BRIDGEPORT, CONN.

PREFACE

From several years' experience in teaching classes in statistics and giving advice at various times to experimentalists, I have come to the conclusion that there is a distinct need for more than one type of textbook. On the one hand there are many who are interested only in knowing something of the theory and principles. In this class we find students who are endeavoring to obtain a broad knowledge of all subjects related to science and art, practicing technicians such as doctors of medicine and technical advisers in agriculture, and administrators of research activities. It would be idle to set students of this type to work on laborious practical examples. It would probably discourage them at the start, and by absorbing time would reduce the possibility of teaching them some of the very attractive philosophical phases of the subject. In a maze of calculations the principles might be lost sight of completely, and the student would emerge with a technique for mechanical operations and no ability to solve actual problems. At the beginning it is not training in actual methods that is required, but the building up of a sound knowledge of fundamental principles.

On the other hand, we have an increasing number of students who, having had some elementary training in statistics and some experience in research work, come to the point finally of requiring a practical knowledge of methods of analysis and some facility in the devices of calculation. There is no denying the fact that two or three years spent in studying the principles and theory of statistics will not fit the student to solve practical problems. To do so is to ignore the many complications that are involved and that training in facility is necessary in order that statistical computations may be attacked with determination and completed in a reasonable length of time. One of the objections very often raised to the use of statistical methods is the time necessary to do the routine work. Frequently this sort of thing can be attributed to insufficient training in the actual methods that should be employed and a lack of organization of the work.

The basis of this book, therefore, is the supplying of a textbook in statistics for students who have passed the elementary stage; who have studied a fair amount of theory and principles and now wish to equip themselves for actual statistical work in their own field of research activities. The experiment station agronomist, the cereal chemist, the plant breeder, and the economic entomologist are all examples of research workers who require a practical knowledge of statistical methods, and undoubtedly there are many others in the same class. It has been my experience that to acquire this knowledge the student must work through a comprehensive series of actual examples, and these should not be miniature examples as they are likely to give him a wrong impression of what will actually be required of him at a later date. Most of the various examples and exercises in this book are therefore of actual size, but every effort has been made to keep them within such limits as will enable the student to work through a representative set in one academic year.

This is not to say that a course in statistical methods should ever be given without emphasis on principles, and this applies particularly to the principles of experimental design. When studying practical methods, the opportunity is prime for the student to acquire a solid grounding in this important phase of the subject. The discussions in the greater part of the book, therefore, are worked out so that they have a direct bearing on the principles of the design of experiments. The first half, for example, while containing material that involves a repetition of elementary work that has already been covered, is nevertheless written so that, in reviewing, the student is brought into contact immediately with the structure of actual experiments. Also in this portion of the book are certain routine calculations which are designed mainly to give the student some facility in calculation before he comes to the heavier problems in the latter part.

There are many to whom I owe thanks in the preparation of this book, but in the first place I must acknowledge a very great debt to Professor R. A. Fisher, who has been mainly responsible for the development of the methods that are set forth. Furthermore, he has been very generous of his own time in explaining how new problems may be solved and in clearing up doubts as to the exact application of previously established methods. I wish also to thank the staff of the Statistical Laboratory at Ames, Iowa, for advice and suggestions, especially Dr. G. W. Snedecor, who in addition has given me permission to use, wholly or in part, any of the tables or material in his excellent new textbook, "Statistical Methods." Thanks are due to many who have called attention to errors in the preprint edition, and to ways in which the explanations and examples could be improved. This applies particularly to my students, who have taken a special interest in suggesting improvements of this kind. They have also taken a particular interest in checking the calculations in order that the book should be as nearly perfect as possible in this respect. In typing the manuscript I must acknowledge the untiring assistance of Misses E. J. Stewart and M. G. White.

C. H. GOULDEN.

February, 1939.

CONTENTS

METHODS OF STATISTICAL ANALYSIS

CHAPTER I

INTRODUCTION

1. The Logic of Statistical Methods. Applying statistical methods to experimental work involves the use of certain logical ideas *appropriate to experimental procedure.* The problems of statistics are, therefore, not entirely mathematical problems; in fact they are very largely problems based on the technique and requirements of the research worker. This important point has not always been clearly understood and hence we find, in the history of the development of statistical methods, various attempts to solve the problems of the experimentalist by the application of purely mathematical methods of reasoning and derivation. Thus we find prodigious attempts being made to apply the method of inverse probability to the testing of the significance of results obtained in experiments. This theory has to do with the evaluation of the probability of the occurrence of certain specified events on the basis of what has happened in some previous event. For example, if 8 balls are drawn from an urn containing black and white balls, and are found to consist of 3 white and 5 black balls; to derive from this result an exact statement of the probability of obtaining a white ball in drawing another single ball is a problem in inverse probability. Everyone will agree that, on the basis of the ratio of white to black balls in the sample drawn, in drawing another ball one's expectation tends towards black, but very few will agree that this expectation can be put in the form of an exact statement of mathematical probability. On first thought, one might be inclined to think that this type of problem is the same as the statistical one of taking samples and reasoning from these samples to the populations from which they were drawn. We shall see, however, that there is a very essential difference between the two situations; that to regard these two situations as the same is merely to misunderstand the true nature of the methods of obtaining new information by experimental methods. To illustrate these points in further detail we shall follow through the procedure of operating a very simple experiment, in which the statistical method will arise as a natural consequence of the efforts of the investigator to get the most out of his experiment.

2. A Simple Experiment in Identifying Varieties of Wheat. This hypothetical experiment is modelled after the famous tea-tasting experiment described by R. A. Fisher (1), but in some respects the procedure is simplified. Fisher's hypothetical experiment will undoubtedly remain as a classic in statistical literature, and after following through the experiment described here the student will do well to make a similar study of the tea-tasting experiment as it discusses certain aspects of this type of problem that cannot be presented here.

A wheat expert claims that, if he is presented with grain samples of two particular varieties which we shall designate as A and B, he can distinguish between them. He does not claim the ability to identify either one of the varieties, if they are presented to him separately, and further there is no special mention of an ability to differentiate between these samples at all times and under all conditions with perfect accuracy. The claim is for a certain power of differentiation, and we must proceed in the planning of the experiment accordingly; that is, we must plan the experiment in such a way that any reasonable power of differentiation possessed by the operator will be demonstrated. With this knowledge we can proceed to set up the experiment.

It will be obvious with a little study that, in order to plan the experiment correctly, it will be necessary to anticipate the possible results. Suppose that we presented the operator with only one pair of samples and he classified them correctly. Without any knowledge whatever of wheat varieties he could, by pure guesswork, name the varieties correctly in 50 per cent of the cases. This follows from the fact that there are only 2 ways of classifying them, and if the operator has no power of differentiating them, these 2 ways are equally likely. Thus in about half of the cases he would place them correctly, and in the remainder of the cases incorrectly. Our conclusion must be that 1 pair of samples would not be sufficient to produce a clear-cut result, regardless of the efficiency or the inefficiency of the operator. What will be the effect of increasing the number of pairs of samples? Obviously, the operator would be much more unlikely to place several pairs of samples correctly than he would just 1 pair. Can this statement be put in more definite terms? Let us assume that 6 pairs are being used and see if we can calculate the probability of a correct result, or, in other words, the proportion of the cases in which the operator, without any power of differentiation of the samples, could be expected to reach a correct placing. If there are 6 pairs of samples, each pair may be placed either rightly or wrongly, so that there are just 7 different kinds of results. These are: 6 right, 5 right, 4 right, 3 right, 2 right, 1 right, and none right. The pairs may be thought of as being presented to the operator one at a time, so there are 2 ways of placing the first pair (right or wrong), 2 ways of placing the second pair, and so forth for all the pairs. Each result for a pair may occur with either result for another pair, so that for 2 pairs we would have 2×2 possible combinations of placings. These are: both right; first pair right and second pair wrong; second pair right and first pair wrong; and both wrong. Continuing with this reasoning, it turns out that for 3 pairs the possible number of combinations of placings is $2 \times 2 \times 2$; and, finally, for 6 pairs the total number is $2^6 = 64$. If now the operator places all 6 pairs of samples correctly, we are in a position to place an evaluation on this result. There is only 1 way of placing all pairs correctly, so that if the operator has no knowledge whatever of wheat varieties he would be expected to place them correctly in only 1 out of 64 trials. This would be a rather odd chance, and we would therefore be inclined, in the event of a successful placing, to attribute it to the ability of the operator in differentiating the varieties. Another way to regard this is to consider the consequences of adopting as a standard, in the examination of a large number of operators, that all pairs must be placed correctly. Then in 1 out of 64 cases we could be expected to attribute to the operator a power of differentiating the varieties that he did not actually possess. This would seem to be a fairly safe standard. In fact it would undoubtedly be argued from the standpoint of the operators being tested that the standard was much too high. In general practice, it is usual to adopt a ratio of 1/20 as an arbitrary level for discriminating between real and chance effects. That is, an event is not regarded as significant unless it would only occur by chance variation in not more than 1 out of 20 trials.

We now have to consider the interpretation that would be made if the operator were to obtain such a result as 5 pairs right and 1 pair wrong. In the above case there was only 1 way of placing 6 of the pairs correctly, but the situation is different now in that any one of the 6 pairs may be the one that is incorrectly placed, making a total of 6 ways, out of the grand total of 64, in which the samples may be placed 5 right and 1 wrong. Then, in considering the experiment from the standpoint of the possibility of its indicating a power of differentiation on the part of the operator, we must also take into consideration the number of ways of placing 6 pairs correctly. That is, we must enumerate the number of ways in which the operator can place 5 pairs of samples correctly, or any other result more favorable to his claim. This makes a total of $1 + 6 = 7$ out of 64 ways in which such a result or one more favorable to the operator could occur, and if the operator has no power of differentiation this result will be expected to occur in just that proportion of the cases. In approximate figures the ratio 7/64 is equal to

1/9; and we note that this is larger than the ratio 1/20, which, as pointed out above, is accepted as a general level of significance. To accept the ratio of 1/9 as indicating a power of differentiation would be to take the risk of being wrong in 1 out of 9 similar trials, and this would probably be too great a risk for most investigators to accept. It might, however, be taken as a sufficient indication to justify further experimentation.

It will be found convenient, in experiments of this type, to set up in the form of a table all the possible results with the corresponding number of ways in which each can occur. Another column of the table may be used to show the ratio that we have taken above to indicate the significance of each result. The figures for this experiment are given in Table 1. Why do we not give more values in the third column?

TABLE 1

POSSIBLE RESULTS, NUMBER OF COMBINATIONS, AND RATIO OF SIGNIFICANCE, FOR A SIMPLE EXPERIMENT IN DIFFERENTIATING SIX PAIRS OF SAMPLES

Possible Results	No. of Combinations	Ratio of Significance
6 right 0 wrong	1	1/64
5 " 1 "	6	7/64
4 " 2 "	15	22/64
3 " 3 "	20	
2 " 4 "	15	
1 " 5 "	6	
0 " 6 "	1	
Total.........	64	

The procedure in this simple experiment may now appear to be quite clear and apparently straightforward in every respect. The reader will then be surprised to learn that we have been guilty of a very serious omission. We have said that, if the operator has actually no power of differentiation, the 64 ways of arranging the pairs are all equally likely to occur. Suppose now that the samples are presented to the operator in pairs with variety A to his left hand and variety B to his right hand. On the off chance that there may be such a systematic arrangement of the pairs, the operator decides to guess this order and then adhere to it throughout the experiment. The result is that the most probable arrangements are 6 right, or 6 wrong, and our theory as to the probable frequency of the different possible results is completely broken down. Another possibility that we have omitted to consider so far is that the 2 samples may show differences as to weight or quality which are actually quite independent of the variety characteristics. Here again the operator may, by guessing, obtain a result that is either all wrong or all right. We could go on and point out a number of factors that would tend to upset our calculations, and in the end the reader might despair as to the possibility of carrying through any experiment that would lead to valid conclusions. Why not take into consideration such factors as we have mentioned and work out the theoretical frequencies of the different combinations accordingly? A little thought will show that this is quite impossible. The vagaries of the minds of operators, for example, in taking advantage of certain orderly arrangements of the pairs, would be quite beyond the possibility of definite enumeration. The situation is not hopeless, however, as there is always at hand an extremely powerful method of overcoming this difficulty. The method is to arrange all factors that may enter into the results, completely at random. Thus, in presenting the pairs to the operator, a random arrangement would be followed that would be determined beforehand by throwing coins, drawing cards, or from a book of random numbers. It could then be stated with absolute confidence that, on the hypothesis that the operator has no knowledge of differentiating the samples, all possible arrangements would be equally likely to occur. It would be possible, for example, to use different colors of trays as containers for the samples. In each pair 1 tray might be red and 1 blue, and, if the varieties are assigned to the trays at random, it will still be true that all possible arrangements are equally likely. Of course a word of caution is needed here. Different colored trays, or any other disturbing influence on the ability of the operator to differentiate the samples, are not recommended, as they tend to reduce the efficiency of the test; but at the same time if such factors are properly randomized they do not affect the validity of the test of significance.

3. **Defining Some Statistical Terms.** In describing our simple experiment, statistical terms were avoided as much as possible. Such terms are, however, a kind of shorthand and will be found very convenient as we proceed to the consideration of more intricate problems. The 6 pairs of samples of grain constitute in themselves a *sample* in the true statistical sense. We were not particularly interested in what the operator did with the 6 pairs except in so far as it indicated his ability to differentiate the varieties in general. In other words, we were trying to obtain an estimate of what would happen if he were presented with a very large group of such pairs. This large group containing an indefinite number of pairs might be said to constitute the *population* that we are

sampling. The general problem of statistics, therefore, is the *estimation* of values for populations by means of determinations made on samples drawn at *random* from these populations. Assuming that the final result of our experiment was 5 pairs of samples placed correctly, the best estimate we would have for what our operator might do with a very large sample is that he would place $\frac{5}{6}$ of the pairs correctly. This value is the *mean* number of successful placings that the operator would make in a population of similar pairs. A value such as this, calculated from a sample, is said to be a *statistic*. The population value of which the statistic is an estimate is referred to as a *parameter*. Statistics are subject to variability in that we will get different results with different samples. The populations sampled are regarded for convenience as being infinite; and therefore for any one *variable*, such as the number of successful placings, there is only 1 value of the parameter.

In all experiments there is a hypothesis to be tested. It will have been noted that in the description of the simple experiment we repeatedly used the words "if the operator has no power of differentiation." This points to the fact that the hypothesis we were testing was just that. In statistical parlance our hypothesis is now, owing to the pertinent suggestion of Professor Fisher (1), referred to as the *null hypothesis*. This null hypothesis was the basis for the calculation of the number of ways out of the total that certain results would be obtained, it being assumed, owing to *randomization* of the experiment, that all the possible ways were equally likely.

4. Summary of Principles. We have now worked through an actual experiment, which, although it was extremely simple, has introduced us to the main principles of the statistical method and has allowed us to obtain an easy introduction to many of the common statistical terms. It will be convenient after this discussion to return to some of the generalizations of Section 1.

It will have been noted that the logic employed in tests of significance is clearly that of the experimentalist. This is true whether or not the experimenter has any knowledge of mathematics. Always, if he is critical of his results, he asks himself whether or not they could have arisen as a chance variation, and on this basis arrives at some conclusion as to their significance. The statistical method, therefore, does not introduce anything new in this sense, but merely supplies him with the technique for planning his experiment so that it is justifiable to ask such a question, and then furnishes him with a method of measuring the confidence to be placed in the findings.

The results from one sample are not used to obtain a statement as to the probability of obtaining a given result in drawing another sample, but they are used to obtain an estimate of the population from which the sample was drawn.

A test of significance is, essentially, the use of the data provided by the sample to test any hypothesis that may be set up. In such tests we do not always realize that a hypothesis is involved, but nevertheless this is true. When we ask the question, "Is my result due to some real effect or to a chance variation?" we can answer this question only by setting up the hypothesis that there is no effect, and determining whether or not the results agree or disagree with the hypothesis.

The mathematical derivations involved in statistical tests arise from attempts to state the proportion of cases, according to a given hypothesis, in which the results obtained will occur. Thus, in the experiment described above, the hypothesis was that the operator had no power of differentiating the varieties; and on this basis we inquired as to the proportion of cases in which a result of 6 right would occur. The order in which the samples were presented having been randomized, it was possible to state that all placings were equally likely; and hence we were able to derive by strictly mathematical methods the proportion of cases in which a given placing would occur.

5. The Functions of Statistical Analysis. The chief functions of statistical analysis as applied to experimental procedure may now be enumerated as follows:

(a) To provide a sound basis for the formulation of experimental designs.

(b) To provide methods for making tests of significance and trustworthy estimations of the magnitude of the effects indicated by the results.

(c) To provide adequate methods for the reduction of data.

The discussion of the previous sections will have given a reasonably clear picture of the manner in which the principles of statistics are made use of in designing experiments. Since this is the most recent development in this field, it is natural that it is with respect to experimental design that the beginner is most likely to err. Frequently an elementary knowledge of statistics, consisting merely of an outline of the facts of variability and the various methods of measuring this variability, is taken as a sufficient knowledge for applying statistical methods to experimental work. The results of this practice are often disastrous. It is the reason why the consulting statistician is frequently presented with a set of data collected from an experiment which has been very badly designed. At the best, in such an experiment, there will be a loss of precision and information; but in addition there may be a decided bias in the results and as a consequence the whole or at least a part of the data may have to be discarded. It is not exaggeration, therefore, to state that to the experimentalist a study of statistical methods is futile unless he endeavors to apply these methods not only to the analysis of data but also to the structure of proposed experiments.

The necessity for tests of significance has already been dealt with, but very little emphasis in the above discussion was placed on methods of estimation. It was pointed out, however, in the hypothetical example, that, if the operator's result was 5 right placings out of a possible 6, this would have to be taken as the best estimate available of the proportion of correct placings the operator could be expected to make if presented with a large series of samples. Obviously the experiment was so small that this may not be very close to the proportion that the operator would actually accomplish, and hence in this respect the experiment was not sufficiently extensive. The methods of statistics are concerned very vitally, therefore, with methods of estimation; and here again we cannot avoid noting the importance of experimental design, in that by careful design we can very largely determine beforehand the accuracy with which a particular estimate can be made.

The necessity for the reduction of data is perfectly obvious, but it may not be clear as to the various methods employed in statistics for bringing this about. It is impossible to list these here, but we can classify them into three general groups: viz., *tables*, *graphs*, and *statistics*. The tables are usually prepared first, and from these we draw graphs to illustrate the main features of the data, and calculate statistics. The statistics are single expressions such as the mean or average which express the general characteristics of the samples studied.

REFERENCE

1. R. A. FISHER. The Design of Experiments. Oliver and Boyd, London and Edinburgh, 1937.

CHAPTER II

THE ARITHMETIC MEAN AND STANDARD DEVIATION—
FREQUENCY TABLES AND THEIR PREPARATION

1. The Arithmetic Mean. This is our first example of a *statistic*. It is called a statistic because we regard it in statistical practice as a value calculated from a sample, and an estimate of the mean of the population from which the sample was drawn. Values for the means of samples will be expected to vary from sample to sample, and are therefore not essentially different from individual variates in that respect. It is for this reason that it is not consistent terminology to speak of the mean or any other statistic calculated from a sample as a *constant*. The only constant values in statistical theory and practice are the values representing the infinite populations from which the samples are drawn. These, as we shall see later, are usually referred to in modern statistical literature as *parameters*.

It is often said of the arithmetic mean that it is the best single value that can be applied to the sample as a whole. Thus we find that the agronomist refers to the average yield of a variety, and not to the individual yields of a series of plots. Many other instances of this kind could be cited; in fact, it is an everyday usage and needs no further explanation.

For a sample of N variates where x_i represents any one variate, the mean $\bar{x}$ is given by:

$$\bar{x} = \frac{x_1 + x_2 + x_3 + \cdots + x_i + \cdots + x_n}{N}$$

which for the sake of abbreviation is written:

$$\bar{x} = \frac{\Sigma(x)}{N} \tag{1}$$

If the values for three variates are 6, 8, and 1, the mean is obviously:

$$\frac{6 + 8 + 1}{3} = \frac{15}{3} = 5$$

Using the short formula means simply that the summation of the three quantities is understood, and, instead of writing out all the values and connecting them with plus signs, we merely write $15/3 = 5$. According to strict mathematical usage, $\Sigma(x)$ should be written $\overset{N}{\underset{1}{\Sigma}}(x)$, to show that N values are summated, but the simpler form may be used when the number of summations is obvious.

One of the most interesting properties of the mean is that the sum of the deviations of all the individual variates from the mean is zero. Again representing an individual variate by x_i, an individual deviation from the mean will be $(x_i - \bar{x})$. Then summing all these we get:

$$\Sigma(x - \bar{x}) = (x_1 - \bar{x}) + (x_2 - \bar{x}) + \ldots + (x_n - \bar{x})$$

$$= (x_1 + x_2 + \ldots + x_n) - N\bar{x}$$

And since

$$N\bar{x} = \frac{N(x_1 + x_2 + \ldots + x_n)}{N}$$

It is clear that

$$\Sigma(x - \bar{x}) = 0$$

Using the summation sign to shorten the algebra we would have

$$\Sigma(x - \bar{x}) = \Sigma(x) - \Sigma(\bar{x}) = \Sigma(x) - N\bar{x}$$

And since

$$N\bar{x} = \frac{N\Sigma(x)}{N}$$

It is again clear that

$$\Sigma(x - \bar{x}) = 0$$

2. The Standard Deviation. In using the mean of a sample to represent the sample as a whole, it must occur to us that the reliability of this method will depend on the degree of variation among the individual variates that make up the sample. If there is no variation the mean would represent the whole set perfectly; but as the variation becomes greater the single value of the mean is less and less descriptive of the entire group, and it becomes more and more necessary in order to describe the sample completely that we have some measure of variability. The average deviation from the mean might suggest itself, but we have seen that the sum of the deviations from the mean is zero, and from this it follows that the mean deviation is also zero. For this reason the statistic that has been adopted as a measure of variability is the root mean square deviation, commonly known as the standard deviation. The formula for the standard deviation, which is usually represented by the Greek letter sigma (σ), is:

$$\sigma = \sqrt{\frac{\Sigma(x - \bar{x})^2}{N}} \qquad (2)$$

The direct method of calculating the standard deviation is to find all the deviations from the mean, square them, summate, divide by N, and then extract the square root. For example, if we have the three figures 6, 8, and 1, for which the mean is 5, the standard deviation would be:

$$\sqrt{\frac{1^2 + 3^2 + 4^2}{3}} = \sqrt{\frac{26}{3}}$$

When there are more variates in the sample, and especially when the deviations contain decimal figures, a much shorter method can be used. The main part of the work is to find the sum of squares of the deviations, and it can be shown very easily that:

$$\Sigma(x - \bar{x})^2 = \Sigma(x^2) - \frac{[\Sigma(x)]^2}{N} \qquad (3)$$

Applying this to our miniature example we have:

$$\Sigma(x - \bar{x})^2 = (6^2 + 8^2 + 1^2) - 15^2/3 = 26$$

This formula is especially useful for machine calculation and is now used almost exclusively in statistical laboratories.

We now have to consider a point which is very important in the practical application of statistical methods, and one over which there is often a great deal of confusion. It was pointed out above that the mean of a sample is taken as the best possible estimate of the mean of the parent population. This practice of estimating values for parent populations is the main object of calculating values for samples. With a little thought this point should be quite clear. We determine the reaction of a crop to a given fertilizer on a sample of plots which may not be more than 6 to 10 in number. It cannot be stated, even by the wildest stretch of the imagination, that we are primarily interested in the reaction to the fertilizer on those 6 to 10 plots. What we are attempting to find out is the general reaction to the fertilizer under farming practice, and hence we must picture a very large population of plots for the mean reaction of which we are trying to obtain an estimate. If we let this population, for purposes of clarity of thinking, be regarded as infinite, it follows that the mean and the standard deviation for this population are fixed values and hence we call them parameters. If the mean of the parent population is denoted by m, then $\bar{x}$, the mean of the sample, is an estimate of the parameter m. Similarly if σ is the standard deviation of the parent population, the value which we calculate from the sample must also be the best possible estimate of σ. Actually this estimate is not the root mean square deviation that we have defined above. This arises from the fact that, if m is the mean of the parent population, the best estimate of σ is:

$$\sqrt{\frac{\Sigma(x - m)^2}{N}}$$

but since we do not know m we use $\bar{x}$ instead, and it can be shown by a simple algebraic derivation that the best estimate of σ is given by:

$$s = \sqrt{\frac{\Sigma(x - \bar{x})^2}{N - 1}} \tag{4}$$

wherein we put this expression equal to s in that it is not σ but the best possible estimate of σ. We keep to this symbolism throughout in order to distinguish the standard deviation calculated from a sample from the true value which is a parameter of the parent population. The divisor $(N - 1)$ is known as the *number of degrees of freedom* available for estimating the standard deviation. We shall learn more of this term in later chapters.

3. Standard Deviation of a Sample Mean. If we take a series of samples and determine a mean for each one, it is obvious that the means for these samples will vary from sample to sample, and that the degree of variation among these means will be related to the degree of variation among the individual variates. If one particular sample is taken, the exact relation is given by the equation:

$$s_{\bar{x}} = \frac{s}{\sqrt{N}} \tag{5}$$

where $s_{\bar{x}}$ is the standard deviation of the mean of the sample, s is the standard deviation for the sample as a whole, and N is the number in the sample. The standard deviation of a mean is therefore inversely proportional to the square root of the number in the sample.

4. The Frequency Table. This is a table which shows, for the sample of variates studied, the frequencies with which they fall into certain clearly defined classes. If the sample is very small the frequency table may not be necessary, and even if prepared may not mean very much; but for moderately large samples it is usually desirable to begin the reduction of the data with a table of this kind. The frequency table provides the values for easy graphical representation, and from it such statistics as the mean and standard deviation may be calculated with much greater ease than from the original set of individual values.

5. Selection of Class Values. Frequency tables may deal with either continuous or discontinuous variables. A continuous variable is one in which a single variate may take any value within the range of variation. Thus the yield of a plot of wheat may take any value within the range from the lowest-yielding plot to the highest. A discontinuous variable can take only certain specified values. For example, in tossing 5 coins we can have 5, 4, 3, 2, 1, or 0 heads, and no other values can occur.

A frequency table for the number of heads in tossing 5 coins 100 times might be as follows:

Class Values	Frequency
5 heads	3
4 heads	16
3 heads	28
2 heads	31
1 heads	17
0 heads	5
	Total = 100

The class values to be selected for such a table are obvious, and this is usually true for discontinuous variables. In some examples, however, it may be necessary to form the class values such that the class interval is greater than unity. In tossing coins 20 at a time, we might use the classes 0–2 heads, 3–5 heads, and so forth.

If the variable is continuous, the classes for which the frequencies are to be determined must be chosen arbitrarily, the choice depending on the accuracy required in the computation of statistics from the table, the range of variation—which is, of course, the difference between the lowest and the highest value of the sample—the number in the sample or total frequency, and the facility with which these classes can be handled in computation. In the first place, the greater the number of classes the greater the accuracy of the calculations made from the table. But there must be a limit to the number of classes we can handle conveniently, and these two opposing factors must be balanced up. A good general rule is to make the class interval not more than one-quarter of the standard deviation. Of course we do not as a rule know what the standard deviation is before the table is made up, but it is possible to make a rough estimate of its value from the range of variation.   Tippett (3) has published detailed tables on the relation between the range of variation and the standard deviation, and these have been summarized in a short table prepared by Snedecor (2).   The following values are taken from Snedecor's table after rounding off the figures to two significant digits.

TABLE 2

VALUES OF THE RATIO, RANGE DIVIDED BY THE STANDARD DEVIATION (*SD*),
FOR SAMPLE SIZES FROM 20 TO 1000

Number in Sample	Range/*SD*	Number in Sample	Range/*SD*
20	3.7	200	5.5
30	4.1	300	5.8
50	4.5	400	5.9
75	4.8	500	6.1
100	5.0	700	6.3
150	5.3	1000	6.5

Now suppose that we have a sample of 500 variates and the range of variation is 0.25 to 2.63.   The difference is 2.38, and if we were to divide this by the standard deviation our table tells us that we would get a quotient of approximately 6.1.   In order to make the standard deviation about one-quarter of the class interval, it is clear that its magnitude will have to be about $2.38/6.1 \times 4 = 0.098$.   It is more convenient to have an odd number for a class interval than an even one, since it means that the midpoint of the interval does not require one more decimal place than we have in the values that define the class range.   In the end we should probably decide in this case on an interval of 0.11.   In making up the classes it is usual to begin with the lower boundary of the first class slightly below the lowest value, so that our classes and midpoints would finally be set up somewhat as follows:

Class Range	Class Value, or Midpoint of Class Range
0.19 to 0.29	0.24
0.30 to 0.40	0.35
0.41 to 0.51	0.46
0.52 to 0.62	0.57
etc.	etc.

By following the above rules we ensure a sufficient degree of accuracy in any statistics that are calculated from the frequency table; but, if the frequency table is required mainly for the preparation of a graph as described below, this method may give classes that are too small, in that some of the classes may contain only very small frequencies or perhaps none at all.   It is desirable in such cases to make the class interval from one-half to one-third of the standard deviation.

In statistical literature one may come across references to Sheppard's corrections for grouping.   These are designed to remove bias from certain statistics that are calculated from grouped data instead of from the individual values.   Thus, in calculating $\Sigma(x - \bar{x})^2/N - 1$, it has been shown that the bias is positive and equal approximately to $1/12$ of the class interval.   In the tests for abnormality described in Chapter III, and in certain other specific calculations, it is necessary to make the adjustments, but in general practice they are usually ignored and in many tests of significance it is more correct to omit them altogether.

The student should note carefully at this point that Sheppard's corrections are for the purpose of removing a definite bias and in no sense do they make allowance for inaccuracies introduced by using groups that are too large.

6. Sorting out the Variates and Formation of the Frequency Table. Sorting is greatly facilitated by writing the value of each variate on cards of a convenient size for handling.   The class ranges are first written out on cards and arranged in order on a table.   The sorting can then be done rapidly, and after it is finished it is very easy to run through the piles and obtain a complete check on the work.   It is very important to have perfect accuracy at this point.   In a series of studies a misplaced card may give a great deal of trouble at a later stage in the work.   The frequency table is finally made up by entering the frequencies opposite the corresponding class values.

Table 3 is a sample of a frequency table.   It represents data on the carotene content of the whole wheat of 139 varieties.   The class values are in parts per million of carotene in the whole wheat.   In this instance a great deal of accuracy in the calculations was not desired, and it will be noted that the class values are larger than they would be if the rules for the formation of these values as outlined above had been followed. Check this point by reference to Table 2.

TABLE 3

FREQUENCY TABLE FOR PARTS PER MILLION OF CAROTENE IN THE WHOLE WHEAT OF 139 VARIETIES OF WHEAT

Class Values...	0.85 to 0.95	0.96 to 1.06	1.07 to 1.17	1.18 to 1.28	1.29 to 1.39	1.40 to 1.50	1.51 to 1.61	1.62 to 1.72	1.73 to 1.83	1.84 to 1.94	1.95 to 2.05	2.06 to 2.16	2.17 to 2.27
Frequency.....	2	6	14	21	24	37	13	10	4	3	2	2	1

7. Graphical Representation of a Frequency Table.   Graphs of two types are in general use.   The best type of graph and the one most commonly used is the *histogram*.   It is a diagrammatic representation of a frequency table in which the class values are represented on the horizontal axis, and the frequencies by vertical columns erected in their appropriate positions on the horizontal axis.   The histogram is most useful when a curve for some theoretical distribution is being fitted.   The nature of any disagreement between the theoretical distribution and the actual frequencies can be located readily when the theoretical curve is

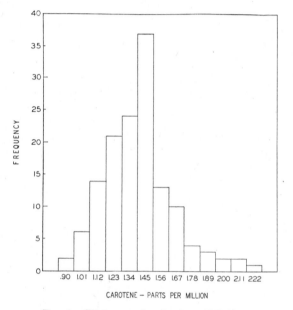

Fig. 1.—Histogram for the data of Table 3.

superimposed on the histogram.   As an example the histogram for the data of Table 3 is shown in Fig. 1.

The other type of graph is usually known as a *frequency polygon*.   A straight line is erected for each frequency at the midpoint of the corresponding class value, and the ends of these connected in sequence by straight lines.   It does not give as accurate a picture for the sample as the histogram, but tends in its shape towards the smooth curve of the population from which the sample was drawn.

8. Calculation of the Mean and Standard Deviation from a Frequency Table.   After the frequency table has been formed, we add two more columns as indicated in the small example given below:

Class Value or Midpoint of Class Range (x)	Frequency f	Frequency Multiplied by Class Value $f \times (x)$	Frequency Multiplied by Square of Class Value $f \times (x^2)$
1	2	2	2
2	4	8	16
3	7	21	63
4	6	24	96
5	1	5	25
Totals............	$20 = N$	$60 = \Sigma(x)$	$202 = \Sigma(x^2)$

On summating the last three columns we get N, $\Sigma(x)$, and $\Sigma(x^2)$, which are the values necessary for the calculation of the mean and the standard deviation. The mean is given by:

$$\bar{x} = \frac{\Sigma(x)}{N}$$

and the standard deviation by:

$$s_m = \sqrt{\frac{\Sigma(x^2) - [\Sigma(x)]^2/N}{N - 1}} \qquad (6)$$

It will be noted that the numerator of the standard deviation is $\Sigma(x - \bar{x})^2$, and that to obtain it we have made use of the identity given in formula (3).

The class values are very frequently numbers containing two to four digits, in which case a great deal of labor can be saved by replacing them by the series of natural numbers 1, 2, 3, 4, $\cdots$ etc. By this method we obtain a mean and a standard deviation that we shall designate by $\bar{x}'$ and s', respectively. These can be converted into the true values by means of the following identities:

$$\bar{x} = (\bar{x}' - 1)i + X_1 \qquad (7)$$

$$s = s'i \qquad (8)$$

where i is the class interval and X_1 is the first *true* class value.

9. Coefficient of Variability. This is the term applied to the standard deviation when it is expressed in percentage of the mean of the sample. It is a statistic of very limited usage owing to the difficulty of determining its reliability by statistical methods. The formula is obviously:

$$C \text{ (coefficient of variability)} = s\left(\frac{100}{\bar{x}}\right) \qquad (9)$$

10. Exercises.

1. Substitute the natural numbers 1, 2, 3, $\cdots$ 13 for the class values of Table 3, and calculate the mean and the standard deviation. Convert the calculated values to actual values using formulas (7) and (8).

$$\bar{x}' = 5.597 \qquad \bar{x} = 1.406 \qquad s' = 2.196 \qquad s = 0.2416$$

2. Table 4 gives the yields in grams of 400 square-yard plots of barley. Make up a frequency table and histogram for these yields, using a class interval of 11, and make the first class 14 to 24.

3. The areas in arbitrary units of 500 bull sperms are given in Table 5.[1] Prepare the frequency table and histogram, using 16 classes, making the first class 123 to 125.

4. For either one of Exercises 2 and 3 above, calculate the mean and the standard deviation from the frequency table, using actual class values. Then replace the actual class values by 1, 2, 3, 4, $\cdots$, and recalculate the mean and the standard deviation.

$$\text{Ex. 2} \quad \bar{x}' = 13.055 \qquad \bar{x} = 151.60 \qquad s' = 2.880 \qquad s = 31.68$$

$$\text{Ex. 3} \quad \bar{x}' = 7.852 \qquad \bar{x} = 144.56 \qquad s' = 2.576 \qquad s = 7.728$$

5. For the data in Tables 4 and 5, determine the class values that should be used to give a high degree of accuracy in the calculations.

6. Prove the identity:

$$\Sigma(x - \bar{x})^2 = \Sigma(x^2) - [\Sigma(x)]^2/N$$

TABLE 4

Yields in Grams of 400 Square-Yard Plots of Barley

185	162	136	157	141	130	129	176	171	190	157	147	176	126	175	134	169	189	180	128
169	205	129	117	144	125	165	170	153	186	164	123	165	203	156	182	164	176	176	150
216	154	184	203	166	155	215	190	164	204	194	148	162	146	174	185	171	181	158	147
165	157	180	165	127	186	133	170	134	177	109	169	128	152	165	139	146	144	178	188
133	128	161	160	167	156	125	162	128	103	116	87	123	143	130	119	141	174	157	168
195	180	158	139	139	168	145	166	118	171	143	132	126	171	176	115	165	147	186	157
187	174	172	191	155	169	139	144	130	146	159	164	160	122	175	156	119	135	116	134
157	182	209	136	153	160	142	179	125	149	171	186	196	175	189	214	169	166	164	195
189	108	118	149	178	171	151	192	127	148	158	174	191	134	188	248	164	206	185	192
147	178	189	141	173	187	167	128	139	152	167	131	203	231	214	177	161	194	141	161
124	130	112	122	192	155	196	179	166	156	131	179	201	122	207	189	164	131	211	172
170	140	156	199	181	181	150	184	154	200	187	169	155	107	143	145	190	176	162	123
189	194	146	22	160	107	70	84	112	162	124	156	138	101	138	141	143	135	163	183
99	118	150	151	83	136	171	191	155	164	98	136	115	168	130	111	136	129	122	120
179	172	192	171	151	142	193	174	146	180	140	137	138	194	109	120	124	126	126	147
115	148	195	154	149	139	163	118	126	127	139	174	167	175	179	172	174	167	142	169
122	163	144	147	123	160	137	161	122	101	158	103	119	164	112	57	94	106	132	122
164	142	155	147	115	143	68	184	183	167	160	138	191	133	160	156	122	111	153	148
103	131	180	142	191	175	146	181	111	110	154	176	168	175	175	146	148	167	106	123
121	154	148	91	93	74	113	79	131	119	96	80	97	98	106	107	69	86	94	129

[1] Data by courtesy of A. Savage, Department of Animal Pathology, University of Manitoba.

TABLE 5

AREAS IN ARBITRARY UNITS OF 500 BULL SPERMS

140	138	140	140	140	139	138	138	138	138
133	132	140	140	138	139	139	145	145	145
147	147	147	149	149	155	160	159	159	160
139	143	142	142	141	141	145	145	144	146
140	148	147	147	149	148	148	148	149	149
153	153	153	153	155	141	149	149	149	149
149	149	149	148	147	147	148	159	161	161
158	157	157	141	141	143	143	143	143	142
141	141	141	139	138	159	161	155	137	136
144	144	145	144	144	146	145	145	144	146
138	149	149	148	148	148	162	162	153	153
144	144	144	146	145	145	145	146	141	143
134	124	124	134	132	136	137	125	123	134
146	146	139	138	138	138	140	140	146	139
139	139	152	150	150	150	152	151	149	149
149	149	149	154	154	153	155	149	149	149
161	160	159	135	154	154	154	155	154	154
142	141	141	141	141	142	142	142	142	141
136	136	135	137	136	135	135	137	137	137
146	146	146	145	140	140	140	138	138	140
155	154	153	153	153	153	153	153	153	155
143	142	142	142	147	147	150	152	152	150
134	131	130	129	131	130	129	129	134	134
140	139	139	139	127	137	134	132	133	133
148	148	147	147	147	147	147	149	148	147
149	149	149	149	149	146	146	146	145	146
137	136	136	137	137	136	134	136	135	129
139	139	152	152	152	152	151	150	152	152
136	136	137	145	144	146	146	145	145	145
153	153	155	135	158	158	157	157	157	158
150	150	150	150	151	151	150	150	152	151
133	133	134	129	130	141	143	142	141	141
134	132	127	137	128	125	136	141	143	143
147	147	169	165	162	162	149	144	144	144
146	145	145	144	146	145	144	146	146	146
135	137	137	127	134	132	135	135	127	126
151	148	148	147	147	149	149	149	150	151
145	144	144	146	144	143	143	143	143	142
157	156	137	137	137	137	136	137	135	133
150	150	152	152	152	152	152	152	152	151
141	141	143	142	142	142	138	140	140	140
143	143	144	144	144	144	146	146	140	139
144	146	145	145	145	138	140	139	138	153
146	146	146	146	146	145	145	145	146	145
134	135	157	156	156	157	157	157	157	156
151	151	151	150	150	150	150	150	150	152
142	141	142	141	141	142	142	142	141	143
135	133	133	150	151	149	139	139	139	138
138	140	140	153	153	148	147	147	156	158
158	152	141	141	142	141	143	139	139	139

REFERENCES

1. R. A. FISHER. Statistical Methods for Research Workers. Oliver and Boyd, London and Edinburgh, 1936.
2. G. W. SNEDECOR. Statistical Methods. Collegiate Press, Inc., Ames, Iowa, 1937.
3. L. H. C. TIPPETT. *Biometrika*, **17**: 386, 1926.

CHAPTER III

THEORETICAL FREQUENCY DISTRIBUTIONS

1. Characteristics of Frequency Distributions of Biological Variates.
A frequency table may be used to furnish an estimate of the frequency
distribution of the population from which the sample has been taken.
For example, we could take any one of the frequency tables of Chapter
II and draw a smooth curve through the upper ends of the columns of the
histogram. We would draw a smooth curve because the parent population is assumed to be infinite and each *point* on the base line could be
represented by a frequency, or, to be more specific, the height of the
perpendicular line from any point on the base line to the curve would
represent the proportion of the total frequency of the population having
the value represented by the point. This method, however, would not
be very satisfactory, as the position of the curve would be, to a considerable extent, a matter of individual judgment. Also, the sample studied
might indicate, owing to errors of sampling, certain irregularities and
lack of symmetry which might be entirely absent in the population.
Furthermore, to be consistent in our logic, it follows that we are not so
much interested in drawing a curve that fits the sample as we are in
setting up a theoretical curve as a hypothesis and then determining
whether or not the data of the sample agree with the theoretical frequencies. In setting up our theoretical curve, it is of course natural
that we set up one that is likely to agree fairly well with the data of the
sample, and this is only saying in other words that we should set up a
reasonable hypothesis. We could set up a whole series of theoretical
curves, the majority of which would have no resemblance whatever to
the histogram of the sample; but obviously this would be a mere waste
of time. To deduce a theoretical distribution into which our sample is
likely to fit, it is necessary to study the characteristics of the frequency
tables for biological variates as a whole and work out a logical theory for
setting up the theoretical values. If we examine the histograms of
Chapter II for three different kinds of biological variates, we find that
they have certain characteristics in common. Close to the mean, the
variates occur with much greater frequency than they do at some distance from the mean; but the reduction in the frequencies from the mean
to the extreme tails of the distribution is not uniform, with the result that

if a smooth curve is drawn through the tops of the columns of the histograms it is seen to resemble an isosceles triangle but with a rounded top and very much flattened base. A curve of this type is found to resemble very closely a definite type of mathematical curve; but to understand more easily the reasoning behind the derivation of this curve it is necessary for us to look into the characteristics of another theoretical distribution that is appropriate for discontinuous variables.

2. **The Binomial Distribution.** In Chapter I we derived a theoretical distribution for the experiment on identifying varieties of wheat. This will be found in Table 1. Each theoretical frequency was derived by the direct application of elementary theorems of probability, and if, instead of dealing with specific numbers of pairs of samples, we had dealt with the problem as a general one for any number of pairs of samples we would have derived the *binomial distribution*. Thus the theoretical frequencies of Table 1 can be written out at once from the terms of the expansion of the expression $(\frac{1}{2} + \frac{1}{2})^6$. These are:

$$\frac{1}{64} \qquad \frac{6}{64} \qquad \frac{15}{64} \qquad \frac{20}{64} \qquad \frac{15}{64} \qquad \frac{6}{64} \qquad \frac{1}{64}$$

wherein we note that the theoretical frequencies are stated as proportions of the total number and express directly the probabilities of particular combinations. In general for similar problems where there are alternative possibilities such as right or wrong placings of pairs of samples, heads or tails in the tossing of a coin, an ace or any other number in the throwing of a die, etc., the theoretical distribution can be written down directly by expanding the binomial $(p + q)^n$, where n is the number of events in any 1 trial, p is the probability of the occurrence of the event in 1 way, q is the probability of the occurrence of the event in the alternative way, and $p + q = 1$. If $p = q$ we obtain a symmetrical distribution, but if p is not equal to q the distribution is asymmetrical or skewed.

There are many applications of the binomial distribution in statistical analysis, and one application of particular interest will be dealt with in Chapter X. For the present it is sufficient to note that the form of the distribution is somewhat similar to the actual distributions of Chapter II, which we have concluded are fairly typical for biological variables in general. However, the binomial distribution is not suitable as a theoretical distribution for continuous variables, as in itself it is essentially discontinuous; so that if we make any use of it for continuous variables it must be as a stepping stone to some more general type of distribution. The biological variables we have studied indicated from the samples for which histograms were made that the parent populations were essentially symmetrical. The comparable situation for the binomial distribution would occur when $p = q$. Starting from this point, therefore, let us suppose that n is infinitely large; and, in graphing the histogram for the theoretical distribution, the columns which will also be infinite in number are represented by vertical lines only. The result will be a smooth curve, and by carrying through this procedure algebraically and making certain approximations we can arrive at an equation for a smooth curve. This is the expression for what is commonly known as the *normal frequency distribution*.

3. The Normal Distribution. Most variables dealt with in biological statistics show in their actual distributions only minor deviations from the theoretical normal distribution defined by:

$$y = \left(\frac{N}{\sigma\sqrt{2\pi}}\right)e^{-\frac{1}{2}\left(\frac{x}{\sigma}\right)^2} \tag{1}$$

where σ is the standard deviation of the population, N is the total number of variates, e is the base of the Napierian system of logarithms, and y is the frequency at any given point x, where x is measured from the

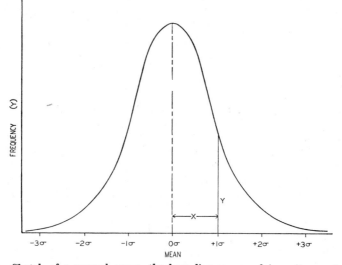

Fig. 2.—Sketch of a normal curve, the base line measured in units equal to the standard deviation (σ).

mean of the population. The curve expresses, therefore, the relation between y and x, with y as the dependent variable. Figure 2 is a sketch of a normal curve. It illustrates the measurement of x from the mean of the population which is located at the point where the dotted line has been erected.   For the value of x taken, y is the perpendicular distance from that point to the curve.

Equation (1) may be written:

$$y\left(\frac{\sigma}{N}\right) = \frac{e^{-\frac{1}{2}\left(\frac{x}{\sigma}\right)^2}}{\sqrt{2\pi}} \qquad (2)$$

and putting z for y (σ/N) we have:

$$z = \frac{e^{-\frac{1}{2}\left(\frac{x}{\sigma}\right)^2}}{\sqrt{2\pi}} \qquad (3)$$

and since x/σ varies in actual practice only from 0 to 6, the values of z have been tabulated for all the values of x/σ from 0 to 6 proceeding by intervals of 0.01.   Any given value of z can then be transformed to y by multiplying by N/σ for the particular population with which we are dealing.   In other words, for a given population for which N and σ are known, we can proceed with a set of tables to plot the theoretical smooth curve.

A smooth curve plotted by the above method is an estimate of the form of the infinite population from which the sample has been drawn; but what we often require is the theoretical frequency distribution corresponding to the actual frequency distribution of the sample.   That is, we require the theoretical normal frequencies for the arbitrarily chosen class values of the actual distribution.   For this purpose, if N is taken as 1, equation (1) becomes:

$$y = \frac{e^{-\frac{1}{2}\left(\frac{x}{\sigma}\right)^2}}{\sigma\sqrt{2\pi}}$$

which can be integrated from $x = $ minus infinity to $x = $ any assigned value.   This gives the area under that portion of the curve, and we will represent it as $\frac{1}{2}(1 + \alpha)$.   The integration is started at $x = $ minus infinity, because the normal curve never actually touches the base line although, at $x = -6$, y is an exceedingly small value.   The reason for expressing the area as $\frac{1}{2}(1 + \alpha)$ or $\frac{1}{2} + \frac{1}{2}\alpha$ will be seen from an examination of Fig. 3.   For any assigned value of x the area within the limits of $\pm x$ is represented by α.   Therefore, from $x = $ minus infinity to $x = $ any assigned value, if the total area of the curve is 1, the area is $\frac{1}{2} + \frac{1}{2}\alpha$.

The tabulated values of z and $\frac{1}{2}(1 + \alpha)$ for values of x/σ from 0 to 6 are given in Sheppard's " Tables of Area and Ordinate in terms of Abscissa."   These are commonly referred to as Sheppard's tables of the probability integral. The detailed application of these tables to a practical example is described below under Section 4.

4. Methods of Calculation.

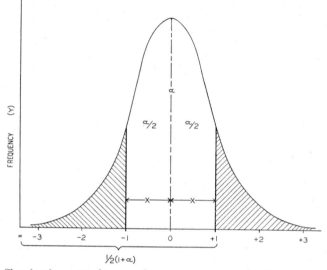

Fig. 3.—Sketch of a normal curve showing ordinates erected at $x/\sigma = +1$, and $x/\sigma = -1$. The unshaded area $= \alpha$, and the shaded area $= (1 - \alpha)$.

Example 1. The calculations necessary to fit a normal curve to an actual frequency distribution and to determine the normal frequencies corresponding to the actual frequencies are given in Table 6. The data are for the transparencies of 400 red blood cells taken from a patient suffering from primary anemia (4). The transparency is taken as the ratio of the total light passing through the cell to the area of the cell. For this distribution $\bar{x}' = 7.06$ and $\sigma = 2.45$.

The calculations can best be described by considering each column of the table. The columns have been numbered at the head of the table for convenient reference.

Column (1): The class ranges are as described in Chapter II. Note that unit class intervals have been used. This is necessary in obtaining y, but makes no difference to the remainder of the calculations. After setting up the class ranges, the actual frequencies may be entered as in column (10), but it is of no consequence when these are entered as they are not used in the calculations.

Column (2): In order to understand clearly the meaning of the class limits, refer to any histogram as in Chapter II, Fig. 1, or Exercises 2 and 3. The limits correspond with the lines bordering the columns of the histogram. The mean of the sample is placed according to the class range in which it falls. In this case the mean is 7.06 and must be placed opposite the class range 6.6–7.5. The limits are then entered by passing in both directions from the mean. The class in which the mean falls will have two limits, but for each of the others we take only the one farthest from the mean.

TABLE 6

CALCULATION OF ORDINATES FOR FITTING A NORMAL CURVE, AND
THEORETICAL NORMAL FREQUENCIES

(1) Class Range	(2) Class Limits	(3) d	(4) d/σ	(5) z	(6) $y=$ $z\left(\dfrac{N}{\sigma}\right)$	(7) $\frac{1}{2}(1+\alpha)$	(8) $\dfrac{N}{2}(1+\alpha)$	(9) Theoretical Normal Frequencies	(10) Actual Frequencies
		9.56	3.90	0.0002	0.03	1.0000	400.00		
		8.56	3.49	0.0009	0.15	0.9998	399.92	0.08	
		7.56	3.08	0.0035	0.57	0.9990	399.60	0.32	
		6.56	2.68	0.0110	1.80	0.9963	398.52	1.08	
0.6– 1.5	1.5	5.56	2.27	0.0303	4.95	0.9884	395.36	3.16	4
1.6– 2.5	2.5	4.56	1.86	0.0707	11.54	0.9686	387.44	7.92	11
2.6– 3.5	3.5	3.56	1.45	0.1394	22.76	0.9265	370.60	16.84	17
3.6– 4.5	4.5	2.56	1.04	0.2323	37.92	0.8508	340.32	30.28	29
4.6– 5.5	5.5	1.56	0.64	0.3251	53.08	0.7389	295.56	44.76	43
5.6– 6.5	6.5	0.56	0.23	0.3885	63.43	0.5910	236.40	59.16	56
6.6– 7.5	7.06	0.00	0.00	0.3989	65.12	0.5000	200.00	64.96	58
7.6– 8.5	7.5	0.44	0.18	0.3925	64.08	0.5714	228.56	60.40	63
8.6– 9.5	8.5	1.44	0.59	0.3352	54.72	0.7224	288.96	47.56	61
9.6–10.5	9.5	2.44	1.00	0.2420	39.51	0.8413	336.52	31.16	25
10.6–11.5	10.5	3.44	1.40	0.1497	24.44	0.9192	367.68	18.24	20
11.6–12.5	11.5	4.44	1.81	0.0775	12.65	0.9648	385.92	8.80	9
12.6–13.5	12.5	5.44	2.22	0.0339	5.53	0.9868	394.72	3.56	4
13.6–14.5	13.5	6.44	2.63	0.0126	2.06	0.9957	398.28	1.24	
		7.44	3.04	0.0039	0.64	0.9988	299.52	0.36	
		8.44	3.44	0.0011	0.18	0.9997	399.88	0.08	
		9.44	3.85	0.0002	0.03	0.9999	399.96	0.04	
		10.44	4.26	0.0000	0.00	1.0000	400.00		
							Total	400	400

Column (3): The deviation of the class limit from the mean. Note that this corresponds to x in the discussion above.

Column (4): Figures in previous column divided by the standard deviation. The latter is calculated using unit class intervals, and from the formula

$$\sigma = \sqrt{\frac{\Sigma(x - \bar{x})^2}{N}}.$$

Column (5): Values of z from Sheppard's "Tables."
Column (6): Corresponding z values multiplied by N/σ.
Column (7): Values of $\frac{1}{2}(1 + \alpha)$ from Sheppard's "Tables."
Column (8): Corresponding $\frac{1}{2}(1 + \alpha)$ values multiplied by N.
Column (9): Differences between consecutive values in column (8). Begin at 400 at each end and go towards the center. At the center the two differences are added. Note that the theoretical frequencies are not kept in line with the values in column (8), but are lined up with the corresponding actual frequencies in column (10).

Column (10): The actual frequencies.

5. Probability Calculations from the Normal Curve. We have observed from the previous exercises and examples that most biological variables tend to follow the normal distribution and that methods are available for making, for any particular sample, an estimate of the form of the normal distribution from which the sample was drawn. Since the normal distribution can be expressed by a mathematical equation, the area of any section of the curve cut off by an ordinate can be determined readily by integration of the equation, and for all practical problems this work has been performed and tabulated in Sheppard's

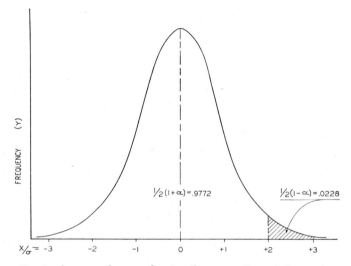

FIG. 4.—Sketch of a normal curve showing the proportions of the total area below and above the ordinate erected at $d/\sigma = +2$.

"Tables." It remains to show how these facts form the basis for tests of significance in statistical problems.

If a variable is normally distributed and the mean and standard deviation of the population are known, we can draw the curve and erect an ordinate at any point. Suppose that such an ordinate is erected at a point which is at a distance, on the positive side of the mean, exactly equal to twice the standard deviation. Thus $d/\sigma = 2$, and from Sheppard's "Tables" we find that $\frac{1}{2}(1 + \alpha) = 0.9772$. Taking the total area of the curve as 1, the area to the left of the ordinate is 0.9772, and that to the right of the ordinate is $(1 - 0.9772) = 0.0228$. Assuming a population of 1000 variates, it is obvious that 22.8 of these variates would be greater than the mean by an amount equal to 2 or more times the standard deviation. Hence if one variate is selected at random from the 1000, it is obvious that the probability that this variate will exceed the mean to the extent of 2 or more times the standard deviation is 22.8/1000. Reference to Fig. 4 will make this point clear.

Looking at the same problem from another angle, we inquire as to the probability, in selecting a variate at random, that this variate shall fall outside the limits of plus or minus twice the standard deviation. We erect two ordinates, one at $d/\sigma = -2$, and one at $d/\sigma = +2$; and our problem is to find the area in both tails of the curve. Obviously this will be $[1 - \frac{1}{2}(1 + \alpha)] \times 2 = (1 - 0.9772) \times 2 = 0.0456$. The probability that a single variate selected at random will deviate by an amount equal to or greater than ± 2 is 45.6/1000, or approximately 1/22.

Probability results are sometimes expressed in terms of odds. If the probability is 1/22, the odds are 1 out of 22, or, as usually stated, 1 to 21.

For the case above, where the deviations in both directions are considered, note that the probability is given directly by $[1 - \frac{1}{2}(1 + \alpha)] \times 2 = 1 - \alpha$. The odds are given by $\alpha/(1 - \alpha) : 1$.

Some examples follow that should make the whole procedure perfectly clear.

Example 2. The mean (m) of a population is 26.4, and the standard deviation (σ) is 2.0. Find the probability that a single variate selected at random will be 29.4 or greater.

The deviation $(d) = 29.4 - 26.4 = +3.0$. Hence $d/\sigma = \frac{3}{2} = 1.5$. For $d/\sigma = 1.5$, $\frac{1}{2}(1 + a) = 0.9332$. The probability $(P) = (1 - 0.9332) = \mathbf{0.0668}$.

Example 3. For the above population, find the probability that a single variate selected at random will deviate from the mean to the extent of 3.5 or more.

$$d = \pm 3.5 \qquad \frac{d}{\sigma} = \frac{3.5}{2} = 1.75$$

For $d/\sigma = 1.75$, $\frac{1}{2}(1 + \alpha) = 0.9599$. $\alpha = (0.4599 \times 2) = 0.9198$

Hence $P = (1 - \alpha) = (1 - 0.9198) = \mathbf{0.0802}$.

Example 4. Determine the value of d/σ corresponding to $P = 0.05$.

$$P = (1 - \alpha) = 0.05$$
$$\alpha = (1 - 0.05) = 0.95$$
$$\tfrac{1}{2}(1 + \alpha) = (0.5 + 0.4750) = 0.9750$$

From Sheppard's "Tables," $d/\sigma = 1.96$.

6. Tests of Departure from Normality.* The χ^2 test of Chapter IX, Example 19, on the goodness of fit of actual to theoretical normal

---

* Students studying statistics for the first time are advised to pass over the remainder of this chapter and come back to it at a later date.

frequencies is a general test of the normality of a distribution, and, by noting those classes that make the greatest contribution to χ^2, we can come to some decision as to the type of departure from normality. The test described here is one that involves the calculation of two statistics that are direct measures of the type and degree of abnormality, Fisher (1).

Types of Abnormality. Frequency distributions that depart significantly from the normal may be divided roughly into three classes:

(a) *Skew Distributions.* The degree of skewness of a given distribution is indicated approximately by the measure

$$\text{Skewness} = \frac{\text{Mean} - \text{Mode}}{\sigma}$$

where the mode is the position on the base line, or x ordinate, of a perpendicular line drawn to the maximum point of the curve. This measure is obviously zero for the normal distribution, as the curve is symmetrical and the mean and the mode coincide. When the mode is greater than the mean we have negative skewness, and when less than the mean, positive skewness.

(b) *Platykurtic,* or flat topped. The shoulders of the curve are filled out and the tails depleted.

(c) *Leptokurtic,* or peaked. At the center the curve is higher and more pointed than the normal, and the tails are extended.

In certain distributions we may have skewness as well as kurtosis as indicated by (b) and (c).

Test for Abnormality. The type of abnormality of a distribution can be determined directly by calculating two statistics known as g_1 and g_2. These are calculated from the k statistics k_1, k_2, k_3, and k_4, that are in turn derived from the sums of the powers up to 4 of the deviations from the mean.

One of the most convenient methods for the calculation of the k statistics is to obtain first a series of values $a_1 \cdots a_4$, defined as follows:

$$a_1 = \frac{\Sigma(x)}{N} \qquad a_3 = \frac{\Sigma(x^3)}{N}$$

$$a_2 = \frac{\Sigma(x^2)}{N} \qquad a_4 = \frac{\Sigma(x^4)}{N}$$

From $a_1 \cdots a_4$, we calculate a series of statistics known as the *moments* $(v_1 \cdots v_4)$, which in this form are uncorrected for grouping in the frequency table.

$$v_1 = a_1$$

$$v_2 = a_2 - a_1^2$$

$$v_3 = a_3 - 3a_1a_2 + 2a_1^3$$

$$v_4 = a_4 - 4a_1a_3 + 6a_1^2a_2 - 3a_1^4$$

The k statistics are then given by:

$$k_1 = v_1$$

$$k_2 = \left(\frac{N}{N-1}\right)v_2$$

$$k_3 = \left(\frac{N^2}{(N-1)(N-2)}\right)v_3$$

$$k_4 = \frac{N^2}{(N-1)(N-2)}\left[\frac{(N+1)v_4 - 3(N-1)v_2^2}{N-3}\right]$$

Two of the k statistics k_2 and k_4 require correction for the interval of grouping of the frequency distribution. For a unit interval the corrected values are given by:

$$k_2' = k_2 - \tfrac{1}{12}, \quad \text{and} \quad k_4' = k_4 + \tfrac{1}{120}$$

Corrections for other intervals will, of course, not be necessary; as it is always possible to use a unit interval for the purpose of calculating the k statistics.

The measures of curve type g_1 and g_2 are given as follows, with their standard errors:

$$g_1 = \frac{k_3'}{(k_2')^{3/2}} \qquad SEg_1 = \sqrt{\frac{6N(N-1)}{(N-2)(N+1)(N+3)}}$$

$$g_2 = \frac{k_4'}{k_2'^2} \qquad SEg_2 = \sqrt{\frac{24N(N-1)^2}{(N-3)(N-2)(N+3)(N+5)}}$$

For normal distributions both g_1 and g_2 are zero. The former is a measure of symmetry and has the same sign as (mean − mode). Figure 5 illustrates positive and negative skewness as indicated by positive and negative values of g_1. A positive value of g_2 indicates a peaked curve, and a negative value a flat-topped curve. These two types are also illustrated in Fig. 5 (see page 31).

Example 5. We shall take as an example to which to apply the test for normality the frequency distribution given in Table 7, which also contains the necessary calculations. We get:

$$g_1 = +0.184 \qquad SEg_1 = 0.227$$

$$g_2 = +0.0188 \qquad SEg_2 = 0.451$$

The signs of g_1 and g_2 indicate that the curve departs slightly from normality in having a slight positive skewness and in being slightly peaked, but the values of g_1 and g_2 are very much less than twice their standard errors so we conclude that there is no evidence of a significant departure from normality.

When the number of classes is fairly large it is desirable to calculate the k statistics using an assumed mean. We measure x in terms of the deviations from the assumed mean and proceed exactly as in Table 7. Table 8 is an example of the calculation of the k statistics by this method, using the same data as in Table 7.

TABLE 7

CALCULATION OF THE k STATISTICS

x	Frequency	fx	fx^2	fx^3	fx^4
1	1	1	1	1	1
2	6	12	24	48	96
3	13	39	117	351	1,053
4	25	100	400	1,600	6,400
5	30	150	750	3,750	18,750
6	22	132	792	4,752	28,512
7	9	63	441	3,087	21,609
8	5	40	320	2,560	20,480
9	2	18	162	1,458	13,122
$\Sigma(x) \ldots \Sigma(x^4)$ $(N = 113)$		555	3007	17,607	110,023
$a_1 \ldots a_4$		4.911,504	26.6106	155.814	973.655
			-24.1229	-392.094	-3061.124
				236.959	3851.545
					-1745.739
$v_1 \ldots v_4$		4.9115	2.4877	0.679	18.337
$k_1 \ldots k_4$		4.9115	2.5098	0.697	0.103
Corrections			-0.0833		0.008
$k_1' \ldots k_4'$		4.9115	2.4265	0.697	0.111

$$g_1 = \frac{0.697}{(2.4265)^{3/2}} = +0.184 \qquad SEg_1 = 0.227$$

$$g_2 = \frac{0.111}{(2.4265)^2} = +0.0188 \qquad SEg_2 = 0.451$$

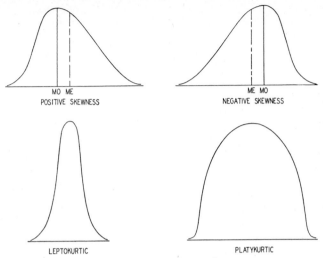

MO ME
POSITIVE SKEWNESS

ME MO
NEGATIVE SKEWNESS

LEPTOKURTIC

PLATYKURTIC

FIG. 5.—Illustrating types of abnormality in frequency distributions.
MO = mode, and ME = mean.

TABLE 8

CALCULATION OF k STATISTICS USING AN ASSUMED MEAN

x	f	Deviations (d) from Assumed Mean	fd	fd^2	fd^3	fd^4
1	1	-4	-4	16	-64	256
2	6	-3	-18	54	-162	486
3	13	-2	-26	52	-104	208
4	25	-1	-25	25	-25	25
5	30					
6	22	1	22	22	22	22
7	9	2	18	36	72	144
8	5	3	15	45	135	405
9	2	4	8	32	128	512
$\Sigma(d) \ldots \Sigma(d^4)$	$(N - 113)$		-10	282	2	2,058
$a_1 \ldots a_4$			$-0.088,496$	2.4956	0.017,699	18.212
				-0.0078	0.662,552	0.006
					$-0.001,386$	0.117
						-0.000
$v_2 \ldots v_4$				2.4878	0.679	18.335
$k_2 \ldots k_4$		etc.		2.5098	0.697	0.103

7. Exercises.

1. Calculate the ordinates (y) and the theoretical normal frequencies for the frequency distribution of either Chapter II, Exercise 2, or Chapter II, Exercise 3. Totalling the theoretical frequencies will provide a check on the calculations.

2. Make two graphs for Exercise 1.

(a) Histogram of actual frequencies and smooth normal curve.

(b) Histogram of theoretical frequencies and smooth normal curve.

3. Examine equation (1) in Section 3 above, and show how the value of σ affects the shape of the curve.

4. If the mean of a population is 21.65 and σ is 3.21, determine the probability that a variate taken at random will be greater than 28.55 or less than 14.75.

$$P = 0.03.$$

5. If, for the population described in Exercise 4, the standard deviation of the mean of a sample of 400 variates is $\sigma/\sqrt{400}$, find the probability that the mean of any one sample of 400 taken at random will fall outside the limits 21.33 to 21.97.

$$P = 0.045.$$

6. Determine d/σ values corresponding to the P values of 0.001, 0.01, 0.02, 0.10, 0.20, and 0.50.

7. Test the following distributions for departure from normality.

(a) $x..$	1	2	3	4	5	6	7	8	9	10	11	12	13	14	15	16
$f...$	1	57	185	217	177	126	87	54	30	20	14	11	13	5	1	2
(b) $x..$	1	2	3	4	5	6	7	8	9	10	11	12	13	14	15	16
$f...$	2	3	4	5	7	11	17	30	50	34	21	10	7	5	2	2
(c) $x..$	1	2	3	4	5	6	7	8	9	10	11	12	13	14	15	16
$f...$	1	7	13	19	23	26	27	28	26	24	22	17	14	9	4	1

(a) $g_1 = 1.360, g_2 = 2.143.$ (b) $g_1 = -0.327, g_2 = 0.939.$ (c) $g_1 = 0.107, g_2 = -0.766.$

REFERENCES

1. R. A. Fisher. Statistical Methods for Research Workers. Sixth Edition Oliver and Boyd, London and Edinburgh, 1936. Reading: Chapter III, Sections 11, 12, 13, 14, 18, and Appendix A.
2. Raymond Pearl. Medical Biometry and Statistics. W. B. Saunders and Company, Philadelphia and London, 1923. Reading: pages 235 to 245.
3. Karl Pearson. Tables for Statisticians and Biometricians. Part I.
4. A. Savage, C. H. Goulden, and J. M. Isa. Can. J. Research, 12:803–811, 1935
5. L. H. C. Tippett. The Methods of Statistics. Williams and Norgate, Ltd., London, 1931. Reading: Chapter II, Sections 2.63, 2.7.
6. G. Udny Yule. An Introduction to the Theory of Statistics. Charles Griffin and Company, Ltd., London, 1924. Reading: Chapter XV.

CHAPTER IV

TESTS OF SIGNIFICANCE WITH SMALL SAMPLES

1. The Estimation of the Standard Deviation. In Chapter II, Section 2, it was pointed out that the best estimate of the standard deviation of a population from which a sample has been drawn is $\sqrt{\Sigma(x - m)^2/N}$, where m is the mean of the population and N is the number in the sample. Since we never know the value of m, we use $\bar{x}$ instead; but the substitution of $\bar{x}$ in the above formula will not give us the best possible estimate of σ; actually it will give us an estimate that is too small. In other words, if we take a large number of samples and calculate a standard deviation for each one, the average value of our standard deviations will be low, and this will be true regardless of how many samples we take. As a matter of fact, if we take a large enough number of samples, we can predict with accuracy the extent of the negative bias in the average of the standard deviations. To the beginner these facts often appear somewhat mysterious, particularly the fact that the bias, in our estimate, can be removed, as pointed out in Chapter II, by using the formula $\sqrt{\Sigma(x - \bar{x})^2/N - 1}$. It may seem peculiar that the bias can be removed in so simple a manner. Now, it is easy enough to work out this proposition algebraically, but this does not settle the question necessarily for the beginner, as it is quite possible to work through a derivation and follow all the steps without really understanding the situation. Consequently, we shall not use the algebraic method here, but will try instead to point out why a bias should exist and why it is reasonable that it should be removed by dividing the sum of squares of the deviations from the sample mean by 1 less than the number in the sample.

In the first place, we have noted already that the sum of the deviations from the mean of a sample or of a population is zero (Chapter II, Section 1). We shall now note that the sum of the *squares* of the deviations from the mean is a *minimum*. If the mean of the population is m and we take a large number of samples of size N and in each case we determine $\Sigma(x - m)^2$, it follows that the sum of all these will be the same as if we had merely gone through the whole population without considering any portion of the variates as a sample. Then, on dividing this total sum of squares by the total number and extracting the square

33

root, we would have the value of σ for the whole population. It obviously does not matter whether we divide the population into samples and determine σ for each one and then average, or merely take the whole population as one sample. However, this procedure is possible only in theory, as m is actually unknown. For each sample, therefore, suppose that we calculate $\sqrt{\Sigma(x - \bar{x})^2/N}$ and then average. Now, since the sum of the squares of the deviations from the mean is a minimum, the use of $\bar{x}$ will give a minimum value for the sample; but, since the values of $\bar{x}$ vary from sample to sample, it is perfectly clear that $\Sigma(x - \bar{x})^2$ for any one sample will be as large as $\Sigma(x - m)^2$ for the same sample only if $\bar{x}$ happens to be equal to m. No matter how slightly $\bar{x}$ varies from m, the sum of the squares of the deviations from the mean of the sample will be smaller than the sum of the squares of the deviations from the population mean, and hence the value of the standard deviation is underestimated by the formula which has N as a divisor. Now let us consider the extent of the bias and how it may be removed. There are N values in a sample, and in theory each of the N variates contributes equally to the estimate of the standard deviation; but in calculating $\Sigma(x - \bar{x})^2$ we use *one* value, $\bar{x}$, which is determined by the sample, and hence the effective weight of the sample is equal to $N - 1$ instead of N. All the values of one sample may be large, and if we could calculate $\Sigma(x - m)^2$ these values would contribute more to the total sum of squares than a set of values in another sample which are closer to m. Actually, since we take the deviations from the mean of the sample, the first sample would not necessarily contribute any more than the second sample. This brings out the idea that the mean used is fixed by the sample and to the extent of reducing the effective weight of the sample by 1. Thus we have the term introduced by R. A. Fisher, "degrees of freedom." When a sample of N variates are used for purposes of estimation, its weight is only that of the number of degrees of freedom. For every statistic calculated from the sample and utilized in forming the estimate, there is a loss of one degree of freedom. Thus, in the present example of estimating the standard deviation, the statistic calculated from the sample is $\bar{x}$, and there is a corresponding loss of one degree of freedom. This principle will be found to hold throughout all statistical procedure.

2. **Terminology and Symbols for Populations and Samples— Introducing the Term Variance.** As pointed out above, we speak of population *parameters* which are true and undeviating values, and *statistics* which are estimates, from the samples, of the population parameters. The statistics we have discussed so far are the mean $\bar{x}$ and the standard deviation s; and the corresponding parameters are m and σ.

Very frequently in statistical procedure the square of the standard deviation, usually referred to as the *variance*, is the more convenient of the two statistics. Most tests of significance can be made by means of the variance, in which case the extraction of the square root in order to obtain the standard deviation is an unnecessary operation. In general, all discussions of methods of estimation refer equally to the standard deviation and the variance, and consequently in Example 6 below we confine our attention to the variance.

Before proceeding with Example 6 it may be of assistance to summarize the symbols and terms that have been used up to this point, and any others that have not been used but are relative to those already discussed. This summary is as follows:

PARAMETERS		STATISTICS	
Mean	m	Mean	$\bar{x}$
Standard deviation	σ	Standard deviation	s
Standard deviation of a mean.	σ_m	Standard deviation or standard error of a mean	$s_{\bar{x}}$
Variance	σ^2 or V	Variance or mean square	s^2 or v
Variance of a mean	σ_m^2 or V_m	Variance of a mean	$s_{\bar{x}}^2$ or $v_{\bar{x}}$
		Number in sample	N or n'
		Degrees of freedom	n

Special notice should be taken of the term *standard error*, which is coming into general use in place of the standard deviation of a sample mean.

Example 6. The Use of Degrees of Freedom in Estimating the Variance. In Table 9 we have a set of random numbers taken from Tippett's tables (6), arranged in 10 groups of 20 numbers each. The variation in these numbers may be assumed to be made up of two portions: (1) *within* the groups, and (2) *between* the groups. But if the numbers have been selected at random these two sources of variation will be equally balanced. They would be unbalanced if, for example, some groups had all small numbers and the other groups all large numbers. The random selection of the numbers ensures that this shall not be the case. In terms of variance, the above statement with respect to variation is simply that the variances for within groups, between groups, and the total variance will all be equal within the limits of random sampling. Now, if for a particular set of numbers, as in this set, the variance for between groups is adjusted until it is almost exactly equal to the total variance, it follows that the variance within groups must also be almost exactly equal to the total. We can determine, therefore, the variance within each group, and if our method is correct these should give an average value very close to that for the whole sample.

The calculation of the variances within groups has been performed in Table 10 by two methods. There are 20 numbers in each group, so that in each group we have 19 degrees of freedom for the estimation of the variance. In column (7) of Table 10 the sums of squares are divided by the degrees of freedom, but in column (8) they are divided by 20, the number in the sample. At the foot of the table the total variance is again calculated by two methods. In the first case we divide by 199 and

TABLE 9

	A	B	C	D	E	F	G	H	I	J
1	29	45	14	25	11	47	28	35	18	25
2	45	39	49	32	32	36	24	27	16	39
3	16	29	29	18	46	42	10	18	34	24
4	37	11	31	28	44	36	27	44	18	30
5	50	12	19	20	28	38	11	25	30	24
6	10	37	20	44	40	21	42	33	29	36
7	26	44	49	41	27	41	22	49	35	31
8	19	15	15	10	28	26	30	11	35	10
9	24	50	11	43	27	17	17	17	42	13
10	10	14	22	19	11	50	33	39	50	43
11	10	22	23	10	48	30	44	26	21	27
12	48	20	41	13	21	39	32	29	11	20
13	22	46	40	31	44	21	23	16	45	39
14	13	14	12	45	16	46	25	47	18	30
15	28	21	39	39	36	22	27	10	31	18
16	32	15	43	23	42	34	16	20	26	11
17	10	37	31	11	12	50	20	12	34	46
18	11	26	34	22	48	13	47	42	22	43
19	30	29	49	35	30	46	38	50	24	44
20	37	22	37	49	30	47	12	34	42	24
Totals....	507	548	608	558	621	702	528	584	581	577

in the second case by 200. We have, therefore, four determinations of the variance as shown below. Note that the last line is calculated independently and does not come from totalling the values above except for columns (2) and (3).

By the first method we obtain for the average variance within groups a value that is 99.94% of the total. By the second method the average variance is only 95.43% of the total, and therefore *underestimates* the true value by 4.57%. Where N is the number of variates in a sample, it follows therefore that the correct estimate of the variance is given by $\Sigma(x - \bar{x})^2/N - 1$.

3. The Distribution of the Estimates of the Standard Deviation.

If a large population is being sampled and each sample contains 100 variates, we will get a series of varying values for the standard deviation calculated from these samples. But, if, instead of taking samples of 100 variates, we take samples of 10, it is to be expected that in the second case we will get values for the standard deviation fluctuating more widely than in the first case. This is the same as saying that the distribution of the standard deviation is dependent on the number of degrees of freedom in the sample. In this respect it is very much the same as a mean. In order to obtain from one sample a value for the mean that

TABLE 10

CALCULATION OF VARIANCE VALUES OF FIGURES IN TABLE 9
BY GROUPS OF 20 AND FOR WHOLE GROUP

(1)	(2) T_x	(3) $\Sigma(x^2)$	(4) $\bar{x}$	(5) T_x^2/N	(6) $\Sigma(x-\bar{x})^2$	(7) $\Sigma(x-\bar{x})^2/19$	(8) $\Sigma(x-\bar{x})^2/20$
A	507	16,159	25.35	12,852.45	3,306.55	174.0289	165.3275
B	548	18,110	27.40	15,015.20	3,049.80	162.8842	154.7400
C	608	21,602	30.40	18,483.20	3,118.80	164.1474	155.9400
D	558	18,620	27.90	15,568.20	3,051.80	160.6210	152.5900
E	621	22,189	31.05	19,282.05	2,906.95	152.9974	145.3475
F	702	27,208	35.10	24,640.20	2,567.80	135.1474	128.3900
G	528	16,132	26.40	13,939.20	2,192.80	115.4105	109.6400
H	584	20,306	29.20	17,052.80	3,253.20	171.2210	162.6600
I	581	19,043	29.05	16,878.05	2,164.95	113.9447	108.2475
J	577	19,045	28.85	16,646.45	2,398.55	126.2395	119.9275
					Av. =	147.6642	140.2810
A to J	T 5814	$\Sigma(x^2)$ 198,414	T^2/N 169,012.98	$\Sigma(x-\bar{x})^2$ 29,401.02	$\Sigma(x-\bar{x})^2/199$ 147.7438	$\Sigma(x-\bar{x})^2/200$ 147.0051	

	Method (1) Using Degrees of Freedom	Method (2) Using Number in Sample
Average within Groups.......	147.66	140.28
Total....................	147.74	147.00

is quite close to the mean of the parent population, we must take a large sample. Small samples will give us unbiassed estimates, but they will be more variable estimates.

Now in Chapter II we observed that, if a population is normally distributed and we know its standard deviation and mean, we can make a direct calculation of the probability of drawing from that population a sample with a mean of a given magnitude. This is, in a sense, a test of the significance of the mean of a particular sample, since if the probability is very small we should conclude that the sample was not drawn from the population in question, but from some other population. However, the standard deviation of the population cannot be determined, and the only value we have is the estimate s which has been calculated from the sample and varies from sample to sample. This brings us therefore to the general question of making tests of significance from the data of samples of any size.

4. Tests of Significance. The method of Chapter II for making probability determinations arose from our knowledge that the ratio of a mean of a sample to the standard deviation of the population from which the sample is drawn is normally distributed. This follows, of course because, if the mean is normally distributed and the standard deviation is constant for the population, the ratio of the two will also be normally distributed. Suppose, however, that we take the ratio of the mean of a sample to the *estimate* of the standard deviation s. Since s is more variable for small samples than for large ones, the ratio will obviously have a distribution that is dependent on the size of the sample, and, in order to determine the probability of the occurrence of any particular value of this ratio, we must know its distribution. This was worked out by "Student" (4) in 1908, and for the first time practical statisticians had placed in their hands a tool which could be applied in tests of significance for samples of all sizes. "Student" gave first a set of tables for the distribution of $\bar{x}/s$, which he designated by the letter Z. Later he prepared a table based on the distribution of t, which is $\bar{x}/s_{\bar{x}}$. Fisher, in "Statistical Methods for Research Workers," gives a compact table of t for degrees of freedom varying from 1 to 30, and the probability levels $P = 0.01, 0.02, 0.05, 0.10,$ and 0.90. These are the most convenient for general use, and are reproduced in part in Table 94.

Example 7. Two varieties of wheat are compared in 4 pairs of plots, there being 1 plot of each variety in each pair. Referring to the two varieties as A and B, we determine the difference in yield $A-B$ for the 4 pairs of plots, and the results are as follows in bushels per acre:

Pair.	1	2	3	4
$A-B$.	2	4	4	6

The differences are all positive and are therefore in favor of the variety A; but we wish to make a test so as to be able to state whether or not the data are in agreement with any hypothesis that we may set up. The obvious hypothesis here is that the varieties are not different in yielding quality, and consequently our theoretical distribution is built up on that basis. If the varieties are not different, the data will be expected to give a value of t that is not improbable. If they are different, we will expect the data to give a value of t which will occur by random sampling in only a small proportion of the cases. Let us proceed to the calculation of t.

We note first that the mean difference is 4, and that the sum of the squares of the deviations of the individual values from the mean is 8. We then have $s^2 = 8/3$, the numerator being the number of degrees of freedom available for estimating the standard deviation s. Then $s = \sqrt{8/3}$, and $s_{\bar{x}} = \sqrt{8/3 \times 4}$, which simplifies to $\sqrt{2/3}$. Finally $t = 4 \times \sqrt{3/2} = 4.87$. Now if we examine Table 94 it is observed that the 5% value of t for 3 degrees of freedom is 3.18, and the 1% value of t is 5.84. Thus the value of t given by the data would occur according to the hypothesis in less than 5% and somewhat more than 1% of the cases. Our conclusion is that the difference observed is due to a real varietal effect, and is not a chance occurrence.

It may be argued that in an example such as the above we are not actually testing the significance of the mean difference, because we are basing it on the distribution of t, wherein an exceptional value of t may be due to extreme deviations in either the mean difference or the standard error. This point is actually only of academic interest, because in either case the two samples are proved to be different regardless of which factor brings about the exceptional value of t. When we consider the actual problem of testing the difference in yield of two varieties, it is obvious that a real difference in the variation of the yields from plot to plot is so unlikely a factor that in general we can disregard this viewpoint, and assume that the significant value of t is at least mainly due to a significant difference in the mean yields.

5. Fiducial Limits. Stress has already been laid on the principle of estimation; and we come now to a method of setting up limiting values according to given probability levels, such that it can be said with a reasonable degree of certainty that the true value which is being estimated lies between these limits. In the example above, the difference between the yields of the two varieties was found to be significant; but no attempt was made to set up two limiting values, one on each side of the mean difference of 4 bushels, and to state that according to a given probability level, the true mean difference was between these limits. If we can perform such an operation it will obviously be of great practical value, because in the end we are not really concerned with being able to say only that one variety is a higher yielder than the other. Unless we can make a reliable estimate of this difference our experiment is not contributing information of value in actual practice.

It was emphasized in Chapter I that a test of significance involves setting up a hypothesis and determining the agreement between the hypothesis and the data of the experiment, and furthermore that any hypothesis whatever can be set up. In the example above, the hypothesis was that the mean difference in yield between the varieties was zero, and what we actually did was to find the value of t from the expression $(\bar{x} - m)/s_{\bar{x}}$, where m, the mean of the parent population according to the hypothesis, was taken to be zero. We can, however, take m equal to any value that we please, and we might choose for example to take m equal to 2. Then $t = (4 - 2) \times \sqrt{3/2} = 2.46$, and this value is less than the 5% point. The inference from this test is that there is no definite evidence that the true difference is greater or less than 2. We begin to see therefore that, though our difference is significant, we cannot specify very closely the range within which the true value lies. Suppose now that we can locate a lower limit such that, if we substituted it for m in the t test, the value of t obtained would be exactly equal to its 5% point, and we determine in addition a similar upper limit. The observed difference could then be said to differ significantly from either of the limiting values, and we could say with a reasonable degree of certainty that the true value lies between these limits. The procedure is simple, as all we have to do is to set up the equation for t with m as an unknown and t equal to its value at the 5% point. Thus:

$$3.18 = (4 - m) \times \sqrt{\tfrac{3}{2}}$$

Solving for m we get an answer of 1.40, and our limits are 0.60 to 3.40. It is now clear that, although our experiment gave a significant result, it did not enable us to estimate very accurately the true difference in yield between the two varieties. These limiting values have been very aptly termed by R. A. Fisher the *fiducial limits*, and in the present example we would describe them as the fiducial limits at the 5% point.

6. General Methods for Testing the Significance of Differences. One of the most common problems in statistics is the testing of the significance of a difference between two means. The reasoning behind such tests involves picturing an infinite population of differences for which the mean is zero. We have two samples for which the means are different; and we wish to know in what proportion of the cases on the average, in the procedure of taking pairs of samples, we will get a difference as large as or larger than the one observed. Tests of this kind fall into two classes:

(*a*) Samples are distinct and the variates are not paired in any way. If there are two blocks of land and we take the yields of a group of plots from each block, and we wish to test the significance of the difference between the means for the blocks, we have a problem that falls into this class. The number of variates in the two samples may be either the same or different. Let the samples be designated as 1 and 2; then:

$\bar{x}_1$ = mean of sample 1.

$\bar{x}_2$ = mean of sample 2.

$\bar{x}_1 - \bar{x}_2$ = mean of difference to be tested.

n_1 = degrees of freedom for sample 1 which contains, therefore, $n_1 + 1$ variates.

n_2 = degrees of freedom for sample 2 which contains, therefore, $n_2 + 1$ variates.

The calculations are carried out as follows:

$\Sigma(x_1 - \bar{x}_1)^2$ = sum of squares for sample 1.

$\Sigma(x_2 - \bar{x}_2)^2$ = sum of squares for sample 2.

$$s = \sqrt{\frac{\Sigma(x_1 - \bar{x}_1)^2 + \Sigma(x_2 - \bar{x}_2)^2}{n_1 + n_2}} \qquad (1)$$

$$s_{\bar{x}} = s\sqrt{\frac{n_1 + n_2 + 2}{(n_1 + 1)(n_2 + 1)}} \qquad (2)$$

$$t = \frac{(\bar{x}_1 - \bar{x}_2)}{s_{\bar{x}}} \qquad (3)$$

We enter the table of t under $n = n_1 + n_2$. If the samples contain an equal number of variates, we have:

$$(n_1 + 1) = (n_2 + 1) = N$$

and

$$s = \sqrt{\frac{\Sigma(x_1 - \bar{x}_1)^2 + \Sigma(x_2 - \bar{x}_2)^2}{2(N - 1)}} \qquad (4)$$

$$s_{\bar{x}} = s\sqrt{\frac{2}{N}} \qquad (5)$$

The table of t is entered under $n = 2(N - 1)$.

Example 8. Let $\bar{x}_1 = 196.42$ and $\bar{x}_2 = 198.82$; then $(\bar{x}_1 - \bar{x}_2) = 2.40$. The samples are taken independently, and consequently there is no reason for assuming that x_1 and x_2 are correlated. In sample 1 we have taken 9 variates, and in sample 2 we have 7 variates. Hence $n_1 = 8$ and $n_2 = 6$. We calculate first $\Sigma(x_1 - \bar{x}_1)^2$ and $\Sigma(x_2 - \bar{x}_2)^2$. We will assume that this is done, and we get:

$$\Sigma(x_1 - \bar{x}_1)^2 = 26.94$$
$$\Sigma(x_2 - \bar{x}_2)^2 = 18.73$$
$$\overline{\text{Total} = 45.67}$$

Then:

$$s = \sqrt{\frac{45.67}{14}} = 1.81$$

and

$$t = \frac{2.40}{1.81}\sqrt{\frac{63}{16}} = 2.62$$

Entering the table of t under $n = 14$ we find that a t value of 2.62 corresponds almost exactly with a P value of 0.02. Between the means of the two samples a difference of 2.40 would occur by chance in only 2 cases out of 100.

(b) Variates are paired; that is, each value of x_1 is associated in some logical way with a corresponding value of x_2. Thus, if two varieties of a field crop are being tested in pairs of plots, each pair containing one plot of both varieties, we would have a problem of this kind. There will, of course, be the same number of variates in the two samples so that, if there are N pairs, there will be $N - 1$ degrees of freedom available for the comparison. This follows logically from the fact that we are now dealing with individual differences and there is one difference for each pair of variates.

The calculations are:

$$s = \sqrt{\left[\Sigma(x_1 - x_2)^2 - \frac{(T_1 - T_2)^2}{N}\right]/N - 1} \tag{6}$$

$$s_{\bar{x}} = \frac{s}{\sqrt{N}} \tag{7}$$

$$t = \frac{\bar{x} - \bar{x}_2}{s_{\bar{x}}} \text{, same as formula (3)}$$

If the student should be confused to find later that s^2 as computed above is not the same as when obtained by the analysis of variance, it may be just as well to adopt the following method, which is identical with that of the analysis of variance. The value of t obtained by the two methods is, of course, the same.

$$s = \sqrt{\left[\tfrac{1}{2}\Sigma(x_1 - x_2)^2 - \frac{(T - T_2)^2}{2N}\right]/N - 1} \tag{8}$$

$$s_{\bar{x}} = s\sqrt{\frac{2}{N}} \tag{9}$$

$$t = \text{same as formula (3)}.$$

Example 9. In this example assume that the variates are paired, as in a feeding experiment where a series of animals are paired up according to initial weight. One animal in each pair is given ration 1 and the other one ration 2. There are 10 pairs of animals, and the difference between the mean gains per 100 pounds of feed at the end of the feeding period is 1.42 pounds. We shall assume that

$$\left[\tfrac{1}{2}\Sigma(x_1 - x_2)^2 - \frac{(T_1 - T_2)^2}{2N}\right] = 15.08$$

Then

$$s = \sqrt{\frac{15.08}{9}} = 1.30$$

and

$$t = \frac{1.42}{1.30}\sqrt{\frac{10}{2}} = 2.44$$

Entering the t table under $n = 9$, we find that the P value is between 0.05 and 0.02, but closer to the former. We can take $P = 0.05$ as approximately correct, so that the difference between the two means could only occur by chance in about 1 out of 20 trials.

7. Exercises.

1. The figures below are for protein tests of the same variety of wheat grown in two districts. In district 1 the average for 5 samples is 12.74, and in district 2, the average for 7 samples is 13.03. If these are the only figures available, test the significance of the difference between the average proteins for the two districts.

Protein Results

District 1.......... 12.6   13.4   11.9   12.8   13.0

District 2.......... 13.1   13.4   12.8   13.5   13.3   12.7   12.4

$$t = 1.04 \qquad P = 0.3, \text{ approximately.}$$

2. Mitchell (2) conducted a paired feeding experiment with pigs on the relative value of limestone and bonemeal for bone development. The results are given in Table 11 below.

TABLE 11

ASH CONTENT IN PERCENTAGE OF SCAPULAS OF PAIRS OF PIGS
FED ON LIMESTONE AND BONEMEAL

Pair	Limestone	Bonemeal
1	49.2	51.5
2	53.3	54.9
3	50.6	52.2
4	52.0	53.3
5	46.8	51.6
6	50.5	54.1
7	52.1	54.2
8	53.0	53.3
Mean....	50.94	53.14

Determine the significance of the difference between the means in two ways: (1) by assuming that the values are paired, and (2) by assuming that the values are not paired. On the basis of your results, discuss the effect of pairing.

(1) Paired: $t = 4.42$, $P = $ less than   0.01.

(2) Unpaired: $t = 2.48$, $P = $ approximately 0.02.

3. In a wheat variety test conducted over a wide area, the mean difference between two varieties was found to be 4.5 bushels to the acre. The standard error of this difference $s_{\bar{x}}$ was 1.5 bushels per acre, and was determined from 100 pairs of plots. Set up the fiducial limits at the 5% probability level for the mean difference in yield between the two varieties.

Note that t can be taken as 1.96, then fiducial limits are 1.56 to 7.44.

REFERENCES

1. R. A. FISHER. Statistical Methods for Research Workers. Oliver and Boyd, London and Edinburgh, 1936. Reading: Chapter V, Sections 23, 24, 24.1.
2. H. H. MITCHELL. Proc. Am. Soc. An. Prod., 63–72, 1930.
3. G. W. SNEDECOR. Statistical Methods. Collegiate Press Inc., Ames, Iowa, 1937. Reading: Chapters II, III, and IV.
4. STUDENT. *Biometrika*, **6**:1, 1908.
5. L. H. C. TIPPETT. The Methods of Statistics. Williams and Norgate, Ltd., London. Reading: Chapter V, Sections 5.1, 5.2, 5.3.
6. L. H. C. TIPPETT. Random Sampling Numbers. Cambridge University Press London, 1927.

CHAPTER V

THE DESIGN OF SIMPLE EXPERIMENTS

1. What is Experimental Design? In Chapter I some ideas relative to experimental design were presented, but in view of what we have now learned of the t test it should be worth while at this point to repeat some of these ideas, and at the same time introduce any new concepts that have arisen out of later discussions. An experiment can be said to have a definite design if it has been carefully planned in advance, and if due attention has been paid to possible results and their interpretation. The latter point is probably the most frequently neglected. A great deal of time may be spent on the various details of procedure, and full preparations made for carrying the experiment through to completion. This may be assumed to be sufficient to ensure a successful experiment, but a long list of such experiments that contribute neither positive nor negative information is good evidence that careful planning of the procedure is in itself incomplete. Only by thinking in terms of the various types of results that an experiment can yield is it possible to obviate some very costly mistakes. If these possibilities are thoroughly worked out it is self-evident that a complete failure is impossible.

2. Planning to Remove Bias. One of the commonest mistakes in experimental design is the failure to guard against biased results. Such experiments *may* give good results but their great weakness is that they are not beyond criticism; and regardless of the truth and importance of the results obtained the investigator may never feel quite happy about presenting them with conviction. Let us examine hypothetical plans of experiments that are subject to a bias of some sort.

Suppose that we are to conduct an experiment on the value of feeding milk to school children. There are two neighboring schools, and milk is given to the children in one of the schools and not to those in the other. At the end of the experiment the children are compared on the basis of height, weight, etc., by means of the t test. The children from the school in which milk was given are found to be significantly heavier than those from the other school. The error in design is so obvious here that it is scarcely necessary to point it out. The experiment has shown that the children of the two schools are significantly different in weight, but this might easily have been the case if no milk had been given or even if

45

the order of giving the milk had been reversed.   In fact the experiment is not at all what it seemed to be at first.   It consists actually of just two variates which are the two schools, and no determination of the error of such an experiment is possible.

Now let us endeavor to improve the plan, and we will confine the giving of milk to pairs of boys or girls, one getting the milk and the other not.   The pairs are selected at random, and in each pair the milk is given to the younger and not to the elder child.   The reader will object that we are again introducing a bias in that the difference observed might easily be due to age and not to the effect of milk in the diet.   This is perfectly true, so in order to overcome this defect we decide to give it to the younger child in one case and the elder child in the second case, alternating in this way throughout the entire group.   Now the experiment seems to be perfect, and in truth it is much improved, but with a little thought it should be clear that we have succeeded in removing only the gross defects—those that are obvious to us at the outset and which anyone can remove with a little thought and a general knowledge of the problem being investigated.   The chief trouble with our design is not that we have knowingly allowed some factor to bias the experiment, but that we have not planned it in such a way that it is impossible for bias to enter in.   A definite method is available for this purpose, which has already been referred to in Chapter I.   It involves merely assigning at *random* which member of each pair of children is to receive milk.   This is a simple device and one which is absolutely trustworthy in the matter of removing bias.

Numerous examples may be cited of experiments that are designed so that bias may enter in.   One of the most common is the field plot test in which the varieties or treatments are arranged systematically in the blocks or replications.   It is not possible to discuss this particular problem and deal with it fully until we have made a study of the methods of the analysis of variance, but we can consider the simple type of experiment in which only two varieties or treatments are being tested and they are arranged in pairs of plots.   Here we are dealing with a series of differences, and we set up a hypothesis as, for example, that the mean difference is normally distributed about zero.   On the basis of this hypothesis we can determine the proportion of the trials in which a difference as great as or greater than the one observed will occur.   The validity of our test depends on its being designed so that if the hypothesis is true the distribution of the results from a large number of trials will be normal and will have a mean of zero.   What would anyone after a little thought say of an experiment designed so that, if the varieties being tested are actually equal in yield, the result turns out according to a large series of tests, either definitely positive or definitely negative? Yet this is just the kind of result that may be expected if the principle of randomization is not used in setting up the experiment.   This applies particularly to the position of the varieties or treatments in the pairs.

3. Designs that Broaden the Scope of the Experiment.   This is another subject than cannot be treated fully at this stage, but a few of the general principles may be pointed out.   Suppose that the all-inclusive subject of the experiment is the effect of milk in the diet of young animals.   Most of us would reject this as a proper subject for experimental investigation at once, because we can see that it is one for which there is no possibility of obtaining a result that will be of practical value. In one group of animals the milk may be beneficial and in another group it may be of no value or even harmful, so that unless the experiment is repeated with all possible kinds of animals and the results with each kind studied separately we cannot expect to gather any valuable information.   The decision with regard to an experiment of this type is likely to be that we should select one kind of animal in which we are particularly interested, and then confine the tests to a limited age group.   In the first case the subject of the investigation called for an experiment of such enormous scope that the entire proposition was absurd.   Now we have limited the scope of the experiment, but we have not gone as far as we might.   Let us suppose that the investigator decides on pigs as the kind of animal to be tested, then he decides to use pigs of one age within the limits of one week, and finally that they shall be from the same litter.   He has now gone to the other extreme and has set up an experiment such that, no matter how significant the results, they will not be of any value except within a very narrow range.   It cannot be assumed that the results will apply to other age groups, to other breeds, or perhaps even to other litters, as it may easily be that the litter selected is peculiar in some respect with regard to the reaction of the individuals of the litter to milk in the diet.   No amount of mathematical knowledge will help the investigator over the difficulty encountered here, of setting up an experiment that will not have too great a scope but will at the same time give results that can be interpreted on a fairly wide basis. Only his own experience and general knowledge of the problem that is to be investigated will give the clue to the correct form for the experiment to take.   In this instance there may be one breed of pigs that is predominant in the area in which the investigator is interested, and consequently it is quite justifiable to confine his experiment to this breed. Again, there will be a definite range in age at which farmers will be concerned with feeding milk, and only this range need be represented.   It will not be wise, however, to use only pigs from one litter; in fact it would seem to be desirable to have as many litters as possible represented in order that the experimental material will be representative of pigs as a whole in the area in which they are being raised. An obviously desirable plan will be to take pairs of pigs of nearly equal weight and condition from a number of litters, assign the alternative diets at random to the members of each pair, and then feed the pigs individually so that individual records may be kept of food eaten and gains made.

4. Replication and the Control of Error. The value of replication in experimental design is easily understood. In the first place, replication increases the accuracy and scope of the experiment; in the second place, it enables us to determine the magnitude of the uncontrolled variation that is usually referred to as the error; and in the third place it allows for designs that give us an effective control over error. The increase in accuracy due to replication is expressible in terms of a mathematical equation. In Chapter II, Section 3, we noted that the standard deviation of a mean is reduced in proportion to the square root of the number in the sample. In ordinary experiments any one treatment is represented by a sample which is made up of one unit in each replication. Therefore in general the accuracy of an experiment, as expressed by the standard error of a mean of any one treatment, is increased in proportion to the square root of the number of replications. This statement should not be interpreted to mean that results of twice the value are obtained by multiplying the replications by 4. This depends on what we mean by the value of the results. In terms of work done or energy expended on an experiment to bring about a given reduction in the standard error this is true, but it may be that the expenditure of additional energy in order to increase the accuracy of the experiment is unnecessary, in which case the value of the results is not enhanced. More will be said on this subject later; but for the present we should note that replication is the primary tool at our disposal for increasing the accuracy of the experimental results.

Another phase of the increased accuracy due to increased replication arises from the distribution of t for different degrees of freedom. From Table 94 we note that, for 1 degree of freedom, t at the 5% point is 12.706 while for 60 degrees of freedom the corresponding value of t is 2.00. In the first case a much larger difference would be necessary to represent a significant effect than in the second case. In a paired experiment the number of degrees of freedom available for estimating the error of the experiment is equal to 1 less than the number of pairs. Suppose then that we have one experiment with 3 pairs and another one with 10 pairs. For the first experiment we would require for significance a difference that is 4.30 times the error, and for the second experiment a difference that is 2.26 times the error, these being the values of t at the 5% point for 2 and 9 degrees of freedom respectively.   It is important for the beginner to note carefully that this increase in accuracy due to increased replication is entirely distinct from that discussed above which results from dividing the standard error of the experiment by the square root of the number of replications in order to determine the standard error of a mean.   Both factors act together and in the same direction but they arise from different sources.

The manner in which replication increases the scope of the experiment will be evident from the discussion of Section 3.   In the example discussed there it was decided purposely to make the replications somewhat different, in order that the results might be of general application. The importance of this is sometimes overlooked, and we will find field plot investigators looking for an exceptionally uniform patch of soil on which to carry out an experiment and putting all the replications on this same patch.   No criticism is offered of this procedure provided that the investigator is not under the impression that by doing so he is necessarily improving the experiment.   Within each replication it is desirable to have as much uniformity as possible, but between the replications it does not improve matters to have a great deal of uniformity; and from the standpoint of increasing the scope of the experiment it may even be harmful.   To put these ideas into concrete form let us assume that two soil treatments are being compared in paired plots.   On the field that is available for the experiment there are several types of soils, and we shall assume for the purpose of argument that all the soil types are present that occur in the area for which the results of the experiment are to apply.   The investigator has three choices.   The pairs of plots can be placed all on one soil type, an equal number of pairs on each type, or at random over the field.   Placing the pairs all on one soil type and close together in the field has in its favor compactness and economy of space; but the results obtained on the one type of soil may not apply to the other types, and consequently to get full information on the problem a separate test must be planned for each condition.   This may be beyond the scope of the facilities of the investigator, so he turns his attention to the other possibilities.   Placing an equal number of pairs on each soil type has decided advantages.   For example, if there are at least four pairs in each location it is possible to regard each set as an individual but very rough experiment, capable of yielding an approximate measure of the particular reaction of the two treatments on the soil type represented.   The average yields of the two treatments over the whole field will, however, be representative for the whole area in which the results are to be put to practical use only if in that area there are about an equal number of acres belonging to each type. This statement, of course, implies that the treatments will give different results under the various substratum conditions, but experience tells us that this is very likely to be the case. We turn now to the third method, that of randomizing the pairs of plots over the whole field. The process of randomization will ensure that the various soil conditions represented in the field will have an equal chance of being used in the experiment. As nearly as possible, therefore, we are obtaining a random sample of the infinite population for which we are endeavoring to obtain an unbiassed estimate of the difference between the two treatments. The only possible criticism of this method is that some of the soil types will not be represented, and hence certain information will be lost. The answer is that with a given type of experiment we cannot perform two functions at once. Without enlarging it considerably we cannot design an experiment that will give us a general average result for the whole area under consideration, and at the same time give us detailed information on the reactions of the treatments under varying conditions. Information regarding the whole area is not lost, but gained, by placing the pairs at random and perhaps missing some of the types. On the assumption that the field is representative of the larger area being sampled it gives us a more correct measure than if we assumed without proper information that each of the types is equally represented.

This somewhat theoretical discussion does not bear precisely on the practical problem with which the investigator is faced, because it is impossible to obtain a field that is really representative of a large area. However, it serves to bring out some very important points that may be put into practice in tests of this kind. Any investigator who gives the problem serious thought will take note of the limitations of one test carried out under very uniform conditions, and at the same time will realize the importance of replication in widening the scope of field plot experiments.

The second important function of replication is to enable us to obtain a measure of the experimental error. This follows directly from the principles of the t test. If there is only one plot of treatment A and one of B there can be only one difference, and the number of degrees of freedom available for estimating the standard error is zero. In non-statistical terms there is only one value, the difference between the two plots, and this difference is the only measure we have of both soil variation and the effect of the treatments. We cannot compare a difference with itself; therefore, we say that there are no degrees of freedom available for estimating the error of the difference. This defect in an experiment is obviously overcome as soon as we introduce replication. Even if we have only two plots of A and two of B we have at least one degree of freedom available for estimating the error, and by means of the t test an unbiassed comparison of the treatments can be made.

The third function of replication has to do with the control of error. Another hypothetical example will make this clear. Again we can suppose that two soil treatments are being compared in paired plots. The measure of error is determined from the variation in the differences within the pairs. Suppose now that the plots are all distributed at random over the field, and the pairs are made up simply by taking the two plots of A and B that happen to fall together in another random selection. This can have only one effect, and that is to increase the variability of the differences, and consequently the accuracy of the test is reduced. A question that may be asked here is whether or not the method that increases the variability of the differences will also increase the average difference between the two treatments. Yes, the average difference will also be increased but it must be remembered that this is due in actual practice to two components. A part is due to the real difference between the treatments and a part to the variability of the soil. The latter component will be increased in the same proportion as the error, but the former will not, and consequently the precision of the experiment becomes correspondingly less as the error component increases.

The benefits to be obtained from the arrangement of treatments in replications wherein each replication contains one of each of the treatments is fairly well known to experimentalists, especially in agronomic research. Variety trials are therefore arranged in compact blocks so that the plots within the blocks are as nearly alike as possible. There are, of course, many applications of the same principle in other types of experimentation; but this subject will be discussed more fully under the heading of the analysis of variance.

REFERENCE

1 R. A. FISHER. The Design of Experiments. Oliver and Boyd, London and Edinburgh, 1937. Reading: Chapters I, II, III.

CHAPTER VI

LINEAR REGRESSION

1. General Observations. In the previous discussions emphasis was placed on the variations that occur in any one variable, such as the yield of wheat plots, the weight of animals, or the height of students. Sometimes the values of one variable are classified in two or more ways, in which case we may be interested in the joint variation of the pairs or groups of values so formed. For example, in Chapter V a problem was discussed in which pairs of plots of two varieties were arranged in different ways over a field. The interest there was largely in the differences between the members of pairs, but it was also pointed out that if the plots were close together they would tend to yield alike, or in other words they would vary together. The present chapter, however, deals with examples wherein there are paired variates but of two different kinds of variables, and in general one of the variables may be regarded as independent and the other as dependent. In a study of the effect of rainfall on yields of field crops, we would have a typical example of a dependent and an independent variable, in that the interest would lie in the degree to which rainfall, acting as an independent variable, would have an effect on yield, the dependent variable. It would be useless, of course, to think of this problem in any other terms, as we could not imagine the yield of field crops having any effect on rainfall.

It is not difficult to see that, for any set of data for paired variates, it should be possible to obtain a measure of the physical relation between the two variables. Suppose that the data are arranged as in Fig. 6, which shows graphically the average yields of groups of plots of Marquis wheat for given percentages of infection with stem rust. It would not be difficult to draw a straight line so that it would represent the general trend of decreasing yield with increasing percentages of infection, and we could then read off the approximate decrease in yield for a given increase in infection. This, of course, would be a very crude method, as the fitting of the line would be purely a matter of eye judgment and different individuals would place the line in slightly different places. Then to develop from the graph a general expression for the relation between the two variables, from which the line could be reconstructed at any time and which could be used for predicting the effect on yield of given percentages of infection, it would be necessary to draw out the graph very accurately and make an average of a number of measurements. In order to arrive at a more precise method of fitting the line, recourse is had to the "method of least squares." This means that a line is fitted such that the sum of the squares of the deviations of the points in the graph from the straight line is a minimum. It gives us a statistic known as the *regression coefficient*, which expresses the increase or decrease in the dependent variable for one unit of increase in the independent variable. From the regression coefficient we can set up a *regression equation*, which can be used to make predictions; and also it defines the straight line known as the *regression straight line*.

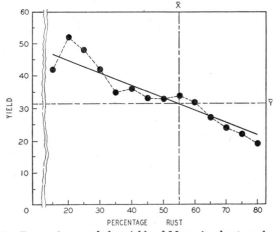

Fig. 6.—Regression graph for yields of Marquis wheat on degree of infection with stem rust.

The essential difference between the treatment of different kinds of variables that are thought to be related and pairs of variables that merely vary together will now be clear. In the first case our concern is to determine a function, in the present case a straight-line function, that will express the average relation between the two variables. In the latter case the function will obviously not be of very much value; we will probably be better satisfied with some expression giving the combined effect of the variables on each other or perhaps, if we cannot think in such terms, the degree to which both variables are acted upon by outside influences that cause them to vary together. Of this second condition we shall learn more in the next chapter.

2. **Fitting the Regression Line.** Let the two variables be represented by x and y, where x is independent and y dependent. Then, if the

relation between x and y can be represented by a straight line, the equation of the line will be of the form:

$$Y = a + bx \tag{1}$$

where a and b are constants and Y represents the values of y estimated from the equation. For any one value of x, say x_i, the corresponding value of y estimated will be Y_i, and the error of estimation will be $(y_i - Y_i)$. The value of y_i would be represented on the graph as in Fig. 6 by one of the points, and the corresponding estimated value Y_i would be a point on the straight line. To fit the line, it is required that the sum of the squares of the errors of estimation $\Sigma(y - Y)^2$ shall be a minimum. It is best to begin with x and y measured from their means, so that our regression line is actually:

$$(Y - \bar{y}) = a + b\,(x - \bar{x}) \tag{2}$$

whence the error of estimation is given by $\Sigma[(Y - \bar{y}) - (y - \bar{y})]^2 = \Sigma(y - Y)^2$, the same as before. Minimizing by the method of least squares for $\Sigma(y - Y)^2$, we obtain the equations: [1]

$$Na + \Sigma(x - \bar{x})b = \Sigma(y - \bar{y})$$

$$\Sigma(x - \bar{x})a + \Sigma(x - \bar{x})^2 b = \Sigma(y - \bar{y})(x - \bar{x})$$

and solving we have:

$$a = 0$$

$$b = \frac{\Sigma(y - \bar{y})(x - \bar{x})}{\Sigma(x - x)^2} \tag{3}$$

In equation (3) we note the expression $\Sigma(y - \bar{y})(x - \bar{x})$, which is usually referred to as the *sum of products*. For two variables, it is the expression that corresponds to the sum of the squares of the deviations from the mean for one variable. We know that the variance for a single variable is given by:

$$s^2 = \frac{\Sigma(x - \bar{x})^2}{N - 1}$$

and now we learn that the *covariance* for two variables is given by:

$$cv = \frac{\Sigma(y - \bar{y})(x - \bar{x})}{N - 1} \tag{4}$$

---

[1] For the method-of-least-squares technique see any good textbook on elementary calculus. If it is confusing to apply these methods to expressions containing the summation sign, Σ, write out one or two sets of values and proceed with them consecutively. The procedure for the entire set of values summated will then be clear.

In (3) if the numerator and denominator are divided by $N - 1$ the equation becomes:

$$b = \frac{\text{Covariance } (xy)}{\text{Variance } (x)} \qquad (5)$$

Going back now to (2) above:

$$Y - \bar{y} = b(x - \bar{x})$$

and: $\qquad\qquad\qquad Y = \bar{y} + b(x - \bar{x}) \qquad\qquad (6)$

or: $\qquad\qquad\qquad Y = (\bar{y} - b\bar{x}) + bx \qquad\qquad (7)$

the last being the form in which this expression is most frequently used. It is known as the *linear regression equation,* and b in the equation is the regression *coefficient.*

3. Properties of the Regression Coefficient. In the equation $Y = \bar{y} + b(x - \bar{x})$, b expresses the probable relation between x and y in terms of the values in which x and y are measured. The coefficient in this equation is usually represented as b_{yx}, which means that it is the regression coefficient for the regression of y on x; and thus in any sample of paired variates studied it represents a kind of average of the increase in y for a given increase in x. Thus if y is bushels per acre and x is tons of fertilizer applied, b_{yx} is an estimate of the increase in yield to be expected from one ton of fertilizer.

For every example where we study the regression of y on x, there is also the theoretical possibility of studying the regression of x on y; but as stated above the theory of linear regression is best confined to examples where we can think clearly in terms of the effect of one variable on the other, and consequently the investigator is concerned with only one aspect of the regression.

The regression coefficient is a measure of the slope of the regression line, but only relative to the class values of the two variables and their range of variation. Suppose that, in a study of the effect of rainfall on yield, the rainfall varies from 0 to 9 and the yields from 20 to 30, and the mean yield is 25 and the mean rainfall 5. In a graph such as Fig. 6 the units could be of the same length for the two variables, and if the regression coefficient is 1 the regression line would go from one diagonal to the other and would have a slope of 1; that is, it would lie at an angle of 45 degrees. However, if rainfall varied from 0 to 20 the slope would be less than 1, even for the case where yield is completely dependent on rainfall.

4. Tests of Significance of the Regression Coefficient. The sampling error of the regression coefficient is related to the error of estimation measured by $\Sigma(y - Y)^2$. Thus we have the *standard error of estimate* given by:

$$s_e = \sqrt{\frac{\Sigma(y - Y)^2}{N - 2}} \tag{8}$$

and the standard error of the regression coefficient by:

$$s_b = s_e / \sqrt{\Sigma(x - \bar{x})^2} \tag{9}$$

The value of $\Sigma(y - Y)^2$ can best be calculated by equating it to $\Sigma(y - \bar{y})^2 - b^2\Sigma(x - \bar{x})$, or $\Sigma(y - \bar{y})^2 - b\Sigma(y - \bar{y})(x - \bar{x})$, depending on which form is the more convenient at the time. In these equalities it is understood that the regression coefficient is b_{yx}.

Then to make the test of significance t is given by:

$$t = \frac{b_{yx}}{s_b} = \frac{b_{yx}\sqrt{\Sigma(x - \bar{x})^2}}{s_e} \tag{10}$$

and the table of t is entered under $N - 2$ degrees of freedom. There are $N - 2$ degrees of freedom because both $\bar{y}$ and b_{yx} are statistics calculated from the sample.

The test for the significance of the difference between two regression coefficients is based on their respective standard errors. For the two regression coefficients b_1 and b_2, with standard errors calculated as in (9) above, the standard error of the difference would be:

$$s_{1-2} = \sqrt{s_1^2 + s_2^2} \tag{11}$$

and

$$t = \frac{(b_1 - b_2)}{s_{1-2}} \tag{12}$$

The two coefficients may be calculated from different numbers of paired values, so that there would be a total of $(N_1 - 2) + (N_2 - 2)$ degrees of freedom available for the comparison of the coefficients, where N_1 and N_2 are the numbers of pairs respectively from which b_1 and b_2 are calculated.

A special case arises when there are two sets of values of the dependent variable. If these are y_1 and y_2, there are two regression coefficients b_{y_1x} and b_{y_2x}; and it may be necessary to test the significance of the difference between them. The simplest and most direct method is to form a new variable from $(y_1 - y_2)$ and calculate $b_{(y_1-y_2)x}$, which may be tested in the ordinary way.

5. Methods of Calculation. It will be remembered from formula (3) that the numerator of the regression coefficient is the sum of products of the deviations from the means of the two variables, and is expressed algebraically as $\Sigma(y - \bar{y})(x - \bar{x})$. The denominator of the coefficient is the already familiar sum of squares of the deviations from the mean, for the independent variable usually indicated by x. Our problem, then, is to learn the most convenient method of calculating the sum of products. The method follows from the identity:

$$\Sigma(y - \bar{y})(x - \bar{x}) = \Sigma(xy) - \frac{T_x T_y}{N} \tag{13}$$

where $\Sigma(xy)$ is the sum of the products of the original values of x and y, taken of course by pairs, and T_x and T_y are the totals for all the original values of x and y, respectively. The latter are somewhat more convenient symbols for the familiar $\Sigma(x)$ and $\Sigma(y)$. Given a series of paired values, therefore, for which a regression coefficient is to be calculated, the first step is to determine T_x and T_y. Then each value of x is multiplied by each value of y (or vice versa), and the sum of the products accumulated in the machine. This gives us $\Sigma(xy)$, and if we subtract from this $T_x T_y/N$, the remainder is the required sum of products of the deviations. $\Sigma(x - \bar{x})^2$ is, of course, calculated in the manner indicated in Chapter II.

In many examples the labor of calculation can be reduced by *coding* the data. This involves either subtracting a uniform quantity from the values of each individual variate or dividing by a constant quantity, or in certain cases both devices are employed at the same time. Supposing that the actual values are as given below on the left; the values on the right are examples of how the coding may be carried out.

UNCODED		CODED		
x	y	x	y	
2402	2785	240	278	Dividing by 10 and rounding off last figure.
		40	78	Subtracting 200.
198	196	8	6	Subtracting 190 from each value.
195	193	5	3	
256	274	56	74	Subtracting 200. It is quite permissible to
229	198	29	−2	have negative values, but usually they complicate the calculations slightly and if a machine is available for calculation most workers avoid them.

The regression coefficient having been calculated, the next step is to determine the regression equation, $Y = (\bar{y} - b\bar{x}) + bx$. The portion

$(\bar{y} - b\bar{x})$ is constant and is computed once and for all. Putting the result for this portion equal to a, we have the working equation:

$$Y = a + b_{yx}x \qquad (14)$$

from which all the Y values that are necessary can be obtained.

It must be remembered that, if the regression equation is calculated from coded data, the resulting equation itself must be decoded before it can be used for prediction purposes. If the data have been coded by subtraction only, the only correction required is to the means of x and y and this correction must be made while the equation is in the form given in equation (7). If in the coding the x and y values are divided by a different constant value, then a correction must be made to the regression coefficient as well as to the means of x and y. For example, if x has been divided by A and y by B, then the regression coefficient calculated from the coded data must be multiplied by B/A.

Example 10. Calculation of the Regression Coefficient and Regression Equation from a Small Series of Paired Values. In a hypothetical example the values from 10 pairs of variates are as given below:

$$x\ldots\ldots\quad 9\quad 8\quad 7\quad 7\quad 6\quad 5\quad 3\quad 3\quad 1\quad 1\quad T_x = 50$$

$$y\ldots\ldots\quad 9\quad 9\quad 8\quad 6\quad 6\quad 5\quad 4\quad 3\quad 1\quad 1\quad T_y = 52$$

Values for the totals are given at the end of each line and $N = 10$. To find the sum of products, and the sum of squares of x, we proceed as follows:

$\Sigma(xy) = (9 \times 9) + (8 \times 9) + (7 \times 8) + \cdots + (1 \times 1) = 335.0$
$T_xT_y/N = (50 \times 52)/10 \qquad\qquad\qquad\qquad = 260.0$
Difference $= \Sigma(y - \bar{y})(x - \bar{x}) \qquad\qquad\qquad = \ \ 75.0$

$\Sigma(x^2) = 9^2 + 8^2 + 7^2 + 7^2 + 6^2 + \cdots + 1^2 \quad = 324.0$
$T_x^2/N = 50^2/10 \qquad\qquad\qquad\qquad\qquad\qquad = 250.0$
Difference $= \Sigma(x - \bar{x})^2 \qquad\qquad\qquad\qquad = \ \ 74.0$

Then $b_{yx} = 75.0/74.0 = 1.014$. $\bar{x} = 50/10 = 5.0$. $\bar{y} = 52.0/10 = 5.2$.

Also $a = (5.2 - 1.014 \times 5.0) = 0.13$.

Finally the regression equation is $Y = 0.13 + 1.014x$.

In order to use this equation for predicting values of y from given values of x, it is only necessary to insert the required value for x and determine the resulting value of Y. For example, if we take x equal to 2 the calculated value of Y is $0.13 + 1.014 \times 2 = 2.158$.

Example 11. Calculation of the Regression Coefficient and Regression Equation from a Large Series of Paired Values. When dealing with large numbers of variates, we found that it was convenient to make up a frequency table in order to summarize the data and reduce the labor of calculating the mean and the standard deviation. Similarly, in regression studies, if a large series of paired values is available it is desirable to make up a table which is a combination of the frequency distributions of the two variables. From long usage such a table has become known as a correlation table, and we shall see in the next chapter that it is likewise of value for calculating the correlation coefficient.

To prepare a correlation table the best plan is to copy the paired values on cards of a size that can be handled conveniently. Thus, if we decided to make up a table for the yields of plots in adjacent rows of Table 4, Chapter II, we would make our cards as follows:

and proceed until all the pairs had been entered. After deciding on the class values in very much the same manner as described in Chapter II, Section 5, we would distribute the cards for one of the variables and then distribute *each pile* for the second variable. Table 12 is the final result of distributing all the cards for the yields of adjacent plots as taken from Table 4. The classes here are somewhat larger than they should be, in order to save space and to make the table more convenient to use as an example. The cards were first distributed for x, giving the frequency distribution as shown in the last row of the table. The 4 cards falling in the first class were then distributed in the vertical column according to the values of y, and so on for each pile. When all the piles were distributed, the cards in each small pile were counted, and the frequencies entered in the table. Notice also that the natural numbers have been inserted in the table to replace the class values. This is the device introduced in Chapter II for reducing the labor of calculating the mean and standard deviation from frequency tables. It may be used here in the same way, in order to reduce the labor of calculating the regression coefficient. It will be noted that this is a form of coding, and consequently the regression coefficient and the regression equation will require correction if they are calculated from a table of this kind.

The next step is to prepare Table 13, in which the first four columns are entered directly from the correlation table. For the column headed " totals for y arrays " we proceed to obtain the totals for each array as follows, where the first array of y is the distribution in the y classes of the variates that fall in the first class for x.

1st array $(2 \times 3) + (1 \times 6) + (1 \times 8)$ $= 20$

2nd array $(2 \times 3) + (4 \times 4) + (5 \times 5) + (1 \times 6) + (1 \times 7) = 60$

The total for this column is obviously T_y, the grand total of y. In the same way we proceed to obtain the totals for the x arrays and T_x, the grand total of x. There are two columns headed $\Sigma(xy)$, the object being to calculate $\Sigma(xy)$ in two ways so as to have a complete check on the calculations. The entries in these columns are obtained by multiplying the totals for the y arrays by the corresponding class values of x, and the totals for the x arrays by the corresponding class values of y. Summating at the foot of the columns we obtain $\Sigma(xy)$.

Finally from the correlation table we have to calculate $\Sigma(x^2)$, and the method is the same as in Chapter II for any frequency distribution. Tabulating our calculations we have:

$$\Sigma(xy) = 5448$$
$$\Sigma(x^2) = 3952$$
$$T_x = 850$$
$$T_y = 1246$$
$$N = 200$$

Then: $\Sigma(y - \bar{y})(x - \bar{x}) = 5448 - (850 \times 1246)/200 = 152.50$

And: $\Sigma(x - \bar{x})^2 = 3952 - 850^2/200 \qquad = 339.50$

The regression coefficient is given by $b_{yx} = 152.50/339.50 = 0.4492$

TABLE 12

Correlation Table for the Yields of Adjacent Barley Plots

	x							
Assumed Classes	1	2	3	4	5	6	7	
Actual Classes	66 88	89 111	112 134	135 157	158 180	181 203	204 226	Frequency y
1 — 20 42				1				1
2 — 43 65			1					1
3 — 66 88	2	2	2					6
4 — 89 111		4	4	3	2	1		14
5 — 112 134		5	11	4	11	3		34
6 — 135 157	1	1	12	15	17	5	2	53
7 — 158 180		1	12	16	13	11	2	55
8 — 181 203	1		1	9	13	4	2	30
9 — 204 226					3	1		4
10 — 227 249						2		2
Frequency x	4	13	43	48	59	27	6	200

(y labels the row axis)

TABLE 13

CALCULATION OF THE REGRESSION COEFFICIENT

y	Frequency y	x	Frequency x	Totals for y Arrays	$\Sigma(xy)$	Totals for x Arrays	$\Sigma(xy)$
1	1	1	4	20	20	4	4
2	1	2	13	60	120	3	6
3	6	3	43	243	729	12	36
4	14	4	48	307	1228	48	192
5	34	5	59	387	1935	132	660
6	53	6	27	187	1122	228	1368
7	55	7	6	42	294	247	1729
8	30	....	......	......	......	143	1144
9	4	....	......	......	......	21	189
10	2	....	......	......	......	12	120
	200	....	200	1246	5448	850	5448
	N	....	N	T_y	$\Sigma(xy)$	T_x	$\Sigma(xy)$

In order to set up the regression equation, the means of x and y are required. These are $\bar{x} = 850/200 = 4.25$, and $\bar{y} = 1246/200 = 6.23$, and the regression equation is written:

$$Y = (6.23 - 0.4492 \times 4.25) + 0.4492x$$

$$= 4.3209 - 0.4492x$$

Since the regression equation has been calculated from coded values, the necessary corrections must be applied. To correct the means we apply formula (7), Chapter II, obtaining:

$$\bar{y} = (6.23 - 1) \times 23 + 31 = 151.29$$

$$\bar{x} = (4.25 - 1) \times 23 + 77 = 151.75$$

Since the class value is 23 for both variables, the regression coefficient does not require any correction, so the new equation is:

$$Y = (151.29 - 0.4492 \times 151.75) - 0.4492x$$

$$= 83.12 - 0.4492x$$

In order to plot the regression straight line, we require only two points on the graph, preferably as far apart as possible. It is simpler to use the coded regression equation to find any values of Y required, and also the graphing may be done in the coded values and the actual values inserted when everything is completed. The end points of the line are

$$Y_1 = 4.3209 - 0.4492 \times 1 = 4.77$$

$$Y_2 = 4.3209 - 0.4492 \times 7 = 7.46$$

The graph is finally as in Fig. 7. If such a graph is required in the final presentation of the results, it would be necessary only to substitute the actual class values for the assumed values. The means of the y arrays are, of course, obtained by dividing the totals for the y arrays by the corresponding frequencies. These may be converted

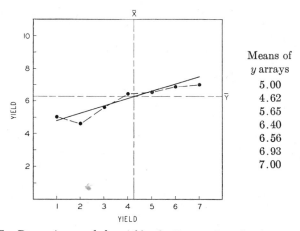

Means of
y arrays
5.00
4.62
5.65
6.40
6.56
6.93
7.00

Fig. 7.—Regression graph for yields of adjacent plots showing regression line and means of y arrays.

to actual values by means of the formula for correcting means as described in Chapter II, and used above for finding the true values of $\bar{x}$ and $\bar{y}$.

To test the significance of the regression coefficient we find

$$s_e = \sqrt{\frac{\Sigma(y - \bar{y})^2 - b^2\Sigma(x - x)^2}{N - 2}} = \sqrt{\frac{417.42 - 0.4492^2 \times 339.50}{198}} = 1.3275$$

$$t = \frac{b\sqrt{\Sigma(x - \bar{x})^2}}{s_e} = \frac{0.4492\sqrt{339.50}}{1.3275} = 6.23.$$

from which it is clear that the regression coefficient is highly significant.

6. Exercises.

1. Table 14 gives the results obtained in an experiment with 25 wheat varieties on the number of days from seeding to heading and the number of days from seeding to maturity. Calculate the regression equation for the regression of days to mature on days to head, and test the significance of the regression coefficient. Code the data before beginning your calculations by subtracting 50 from the days to head and 85 from the days to mature. Find the fiducial limits at the 5% point of the regression coefficient, and decide as to the practicability of using days to head to replace days to mature on the basis of the data provided by this sample.

Regression coefficient = 105.23/125.68 = 0.8373. (Coded data.)

TABLE 14

DATA ON DAYS TO HEAD AND DAYS TO MATURE OF 25 WHEAT VARIETIES

Variety	Days to Head	Days to Mature	Variety	Days to Head	Days to Mature
1	60.0	94.4	14	58.2	92.4
2	53.6	89.0	15	58.0	91.6
3	59.0	94.0	16	59.4	94.0
4	61.8	95.4	17	55.4	90.8
5	53.8	88.2	18	61.6	95.2
6	57.8	93.4	19	63.0	97.2
7	57.8	93.6	20	60.2	94.6
8	58.4	92.0	21	61.6	96.0
9	57.8	92.8	22	57.6	92.6
10	59.0	93.4	23	60.8	95.4
11	59.2	93.8	24	61.2	94.4
12	59.0	92.8	25	58.2	94.0
13	58.6	94.2			

2. Table 15 contains data on the carotene content determined by two methods for 139 wheat varieties. By one method carotene was determined on the whole wheat, and by the other method, on the flour. The figures for carotene in the wheat are lower than for carotene in the flour, which is of course the reverse of the actual condition. This was due to a different method of extraction used for the whole wheat which gave lower but relative results.

Make out cards, one for each pair of values, and prepare a correlation table, letting the flour carotene represent the dependent variable y. In order to reduce the labor of calculation make the classes fairly large; for example, let the first class for x be 0.85 to 0.95, and the first class for y be 1.33 to 1.49. Also do not forget to replace the actual class values by the natural numbers, beginning at 1, before going ahead with the calculations. Determine the regression equation and prepare a graph similar to Fig. 7. $b_{yx} = 438.39/665.96 = 0.6583.$ (Coded data.)

3. Prove: (a) $\Sigma(y - \bar{y})(x - \bar{x}) = \Sigma(xy) - T_xT_y/N,$

(b) $\Sigma(y - Y)^2 = \Sigma(y - \bar{y})^2 - b_{yx}^2\Sigma(x - \bar{x})^2.$

REFERENCES

1. M. EZEKIEL. Methods of Correlation Analysis. John Wiley & Sons, New York, 1930. Reading: Chapter V.
2. R. A. FISHER. Statistical Methods for Research Workers. Oliver and Boyd, London, 1936. Reading: Chapter V, Sections 25, 26, 26.1.
3. G. W. SNEDECOR. Statistical Methods. Collegiate Press, Inc., Ames, Iowa, 1937. Reading: Chapter VI.
4. L. H. C. TIPPETT. The Methods of Statistics. Williams and Norgate Ltd., London, 1931. Reading: Chapter VII, Section 7.22 and Appendix.

TABLE 15
CAROTENE CONTENT OF FLOUR AND WHOLE WHEAT FOR 139 VARIETIES

Variety No.	Carotene in Flour	Carotene in Wheat	Variety No.	Carotene in Flour	Carotene in Wheat	Variety No.	Carotene in Flour	Carotene in Wheat
1	2.39	1.18	48	1.71	1.16	95	1.97	1.33
2	3.11	2.13	49	1.93	1.14	96	1.83	1.14
3	2.15	1.41	50	1.81	1.30	97	2.00	1.51
4	1.96	1.42	51	1.89	1.32	98	1.96	1.28
5	2.02	1.50	52	1.65	1.32	99	2.00	1.33
6	1.76	1.25	53	1.93	1.28	100	2.02	1.32
7	2.10	1.65	54	2.12	1.48	101	1.78	1.17
8	2.12	1.24	55	2.25	1.50	102	1.83	1.10
9	2.28	1.48	56	1.92	1.42	103	1.93	1.22
10	1.86	1.35	57	2.25	1.66	104	2.14	1.44
11	2.60	1.58	58	2.25	1.63	105	2.15	1.54
12	2.11	1.45	59	1.65	1.18	106	2.13	1.46
13	2.30	1.74	60	1.63	1.14	107	1.97	1.40
14	1.80	1.42	61	1.70	1.22	108	1.83	1.11
15	2.00	1.45	62	1.61	1.20	109	2.10	1.40
16	2.05	1.87	63	1.83	1.33	110	1.84	1.19
17	2.09	2.00	64	1.60	1.13	111	1.98	1.39
18	2.33	1.65	65	1.37	.92	112	2.31	1.60
19	2.29	1.64	66	1.96	1.20	113	2.29	1.53
20	2.30	1.62	67	1.88	1.26	114	2.15	1.45
21	1.97	1.55	68	1.92	1.34	115	1.96	1.44
22	2.36	1.68	69	1.89	1.04	116	1.98	1.40
23	1.73	1.32	70	1.99	1.26	117	1.89	1.30
24	1.72	1.47	71	1.82	.98	118	2.08	1.33
25	1.70	1.53	72	2.12	1.31	119	2.00	1.42
26	1.63	1.50	73	2.16	1.16	120	2.06	1.44
27	1.93	1.48	74	2.14	1.04	121	1.96	1.36
28	1.50	1.25	75	1.63	.88	122	2.07	1.38
29	1.77	1.33	76	2.76	1.91	123	2.24	1.51
30	1.60	1.40	77	2.07	1.20	124	2.15	1.38
31	2.31	1.49	78	1.67	1.07	125	1.83	1.18
32	2.17	1.42	79	2.78	1.80	126	1.84	1.20
33	2.10	1.35	80	3.40	2.02	127	2.03	1.45
34	2.90	1.58	81	3.67	2.10	128	1.87	1.05
35	2.17	1.50	82	2.41	1.61	129	2.24	1.44
36	2.15	1.40	83	2.23	1.38	130	2.14	1.06
37	2.01	1.40	84	3.07	1.93	131	2.13	1.10
38	2.35	1.67	85	2.22	1.44	132	2.03	.98
39	2.34	1.62	86	2.55	1.58	133	2.25	1.31
40	2.00	1.47	87	2.12	1.39	134	2.33	1.08
41	2.18	1.55	88	1.94	1.27	135	2.01	1.14
42	2.47	1.73	89	1.95	1.41	136	1.89	1.41
43	2.25	1.62	90	1.59	1.08	137	3.00	2.20
44	1.77	1.39	91	2.00	1.30	138	2.16	1.73
45	1.68	1.34	92	1.77	1.22	139	2.29	1.61
46	2.46	1.29	93	1.98	1.26			
47	1.86	1.28	94	1.97	1.30			

CHAPTER VII

CORRELATION

1. Covariation. This is a term that is very expressive with respect to the fundamental situation regarding two variables, from which the methods of correlation arise. In the previous chapter it was pointed out that, when two variables are so related that one may logically be considered as being dependent on the other one, the method of regression is completely applicable to a study of this relation; but when the two variables cannot be considered in the light of dependence and independence, the method of regression does not appear to be satisfactory. Suppose that a study is to be made of the relation between the heights of brothers and sisters. It would not be logical to consider the height of one member of the pair as being dependent on the height of the other one, yet we may be fairly certain that there is a relation of some sort and we may wish to estimate what this relation is. The question that is asked with respect to two such variables seems to be this. "To what extent do the heights of brother and sister vary together"? Thus we have the term covariation, and the conventional statistic for the measurement of covariation is the *correlation coefficient*.

2. Definition of Correlation. In Table 16 there are three sets of figures that may be taken as measurements on two variables that we shall designate as x and y. On examining these three sets of values it will be noted that the relation between x and y is different in each case. In set 2 we have high values of x associated with high values of y, and in set 3 we have high values of x associated with low values of y. In both cases there is an obvious relation but one is the reverse of the other. In set 1, on the other hand, there is no apparent relation between the two variables. These sets may be regarded as samples from infinite parent populations of paired variates. In the population from which set 2 is drawn, whenever a pair of variates is selected, we expect to find, if the pair contains a high value of x, that there will be a high value of y associated with it. In the population represented by the sample in set 3 it is to be expected that high values of x will be found associated with low values of y. These two opposite situations are referred to as positive and negative correlation. Set 1 represents still another situation. High values of x do not appear to be associated with either high

TABLE 16

THREE SAMPLES OF PAIRED VARIATES ILLUSTRATING THE
PHENOMENON OF CORRELATION

Set 1	x....	7	7	1	6	5	3	8	9	3	1	Total = 50
	y....	5	9	6	1	3	1	9	4	6	8	Total = 52
Set 2	x....	9	8	7	7	6	5	3	3	1	1	Total = 50
	y....	9	9	8	6	6	5	4	3	1	1	Total = 52
Set 3	x....	1	1	3	3	5	6	7	7	8	9	Total = 50
	y....	9	9	8	6	6	5	4	3	1	1	Total = 52

or low values of y. In other words, we shall expect that in the parent population the two variables vary independently. A graphical picture of the results with these three samples is given in Fig. 8. For each sample we have prepared what is usually known as a *dot diagram*. The values of y are represented as ordinates and the values of x as abscissae, so that each pair can be represented by a dot on the diagram. The final

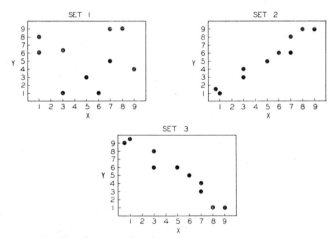

FIG. 8.—Dot diagrams for the sets of values given in Table 16.

result is a figure which represents in a general way, by the scatter of the dots, the relation between the two variables. For set 1 the dots are scattered more or less uniformly over the whole surface. For sets 2 and 3 there is a definite relation between the variables, as shown by the tendency for the dots to arrange themselves in a straight line along the diagonals of the square. We are reminded here of the regression graphs of the previous chapter. The difference is that we are not now studying the effect of one variable on the other, but rather the degree to which the variables vary together owing presumably to influences that are common to both. If such measurements represented heights of brothers and sisters, it is apparent that this common influence might be the similarity of their genes.

This rough illustration is sufficient to give a general idea of the nature of correlation, but it is not adequate to give a complete picture of correlation as it occurs in nature. The student who is specially interested in this subject should make a thorough study of the references given at the end of this chapter. Each writer on this subject presents the situation in a somewhat different manner, and after a study of several viewpoints the student will begin to grasp the fundamental points very clearly. We are concerned here mainly with the viewpoint that correlation is a measure of the degree to which two variables vary together, as we believe this to be the most useful viewpoint from the standpoint of the research worker. Since we have become acquainted with the variance and the standard deviation as measures of variability, it is of interest now to inquire how the combined variation of two variables can be measured, and how much of the variability of one variable is tied up with the variability of some other variable. In the first place, however, we must consider a few points that are fundamental to the methods of measurement that will be employed.

The dot diagrams given in Fig. 8 will result from combining the frequency distributions of two variables. Since they represent samples only, they give merely an estimate of the combined frequency distributions of the two variables in the parent populations. The single or *univariate* distributions are represented by a curve, but the combined or *bivariate* distributions must be represented by a surface. On extending the diagrams of Fig. 8 to much larger samples it is evident that the dots will begin to form into swarms of some definite shape, depending on the degree of correlation between the variables. If the correlation is high the swarm will evidently be of the greatest density along the diagonal of the figure; if there is no correlation the swarm is likely to be almost circular in shape. The theoretical bivariate frequency distribution will obviously be represented by a volume, in contradistinction to that of the univariate distribution which is represented by an area. These points give us some clue as to how we may obtain a measure of correlation.

3. The Measurement of Correlation. Figure 9 illustrates the shape of the swarm in a correlation surface for three different degrees of correlation. The circular swarm at (*a*) represents zero correlation. In (*c*) the swarm falls entirely on the diagonal and must represent perfect correlation. In (*b*) we have a condition between the other two extremes.

Now each surface is divided into quadrants by lines erected at the positions of the means, and in each quadrant are plus and minus signs that represent the signs of the products of the x and y deviations from their means. Thus in the upper right-hand quadrant (1) the deviations of x and y are both positive so that the product of the deviations is positive. Therefore we have positive products in quadrants (1) and (3) and nega-

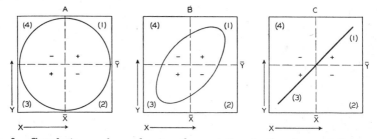

FIG. 9.—Correlation surfaces showing the variation in the shape of the swarm with increasing correlation.

tive products in quadrants (2) and (4). Now if we obtain the sum of the products it is obvious that in (a) the plus and minus products will cancel each other and the sum will be zero. In (c) all the products will be positive so that their sum will be a maximum. In (b) the condition is intermediate between (a) and (c). The plus products are greater than the negative products; hence we have a positive but not a perfect correlation.

Let us consider now the sets of figures in Table 16. If we calculate the sum of the products $\Sigma(x - \bar{x})(y - \bar{y})$ for each set we should find an agreement with the theory outlined above. To carry out these calculations we shall make use of the identity:

$$\Sigma(x - \bar{x})(y - \bar{y}) = \Sigma(xy) - \frac{T_x T_y}{N} \qquad (1)$$

where T_x is the total of the x values, T_y the total of the y values, and N is the number of pairs. Our calculations then come out as follows:

	$\Sigma(xy)$	$T_x T_y / N$	$\Sigma(x - \bar{x})(y - \bar{y})$
Set 1	262	260	2
Set 2	335	260	75
Set 3	186	260	−74

The result is in perfect agreement with the theory that the sum of products is a measure of correlation.

The sum of products is an absolute measure of correlation but will not serve as a relative measure, since it is dependent on several factors that have nothing to do with the correlation between the two variables with which we are concerned. It depends on the number of pairs of measurements or variates, on the units in which the two sets of variates are measured, and on the variability of both of the variables. The first objection can be overcome by dividing by the number of pairs of variates, and we now find that we have $\Sigma(x - \bar{x})(y - \bar{y})/N$, which was defined in the previous chapter as the covariance cv of x and y. The covariance, however, is still not a relative measure of correlation, as it is affected by the units of measurement and the variability of x and y. To overcome this difficulty it is clear that the covariance must be divided by some factor which measures the variability of x and y and is expressible in terms of the units in which these variables are measured. The first factor which suggests itself is the product of the two standard deviations, and this actually gives the formula for the correlation coefficient, usually designated by the symbol r. Thus we have:

$$r_{xy} = \frac{\Sigma(x - \bar{x})(y - \bar{y})/N}{\sigma_x \cdot \sigma_y} \tag{2}$$

Another formula can be given using the variances of x and y in place of their standard deviations. This must of course be:

$$r_{xy} = \frac{\Sigma(x - \bar{x})(y - \bar{y})/N}{\sqrt{v_x \cdot v_y}} \tag{3}$$

where v_x is the variance of x and v_y is the variance of y. Formula (3) shows also the algebraic relationship between the regression coefficient b_{yx} and the correlation coefficient. Since:

$$r_{xy} = \frac{cv}{\sqrt{v_x \cdot v_y}} \quad \text{and} \quad b_{yx} = \frac{cv}{v_x}$$

it follows that:

$$r^2_{xy} = \left(\frac{cv}{v_x}\right)\left(\frac{cv}{v_y}\right) = b_{yx}\left(\frac{cv}{v_y}\right)$$

and $\dfrac{cv}{v_y}$ is obviously the regression coefficient b_{xy} where x is taken as the dependent variable instead of y. Of course in all regression problems there are two regression coefficients, although, in the type of problem we have referred to in the chapter on regression, one of these will be of theoretical interest only. The correlation coefficient is finally:

$$r_{xy} = \sqrt{b_{yx} \cdot b_{xy}} \tag{4}$$

In other words, it is merely the geometric mean of the two regression coefficients.

A brief inspection of the formula of the correlation coefficient will show that it has a maximum value of $+1$ and a minimum value of -1 under conditions that we would ordinarily take to represent perfect correlation. (1) Let $y_i = kx_i$, where y_i and x_i represent any pair of values of y and x, and k is a constant. We have therefore a constant positive relationship between x and y.

Then
$$(y_i - \bar{y}) = (kx_i - k\bar{x}) = k(x_i - \bar{x})$$
and
$$(y_i - \bar{y})(x_i - \bar{x}) = k(x_i - \bar{x})^2$$
Hence
$$\Sigma(x - \bar{x})(y - \bar{y}) = k\Sigma(x - \bar{x})^2$$
Also
$$\Sigma(y - \bar{y})^2 = k^2\Sigma(x - \bar{x})^2$$
Therefore
$$\sigma_y = k\sigma_x$$
And finally
$$\frac{\Sigma(x - \bar{x})(y - \bar{y})/N}{\sigma_x\sigma_y} = \frac{k\Sigma(x - \bar{x})^2/N}{k\sigma_x^2} = \frac{\sigma_x^2}{\sigma_x^2} = 1$$

(2) Let $y_i = -kx_i$. Here we have a constant negative relationship between x and y. Then
$$(y_i - \bar{y}) = -(kx_i - k\bar{x}) = -k(x_i - \bar{x})$$
and
$$(y_i - \bar{y})(x_i - \bar{x}) = -k(x_i - \bar{x})^2$$
Hence
$$\Sigma(x - \bar{x})(y - \bar{y}) = -k\Sigma(x - \bar{x})^2$$
Also
$$\Sigma(y - \bar{y})^2 = k^2\Sigma(x - \bar{x})^2$$
Therefore
$$\sigma_y = k\sigma_x$$
Finally
$$\frac{\Sigma(x - \bar{x})(y - \bar{y})/N}{\sigma_x\sigma_y} = \frac{-k\Sigma(x - \bar{x})^2/N}{k\sigma_x^2} = -\frac{\sigma_x^2}{\sigma_x^2} = -1$$

These two conditions that we have postulated are those for which we should expect a satisfactory coefficient to give us a maximum value of $+1$ and a minimum value of -1. Between these two extremes we should expect the coefficient to give us values varying between $+1$ and -1, and this is what it actually does. Our proof as given above indicates this also, but it is not a rigid proof in that particular respect.

Having satisfied ourselves that when we have perfect positive correlation the coefficient will be $+1$, and when we have perfect negative correlation the coefficient will be -1, it remains to decide how the coefficient will measure correlations that fall within this range. As a matter of fact it is easy to state this proposition, but quite difficult to explain it in a simple and satisfactory manner. Perhaps the best interpretation arises from considerations that actually are more closely related to the theory of linear regression than that of correlation. For example, if we take y to be the independent variable, then we can work out the relation between the correlation coefficient and the two variances, the total for y, and the variance of the errors of estimation. As pointed out in the previous chapter, the sum of squares of the errors of estimation is $\Sigma(y - Y)^2$, where Y represents points on the regression straight line corresponding to each value of y. The variance of the errors of estimation is therefore given by:

$$v_e = \frac{\Sigma(y - Y)^2}{N - 2} \tag{5}$$

Now the variance of y is related to the above variance in the manner indicated by the following equations:

$$v_y = \frac{\Sigma(y - \bar{y})^2}{N - 1} \tag{6}$$

$$v_e = \frac{(1 - r^2)\Sigma(y - \bar{y})^2}{N - 2} \tag{7}$$

From which it follows that the ratio of the two variances is:

$$\frac{v_e}{v_y} = (1 - r^2)\frac{N - 1}{N - 2} \tag{8}$$

On the same basis, if we examine the relation between v_y and the variance due to the regression function, the latter being given by:

$$v_b = b_{yx}^2 \Sigma(x - \bar{x})^2/1 \quad \text{or} \quad r^2\left[\frac{\Sigma(y - \bar{y})^2}{1}\right] \tag{9}$$

we find that:

$$\frac{v_b}{v_y} = r^2(N - 1) \tag{10}$$

Finally, the ratio v_b/v_e is given approximately by:

$$\frac{v_b}{v_e} = \frac{r^2}{(1 - r^2)} (N - 2) \tag{11}$$

The variance v_e is frequently taken as representing that portion of the variation in y which is independent of x; hence we note that from this standpoint equation (8) is the most important. If v_e is expressed in percentage of v_y, then it is clear from (8) that this percentage is almost proportional to $(1 - r^2)$. This is another way of expressing the commonly known fact that differences between high correlation coefficients are much more significant than similar differences between small correlation coefficients. As a measuring stick for general use it is therefore much more convenient to think in terms of r^2 than in terms of r. For example, if we have a correlation coefficient of 0.5, the ratio $v_e/v_y = 0.75$, and the ratio does not fall to 0.5 until r reaches 0.75.

Considerable space might be devoted to further viewpoints on the interpretation of the correlation coefficient, and the student who is especially interested in this phase of statistics should refer to the discussions in the references cited at the end of this chapter. Special notice should be taken of the discussions by R. A. Fisher (1) of the distribution of the correlation coefficient; by G. W. Snedecor (4) of the relation between "common elements" and the correlation coefficient; and by A. E. Treloar (6) of many phases of the entire subject of correlation.

4. Testing the Significance of the Correlation Coefficient. R. A. Fisher (1) has shown that for small samples the distribution of r is not sufficiently close to normality to justify the use of a standard error or a probable error to test its significance. A more accurate method has been developed by Fisher, based on the distribution of t. For a correlation coefficient:

$$t = \frac{r\sqrt{n}}{\sqrt{1 - r^2}} \tag{12}$$

where $n =$ the number of degrees of freedom available for estimating the correlation coefficient. The degrees of freedom can always be taken equal to $N - 2$, because there is a loss of one degree of freedom for each statistic calculated from the sample in order to obtain r. These are $\bar{y}$ and b_{yx} (the regression coefficient). Although b_{yx} may not actually have been calculated, it is involved in the formula of the correlation coefficient through the sum of products $\Sigma(x - \bar{x})(y - \bar{y})$. This point will be clear from a consideration of equation (8) which shows that the ratio v_e/v_y is a function of the correlation coefficient. Now v_e measures the discrepancies between individual values of y and the corresponding values of Y estimated from the regression equation. It follows from this that the correlation coefficient can measure only that portion of the relation between x and y which is represented by the regression equation.

Since the use of t provides a correct method of testing the significance of a correlation coefficient regardless of the size of the sample, in general practice one uses this method for samples of all sizes. For large samples one might calculate a standard error of r, but even this procedure would be subject to criticism if the value of the correlation coefficient was high.

For testing the significance of the difference between two correlation coefficients t is not suitable, and Fisher (1) has developed an accurate method which involves transforming the values of r as follows:

$$z' = \tfrac{1}{2}\{\log_e(1 + r) - \log_e(1 - r)\} \tag{13}$$

The values of z' can be shown to be normally distributed even for small samples and with a standard deviation given by:

$$\sigma_{z'} = \frac{1}{\sqrt{N - 3}} \tag{14}$$

To test the significance of the difference between two correlation coefficients r_1 and r_2, we proceed as follows:

$$z_1' = \tfrac{1}{2}\{\log_e(1 + r_1) - \log_e(1 - r_1)\}$$
$$z_2' = \tfrac{1}{2}\{\log_e(1 + r_2) - \log_e(1 - r_2)\}$$
$$\overline{z_1' - z_2' = \text{difference}}$$

$$\sigma_{z_1' - z_2'} = \sqrt{\frac{1}{N_1 - 3} + \frac{1}{N_2 - 3}} \tag{15}$$

where N_1 and N_2 are the numbers in the two samples from which r_1 and r_2 respectively have been calculated. Finally:

$$t = \frac{z'_1 - z'_2}{\sigma_{z_1' - z_2'}}$$

The table of t is entered under $N_1 + N_2 - 6$ degrees of freedom.

5. Calculation of the Correlation Coefficient. From the previous chapter, the methods for calculating the sum of products $\Sigma(x - \bar{x})(y - \bar{y})$, either directly from paired values or from a correlation table, will have been noted. It is sufficient therefore to note that the formulae given in (2) and (3) may be written as follows in convenient form for calculation.

$$r_{xy} = \frac{\Sigma(xy)/N - \bar{x}\bar{y}}{\sqrt{(\Sigma(x^2)/N - \bar{x}^2)(\Sigma(y^2)/N - \bar{y}^2)}} \qquad (16)$$

$$r_{xy} = \frac{\Sigma(xy) - T_x T_y/N}{\sqrt{(\Sigma(x^2) - T_x^2/N)(\Sigma(y^2) - T_y^2/N)}} \qquad (17)$$

$$r_{xy} = \frac{N\Sigma(xy) - T_x T_y}{\sqrt{(N\Sigma(x^2) - T_x^2)(N\Sigma(y^2) - T_y^2)}} \qquad (18)$$

Formula (17) is the most direct, but (16) and (18) are perhaps better suited to machine calculation. In (18) there are no divisions in either the numerator or the denominator; and after all the preliminary calculations of the values of $\Sigma(xy)$, T_x, T_y, $\Sigma(x^2)$, and $\Sigma(y^2)$ have been performed, each of the three factors in the formula may be obtained without removing any figures from the machine and recording them elsewhere.

The methods of calculating $\Sigma(xy)$, T_x, T_y, $\Sigma(x^2)$, and $\Sigma(y^2)$ will of course be the same as described in Chapters II and VI. They may be calculated either from the correlation table or directly from the paired values. For $N = 50$ or less it is probably best to proceed directly, as setting up the correlation surface is not likely to save any time. When the numbers are fairly large it is nearly always best to have a correlation table, as we shall learn later of a test to determine the agreement between the actual data and the straight line fitted by the regression equation, and to carry out this test the correlation table must be set up.

Example 12. Direct Calculation of the Correlation Coefficient from Paired Values. For the sets of paired values given in Table 16 the calculations of $\Sigma(xy)$ were performed and the results given in Section 3 of this chapter. Let us assume that we wish to calculate the correlation coefficients using formula (17).

Set 1.
$$\Sigma(xy) - T_x T_y/N = 262 - 260 \quad = 2.0$$
$$\Sigma(x^2) - T_x^2/N \quad = 324 - 250 \quad = 74.0$$
$$\Sigma(y^2) - T_y^2/N \quad = 350 - 270.4 = 79.6$$
$$r_{xy} = \frac{2.0}{\sqrt{74.0 \times 79.6}} = +0.026$$

Set 2.
$$\Sigma(xy) - T_x T_y/N = 335 - 260 = 75.0$$
$$\left.\begin{array}{l} \Sigma(x^2) - T_x^2/N \quad = \\ \Sigma(y^2) - T_y^2/N \quad = \end{array}\right\} \text{Same as Set 1}$$
$$r_{xy} = \frac{75.0}{\sqrt{74.0 \times 79.6}} = +0.997$$

Set 3. $\Sigma(xy) - T_xT_y/N = 186 - 260 = -74.0$

$\left.\begin{array}{l} \Sigma(x^2) - T_x^2/N = \\ \Sigma(y^2) - T_y^2/N = \end{array}\right\}$ Same as Set 1

$$r_{xy} = \frac{-74.0}{\sqrt{74.0 \times 79.6}} = -0.964$$

To calculate r_{xy} for Set 2 using formula (18) we would write directly:

$$r_{xy} = \frac{10 \times 335 - 50 \times 52}{\sqrt{(10 \times 324 - 50^2)(10 \times 350 - 52^2)}}$$

and performing one operation with the machine for each factor we obtain:

$$r_{xy} = \frac{750}{\sqrt{740 \times 796}}$$

By one more operation we find the denominator and have:

$$r_{xy} = \frac{750}{767.58} = +0.977$$

Example 13. Calculation of the Correlation Coefficient from a Correlation Table. Suppose that we wish to calculate the correlation coefficient for Table 12, Chapter VI. The first step is to prepare Table 13, which we have already used in Example 11 to calculate the regression coefficient. From this table we have:

$$\Sigma(xy) = 5448 \qquad T_x = 850$$

$$\Sigma(x^2) = 3952 \qquad T_y = 1246$$

$$\Sigma(y^2) = 8180$$

And making use of formula (18) above we calculate:

$$r_{xy} = \frac{200 \times 5448 - 850 \times 1246}{\sqrt{(200 \times 3952 - 850^2)(200 \times 8180 - 1246^2)}}$$

$$= \frac{30,500}{\sqrt{67,900 \times 83,484}} = \frac{30,500}{260.58 \times 288.94} = 0.4051$$

Example 14. Tests of Significance. Although the correlation coefficients calculated in Example 12 were for only 10 pairs of values, the t test will give a reliable measure of their significance. The t values are determined as follows:

Set 1. $r_{xy} = +0.026$ $t = \dfrac{0.026\sqrt{8}}{\sqrt{1 - 0.026^2}} = 0.07$

Set 2. $r_{xy} = +0.977$ $t = \dfrac{0.977\sqrt{8}}{\sqrt{1 - 0.977^2}} = 129.7$

Set 3. $r_{xy} = -0.964$ $t = \dfrac{0.964\sqrt{8}}{\sqrt{1 - 0.964^2}} = 102.5$

Turning to Table 94 we note that for $n = 8$ and $P = 0.05$ the value of t required is 2.306. The coefficient 0.026 is therefore quite insignificant, but the other two are highly significant.

Example 15. The Significance of Differences between Correlation Coefficients. In a study of the relation between the carotene content of wheat flour and the crumb color of the bread, Goulden, et al. (2), obtained the following results with 139 varieties.

Carotene in whole wheat with crumb color, $r_1 = -0.4951$

Carotene in flour　　　with crumb color, $r_2 = -0.5791$

The most accurate method for this test is to make use of Fisher's z' transformation. For the z' test we write:

$$z'_1 = \tfrac{1}{2}\{\log_e (1 + 0.4951) - \log_e (1 - 0.4951)\}$$

$$= \tfrac{1}{2} (\log_e 1.4951 - \log_e 0.5049)$$

$$= \tfrac{1}{2} \log_e \left(\frac{1.4951}{0.5049}\right) = \tfrac{1}{2} \log_e 2.9612 = \log_{10} 2.9612 \times 1.1513$$

$$= 0.47147 \times 1.1513 = 0.5428$$

$$z'_2 = \tfrac{1}{2} (\log_e 1.5791 - \log_e 0.4209)$$

$$= \tfrac{1}{2} \log_e \frac{1.5791}{0.4209} = \tfrac{1}{2} \log_e 3.7517 = 0.57423 \times 1.1513 = 0.6611$$

$$z'_2 - z'_1 = 0.6611 - 0.5428 = 0.1183$$

$$\sigma_{z'_2 - z'_1} = \sqrt{\tfrac{1}{136} + \tfrac{1}{136}} = \sqrt{\tfrac{2}{136}} = 0.1213$$

Since the difference is less than its standard deviation it is not significant.

Note that in writing out the formula for z' we pay no attention to the sign of r as it is the *numerical* difference between the coefficients that we are testing.

6. Exercises.

1. The figures in Table 17 are the physics and English marks [1] for home economics students in the University of Manitoba. Determine the correlation coefficient for the relation between the marks in the two subjects. Use the direct method, and test the significance of the coefficient. $r = +0.705$.

2. For the same 50 students the correlation coefficient for the marks in art and clothing is +0.7300, and for art and physics it is +0.6491. Is this a significant difference?

3. Determine the correlation coefficient for days to head and days to mature of 25 wheat varieties, using the data from Table 14. Find the fiducial limits at the 5% point for this coefficient. $r = +0.946$.

[1] By courtesy of the Registrar, University of Manitoba.

TABLE 17

MARKS IN PHYSICS AND ENGLISH OF 50 STUDENTS IN HOME ECONOMICS
OF THE UNIVERSITY OF MANITOBA

Student	Physics	English	Student	Physics	English	Student	Physics	English
1	20	21	18	26	29	35	23	26
2	25	26	19	24	27	36	26	27
3	24	27	20	19	26	37	22	21
4	22	24	21	25	25	38	26	25
5	27	27	22	18	20	39	23	21
6	26	28	23	20	24	40	29	26
7	26	24	24	23	24	41	23	19
8	32	26	25	22	20	42	20	19
9	22	24	26	23	26	43	23	30
10	27	26	27	31	27	44	33	32
11	22	23	28	24	25	45	21	19
12	22	25	29	28	30	46	28	30
13	22	24	30	25	28	47	24	21
14	29	30	31	26	32	48	26	28
15	26	30	32	24	25	49	24	22
16	24	28	33	27	30	50	30	25
17	25	29	34	28	30			

REFERENCES

1. R. A. FISHER. Statistical Methods for Research Workers. Oliver and Boyd, London, 1936. Reading: Chapter VI, Sections 30, 31, 33, 34, 35, 36.
2. C. H. GOULDEN, W. F. GEDDES, and A. G. O. WHITESIDE. Cereal Chem., 11: 557–566, 1934.
3. RAYMOND PEARL. Medical Biometry and Statistics. W. B. Saunders Co., Philadelphia, 1923. Reading: Chapter XIV, first section.
4. G. W. Snedecor. Statistical Methods. Collegiate Press, Inc., Ames, Iowa, 1937. Reading: Chapter VII.
5. L. H. C. TIPPETT. The Methods of Statistics. Williams and Norgate, Ltd., London, 1931. Reading: Chapter VII, Sections 8.1, 8.2, 8.21, 8.22.
6. A. E. TRELOAR. An Outline of Biometric Analysis. Burgess Publishing Co., Minneapolis, 1936. Reading: Part I, Chapters X, XI, XII, XIII.
7. G. UDNY YULE. The Theory of Statistics. Charles Griffin and Company, Ltd., London, 1924. Reading: Chapter IX.

CHAPTER VIII

PARTIAL AND MULTIPLE REGRESSION AND CORRELATION

1. The Necessity for Dealing with More Than One Independent Variable. In many regression problems the investigator is concerned purely with the effect of one variable on another, and this holds true regardless of other complicating factors. Suppose that a new rapid method has been developed for determining the protein content of grain samples and this method is to be compared with an older and thoroughly tested method which is known to give very accurate results. The two methods are used on a large series of samples and for the entire series the linear regression equation is determined for the regression of protein by the *old* method on protein by the *new* method. Regardless of how these two variables are related, from the practical standpoint of studying the efficiency of the new method as a substitute for the old method, it is clear that the investigator is concerned purely with the closeness of the relationship between the two variables. The new method may not actually measure protein content but some other factor that is so closely associated with protein content that if we know one we know the other. Hence, although the relation between the two variables may be indirect, it is the total relation with which we are concerned, as we require merely a measure of the accuracy with which we can predict one variable from individual measurements of the other variable. In examples of a somewhat different nature it may be quite misleading to study only the total relation between two variables. Suppose that we find a correlation of +0.60 between the yield of wheat and temperature. Can we conclude from this result that, if all other conditions remain constant, there will be an increase in yield with increases in temperature? The answer is no, because temperature may be associated with some other factor influencing yield and this second factor may be the one that is actually causing the variations in yield. Suppose that the second factor is rainfall, which is probably the most important of the meteorological factors influencing the yield. If rainfall is itself associated with temperature, it is clear that there must also be a correlation between yield and temperature. The latter correlation, however, does not provide us with any information of a fundamental nature with respect to the actual

78

changes in yield brought about by changes in temperature. What we require here is a measure of the association between yield and temperature when the rainfall remains constant. To the extent that the relations between the three variables in a problem of this kind can be expressed by linear functions, the measure that we require can be obtained by the method of partial regression or partial correlation. Thus the partial correlation of yield and temperature will measure the degree of covariation for these two variables with a constant rainfall. The partial regression coefficient for yield and temperature will give the actual increase in yield for one unit of increase in temperature when the rainfall is constant. If the correlation coefficients for the three variables are as follows:

$$r_{yt} \text{ (yield and temperature)} \quad = + 0.60$$

$$r_{yr} \text{ (yield and rainfall)} \quad\quad = + 0.82$$

$$r_{tr} \text{ (temperature and rainfall)} = + 0.78$$

the partial correlation coefficient for yield and temperature with rainfall constant may be represented by $r_{yt.r}$, in which the variable placed after the period is the one that is held constant. Applying the partial correlation method as illustrated below we find $r_{yt.r} = + 0.09$. Therefore the actual effect of temperature when rainfall is constant is practically nil.

It is just as well to emphasize by means of this example that the method of partial regression and partial correlation as we are considering it here has to do only with the linear relation between the variables. If the effect of temperature on yield is not the same for a constant low rainfall as it is for a constant high rainfall, then the linear measures are inadequate to express the actual relation.

2. Derivation of Partial Regression and Partial Correlation Methods. The method of simple correlations is derived from the regression equation:

$$y - \bar{y} = b_{yx}(x - \bar{x})$$

where b_{yx} is the regression coefficient. Similarly, when there are three variables y, x, z, the regression equation is:

$$y - \bar{y} = b_{yx}(x - \bar{x}) + b_{yz}(z - \bar{z})$$

In order to simplify the writing of these equations we use x_1 for the dependent variable and x_2, $x_3 \cdots x_n$ for the independent variables. Also b_{12} represents the regression coefficient for x_1 on x_2, and to abbreviate further we write x_1 for $(x_1 - \bar{x}_1)$ and x_2 for $(x_2 - \bar{x}_2)$. Hence the general regression equation for n variables is:

$$x_1 = b_{12}x_2 + b_{13}x_3 + b_{14}x_4 + \cdots + b_{1n}x_n \qquad (1)$$

The error in estimating x_1 from this regression equation will be:

$$(x_1 - b_{12}x_2 - b_{13}x_3 - \cdots - b_{1n}x_n)$$

and it is required to find values of the regression coefficients such that the sum of the squares of these errors is a minimum. That is, we must find values of the regression coefficients such that

$$\Sigma(x_1 - b_{12}x_2 - b_{13}x_3 - \cdots - b_{1n}x_n)^2$$

is a minimum. For 4 variables this leads by mathematical treatment to the following "Normal Equations"

$$\Sigma(x_1x_2) = b_{12}\Sigma(x_2)^2 + b_{13}\Sigma(x_2x_3) + b_{14}\Sigma(x_2x_4)$$

$$\Sigma(x_1x_3) = b_{12}\Sigma(x_2x_3) + b_{13}\Sigma(x_3)^2 + b_{14}\Sigma(x_3x_4) \qquad (2)$$

$$\Sigma(x_1x_4) = b_{12}\Sigma(x_2x_4) + b_{13}\Sigma(x_3x_4) + b_{14}\Sigma(x_4)^2$$

For a set of n variables there are $(n - 1)$ simultaneous equations for which the sums of squares and sums of products are known, and by solving these we arrive at the values for the regression coefficients.

Any partial correlation can then be determined as follows:

$$r_{12 \cdot 3 \cdots n} = \sqrt{b_{12 \cdot 3 \cdots n} \times b_{21 \cdot 3 \cdots n}} \qquad (3)$$

For three variables x_1, x_2, x_3, the normal equations are as follows:

$$\Sigma(x_1x_2) = b_{12}\Sigma(x_2)^2 + b_{13}\Sigma(x_2x_3)$$

$$\Sigma(x_1x_3) = b_{12}\Sigma(x_2x_3) + b_{13}\Sigma(x_3)^2$$

from which it can be proved that

$$r_{12 \cdot 3} = \frac{r_{12} - r_{13} \cdot r_{23}}{\sqrt{(1 - r_{13}^2)(1 - r_{23}^2)}}$$

Similarly

$$r_{13 \cdot 2} = \frac{r_{13} - r_{12} \cdot r_{23}}{\sqrt{(1 - r_{12}^2)(1 - r_{23}^2)}} \qquad (4)$$

and

$$r_{23 \cdot 1} = \frac{r_{23} - r_{12} \cdot r_{13}}{\sqrt{(1 - r_{12}^2)(1 - r_{13}^2)}}$$

This is the most rapid method of obtaining the partials for only three variables. For four or more variables it is best to make use of the fact that the normal equations can be written as follows, taking as an example the equations for five variables:

$$r_{12} = \beta_{12} \qquad + \beta_{13}r_{23} + \beta_{14}r_{24} + \beta_{15}r_{25}$$

$$r_{13} = \beta_{12}r_{23} + \beta_{13} \qquad + \beta_{14}r_{34} + \beta_{15}r_{35}$$

$$r_{14} = \beta_{12}r_{24} + \beta_{13}r_{34} + \beta_{14} \qquad + \beta_{15}r_{45}$$

$$r_{15} = \beta_{12}r_{25} + \beta_{13}r_{35} + \beta_{14}r_{45} + \beta_{15}$$

$$(5)$$

The correlation coefficients are the known values, and the beta (β) values the unknown. The latter can be used as illustrated below to compute the partial correlation coefficients.

Tabular methods of solving these equations for the beta values have been devised which reduce the labor to a minimum. The beta values are defined by:

$$b_{12\cdot3\ \ldots\ n} = \left(\frac{\sigma_1}{\sigma_2}\right) \beta_{12\cdot3\ \ldots\ n} \tag{6}$$

and

$$b_{21\cdot3\ \ldots\ n} = \left(\frac{\sigma_2}{\sigma_1}\right) \beta_{21\cdot3\ \ldots\ n} \tag{7}$$

Hence, on referring to equation (3) above, we find that:

$$\beta_{12\cdot3\ \ldots\ n} \cdot \beta_{21\cdot3\ \ldots\ n} = \left(\frac{\sigma_2}{\sigma_1}\right) b_{12\cdot3\ \ldots\ n} \times \left(\frac{\sigma_1}{\sigma_2}\right) b_{21\cdot3\ \ldots\ n}$$

$$= b_{12\cdot3\ \ldots\ n} \cdot b_{21\cdot3\ \ldots\ n} = r^2_{12\cdot3\ \ldots\ n} \tag{8}$$

And hence:

$$\sqrt{\beta_{12\cdot3\ \ldots\ n} \cdot \beta_{21\cdot3\ \ldots\ n}} = r_{12\cdot3\ \ldots\ n} \tag{9}$$

In order to obtain all the beta values, it is necessary to rewrite the normal equations in different ways and solve. For example, in order to obtain β_{21}, the equations for five variables must be written.

$$r_{21} = \beta_{21} \qquad + \beta_{23}r_{13} + \beta_{24}r_{14} + \beta_{25}r_{15}$$

$$r_{23} = \beta_{21}r_{13} + \beta_{23} \qquad + \beta_{24}r_{34} + \beta_{25}r_{35}$$

$$r_{24} = \beta_{21}r_{14} + \beta_{23}r_{34} + \beta_{24} \qquad + \beta_{25}r_{45}$$

$$r_{25} = \beta_{21}r_{15} + \beta_{23}r_{35} + \beta_{24}r_{45} + \beta_{25}$$

Correlation coefficients are often referred to as coefficients of the pth order, where p is the number of variables held constant. Thus the simple coefficient r_{12} is of zero order, and the partial coefficient $r_{12 \cdot 345}$ is of the third order.

3. Example 16. Calculation of Partial Regression and Partial Correlation Coefficients. The simple correlation coefficients in Table 18 were obtained in a study (2) of the effect of the physical characteristics of wheat on the yield and quality of flour.

TABLE 18

SIMPLE CORRELATION COEFFICIENTS FOR THE
RELATIONS BETWEEN SIX VARIABLES

	1	2	3	4	5
6	0.6412	−0.3190	−0.4462	−0.3511	−0.3092
5	−0.3123	0.2861	0.1467	0.1882	
4	−0.3947	0.0429	−0.0655		
3	−0.5612	0.3114			
2	−0.4589				

where 1 = yield of straight grade flour.   4 = per cent immaturity.

     2 = per cent bran frost.   5 = per cent green kernels.

     3 = per cent heavy frost.   6 = weight per bushel.

In order to use the above method to determine the effects on yield of flour of any one of the forms of damage or of weight per bushel, it is necessary to determine the partial correlation coefficients:

$$r_{12 \cdot 3456}, \quad r_{13 \cdot 2456}, \quad r_{14 \cdot 2356}, \quad r_{15 \cdot 2346}, \quad r_{16 \cdot 2345}$$

For which we will require

$$\beta_{12} \cdot \beta_{21}, \quad \beta_{13} \cdot \beta_{31}, \quad \beta_{14} \cdot \beta_{41}, \quad \beta_{15} \cdot \beta_{51}, \quad \beta_{16} \cdot \beta_{61}$$

We solve for these by the method illustrated in Table 19. It is a tabular method of solving the simultaneous equations and is best understood from a study of the table.

Note that the calculations of Table 19 give β_{12}, β_{13}, β_{14}, β_{15}, and β_{16}, and that in order to obtain the other beta values the simple correlation coefficients must be rearranged and the calculations repeated. The rearrangement in the order 6, 5, 4, 3, 1, 2, will give β_{21}, β_{23}, β_{24}, β_{25}, β_{26}. The next logical rearrangement is 6, 5, 4, 1, 2, 3, giving β_{32}, β_{31}, β_{34}, β_{35}, β_{36}. We continue rearranging the simple correlation coefficients until all the beta values have been calculated. Then they are put together in a table and we select those necessary in order to give the required partials.

The following instructions will be found useful in carrying through the tabular method of solving the equations.

(1) Rule a sheet of paper as in Table 19.

(2) Enter all the correlation coefficients as indicated in lines 1, 3, 7, 12, and 18.

(3) Sum the correlation coefficients to obtain values given in column S. Note that the first sum, line 1, is $r_{61} + r_{62} + r_{63} + r_{64} + r_{65} + r_{66}$, the sum in line 3 is $r_{51} + r_{52} + r_{53} + r_{54} + r_{55} + r_{56}$, the sum in line 7 is $r_{41} + r_{42} + r_{43} + r_{44} + r_{45} + r_{46}$, etc.

The S column provides a check for all the preceding work. The values 1.0662 and -1.1789 must check with the sum of the values in lines 5 and 6 respectively. There are similar checks in the S column of lines 10 and 11, 16, and 17, and 23 and 24. All these checks are approximate, and therefore the values obtained in the check column will not agree with those calculated from the body of the table to the last decimal figure.

(4) The last value calculated in line 24 is β_{12} with its sign changed. It is written below in line 1 of the reverse with the correct sign, and also in column 2 line 1 of the reverse. The remaining values in column 1 come from lines 17, 11, 6, and 2, of the same column but with their signs reversed.

In column 2 the values are:

$$\beta_{12}$$

$$\beta_{12} \times (17 \cdot 2)$$

$$\beta_{12} \times (11 \cdot 2)$$

$$\beta_{12} \times (6 \cdot 2)$$

$$\beta_{12} \times (2 \cdot 2)$$

In line 2 (reverse) add from right to left and obtain β_{13}, then the remaining values in column 3 are:

$$\beta_{13} \times (11 \cdot 3)$$

$$\beta_{13} \times (6 \cdot 3)$$

$$\beta_{13} \times (2 \cdot 3)$$

In line 3 (reverse) add from right to left and obtain β_{14}, then the remaining values in column 4 are:

$$\beta_{14} \times (6.4)$$

$$\beta_{14} \times (2.4)$$

In line 4 (reverse) add from right to left and obtain β_{15}, then the remaining value in column 5 is:

$$\beta_{15} \times (2.5)$$

In line 5 (reverse) add from right to left and obtain β_{16}.

After completing the calculations as in Table 19 the correlation coefficients are arranged in the order 6, 5, 4, 3, 1, 2, in a new table and the calculations carried out as before. For 6 variables there will be 6 tables to calculate, each table giving 5 of the total of 30 beta values. When the latter have all been calculated they can be tabulated, and all that remains is to work out the partials. It is convenient to make a table such as Table 20 for entering the beta values and the corresponding partial correlation coefficients.

TABLE 19

SOLUTION OF NORMAL EQUATIONS FOR SIX VARIABLES

	Line	6	5	4	3	2	1	S
Enter $r_{66}, r_{65}...r_{61}$	1	1.0000	−0.3092	−0.3511	−0.4462	−0.3190	0.6412	0.2157
Change signs	2	−1.0000	0.3092	0.3511	0.4462	0.3190	−0.6412	
Enter $r_{55}, r_{54}...r_{51}$	3		1.0000	0.1882	0.1467	0.2861	−0.3123	0.9995
Multiply line 1 by 2.5	4		−0.0956	−0.1086	−0.1380	−0.0986	0.1983	0.0667
Add lines 4 and 3	5		0.9044	0.0796	−0.0087	−0.1875	−0.1140	1.0662
Divide line 5 by 5.5 and change signs	6		−1.0000	−0.0880	−0.0096	−0.2073	0.1260	−1.1789
Enter $r_{44}, r_{43}, r_{42}, r_{41}$	7			1.0000	−0.0655	0.0429	−0.3947	0.4198
Multiply line 1 by 2.4	8			−0.1233	−0.1567	−0.1120	0.2251	0.0757
Multiply line 5 by 6.4	9			−0.0070	−0.0008	−0.0165	0.0100	−0.0938
Add lines 9 to 7	10			0.8697	−0.2230	−0.0856	−0.1596	−0.4017
Divide line 10 by 10.4 and change signs	11			−1.0000	0.2564	0.0984	0.1835	−0.4619
Enter r_{33}, r_{32}, r_{31}	12				1.0000	0.314	−0.5612	0.3852
Multiply line 1 by 2.3	13				−0.1991	−0.1423	0.2861	0.0962
Multiply line 5 by 6.3	14				−0.0001	−0.0018	0.0011	−0.0102
Multiply line 10 by 11.3	15				−0.0572	−0.0219	−0.0409	−0.1030
Add lines 15 to 12	16				0.7436	0.1454	−0.3149	0.5742
Divide line 16 by 16.3 and change signs	17				−1.0000	−0.1955	0.4235	−0.7722
Enter r_{22}, r_{21}	18					1.0000	−0.4589	0.8625
Multiply line 1 by 2.2	19					−0.1018	0.2045	0.0688
Multiply line 5 by 6.2	20					−0.0389	0.0236	−0.2210
Multiply line 10 by 11.2	21					−0.0084	−0.0157	0.0395
Multiply line 16 by 17.2	22					−0.0284	−0.0616	−0.1123
Add lines 22 to 18	23					0.8225	0.1849	0.6375
Divide line 23 by 23.2 and change signs	24					−1.0000	0.2248	−0.7751
Reserve	1					−0.2248	0.2248	
	2				−0.3796	0.0439	0.4235	
	3			−0.3029	−0.0973	0.0221	0.1835	
	4		−0.0492	0.0266	0.0036	0.0466	0.1260	
	5	0.2786	−0.0152	−0.1063	−0.1694	−0.0717	0.6412	

$\beta_{12} = -0.2248$
$\beta_{13} = -0.3796$
$\beta_{14} = -0.3029$
$\beta_{15} = -0.0492$
$\beta_{16} = 0.2786$

NOTE: In the instructions 2.5 represents the value 0.3092 in line 2, column 5. Similarly, 6.4 represents the value in line 6, column 4, and so forth.

TABLE 20

BETA VALUES AND PARTIAL CORRELATION COEFFICIENTS

Subscript	β	Subscript	β	r Subscript	r
12	−0.2575	21	−0.5844	12.3456	−.388
13	....	31		13.2456	
14	....	41		14.2356	
.	.	.		.	
.	.	.		.	
.	.	.		.	
56		65		56.1234	

4. Tests of Significance. The t test is applicable to partial correlations in the same way as to simple correlations but the degrees of freedom are different. If p is the number of variables held constant, for partial correlation coefficients we have

$$t = \frac{r}{\sqrt{1 - r^2}}\sqrt{N - p - 2} \tag{10}$$

5. Multiple Correlation. In our example, if we consider not the separate but the total effect of weight per bushel and the different forms of damage on the yield of flour, the problem is one of multiple correlation. Since all these variables have some effect on flour yield the more information we have on them the more closely we can predict the flour yield of a particular sample of wheat.

A simple correlation coefficient measures the relation between a dependent and one independent variable. A multiple correlation coefficient measures the combined relation between a dependent variable and a series of independent variables.

Equation (1):

$$x_1 = b_{12}x_2 + b_{13}x_3 + b_{14}x_4 + \cdots + b_{1n}x_n$$

is in reality a multiple regression equation as it may be used to predict values of x_1 from the known values of $x_2, x_3, x_4 \cdots x_n$.

6. Calculation of Multiple Correlation Coefficients. Two methods are in use for the calculation of the multiple correlation coefficient. These arise from the two equations (11) and (12) below:

$$1 - R^2_{1\cdot23}\ldots{}_n = (1 - r^2_{12})(1 - r^2_{13\cdot2})(1 - r^2_{14\cdot23})(1 - r^2_{15\cdot234})\ldots$$

$$(1 - r^2_{1n\cdot23}\ldots{}_{n-1}) \tag{11}$$

$$R^2 = \beta_{12}\cdot r_{12} + \beta_{13}\cdot r_{13} + \beta_{14}\cdot r_{14} + \ldots + \beta_{1n}\cdot r_{1n} \tag{12}$$

Method (11) can be used only when all the partial correlation coefficients of the first, second, third, to the $(n - 2)$ order are known, and hence it is impossible when the partials have been obtained by solving the normal equations. It is very useful, however, when only three variables are being studied. For three variables we have:

$$1 - R_{1\cdot23}^2 = (1 - r_{12}^2)(1 - r_{13\cdot2}^2)$$

Method (12) is directly applicable when the partial correlation coefficients have been obtained by solving the normal equations for the beta values.

7. Testing the Significance of Multiple Correlations. It should be noted that, in equation (11) above, any one of the factors such as $1 - r^2_{13\cdot2}$ cannot be greater than unity, since the square of a correlation coefficient cannot be less than zero. Hence if we compare

$$(1 - R_{1\cdot23\,\ldots\,n}^2) \quad \text{and} \quad (1 - r_{12}^2)$$

giving

$$1 - R_{1\cdot23}^2 \,\ldots\, _n < 1 - r_{12}^2$$

$$R_{1\cdot23}^2 \,\ldots\, _n - 1 > r_{12}^2 - 1$$

or

$$R_{1\cdot23}^2 \,\ldots\, _n > r_{12}^2$$

Similarly for any other factor on the right of the equation; hence:

$$R_{1\cdot23}^2 \,\ldots\, _n > r_{12}^2, r_{13\cdot2}^2, \ldots r_{1n\cdot23}^2 \,\ldots\, _{n-1}$$

The multiple correlation coefficient is greater therefore than any of the constituent coefficients; and its minimum value is zero and not -1, as is the case with a simple or partial coefficient. For this reason a special table must be used for testing the significance of multiple correlations.[1] The calculation of t values, standard errors, or probable errors will give entirely erroneous results. Two tables that may be used are in the references given below.

8. Exercises.

1. Complete the calculation of the partial correlation coefficients begun in Example 16. The following values will assist in checking the work:

$$r_{12\cdot3456} = -0.3177$$

$$r_{16\cdot2345} = 0.3367$$

$$r_{35\cdot1246} = -0.0393$$

$$r_{56\cdot1234} = -0.1373$$

[1] A test is described in Chapter XIII that is based on the analysis of variance.

2. If N is 36, determine the minimum value of a fourth order correlation coefficient that is significant. Put r in terms of t and the number of degrees of freedom.

The value obtained should be 0.3493.

3. Calculate the multiple correlation coefficient $R_{1.23456}$ for the same data as in Example 16, and determine its significance. $R = 0.7936$.

4. Write the simultaneous equations for three variables in the same form as (5) above. Then prove:

$$r_{12\cdot3} = \frac{r_{12} - r_{13}\cdot r_{23}}{\sqrt{(1 - r_{13}^2)(1 - r_{23}^2)}}$$

REFERENCES

1. R. A. FISHER. Statistical Methods for Research Workers. Oliver and Boyd, London, 1936. Reading: Chapter VI, Sections 32, 33, Example 28.

2. W. F. GEDDES, G. J. MALLOCH, and R. K. LARMOUR. *Can. J. Research*, **6**:119–155, 1932.

3. L. H. C. TIPPETT. The Methods of Statistics. Williams and Norgate, Ltd., London, 1931. Reading: Chapter XI, Sections 11.1, 11.2, 11.5, 11.6, 11.7.

4. H. A. WALLACE and G. W. SNEDECOR. Correlation and Machine Calculation. Iowa State College, Bull. 4, 1931.

5. J. WISHART. Table of the Significant Values of the Multiple Correlation Coefficient. *Jour. Roy. Met. Soc.*, No. 54, 1928.

CHAPTER IX

THE χ^2 (CHI-SQUARE) TEST

1. Data Classified in Two Ways. On reviewing the types of problems that have been presented in the previous chapters, it will be recalled that they have dealt with data of two kinds. In the first place we studied an example in which an operator attempted to classify grain samples according to variety. The samples were placed either rightly or wrongly, and there was no intermediate condition. The power of the operator to differentiate the samples was therefore measured in terms of the number of samples placed correctly. With a little thought it will be clear that a great many problems must occur in which the data are of this type. Thus, in describing the health of a population, an obvious criterion will be the proportion of the population that are ill, or perhaps the percentage dying within the year. Again, a set of varieties of a cereal crop may be differentiated by the number of seeds that are viable, and so forth. In further examples the data were of a different type as in the case of yields of wheat plots, weights and heights of men, and degree of infection. We may be reminded, by these remarks, of the classification of variables as continuous and discontinuous, wherein the distinction between the two is fairly clear cut. Will data arising from discontinuous variables always fall into the first class mentioned above, and data from continuous variables into the second class? The answer is that they will not be so easily separated in this way, as we can easily imagine a situation in which data for a continuous variable may be treated by the two methods. We may take as an example a comparison of the yields of two varieties of wheat. In the first place, if there are a sufficient number of plots we may compare the two varieties according to the number of plots that fall into an arbitrarily determined low-yielding class, or an arbitrarily determined high-yielding class; or better still we may compare the numbers of plots falling into both classes. In the second case we may simply compare the average yields of the two varieties on all the plots. Which method shall we use? This question is also very easily answered, as it will be clear that the first method applied to an example of this kind is cumbersome and unwieldy, and will be used only when the numbers are fairly large and the method of classifying the plots according to yield is only approximate. For example, in a comparison of two varieties as grown by farmers it may be impossible to obtain accurate yields, but it may be possible to classify the fields quite accurately into the groups low-yielding and high-yielding. Then, with a fairly large number of fields to work with, a good comparison of the varieties may be made simply by determining the number in each group. For discontinuous variables, on the other hand, comparisons will usually be found to be most conveniently made by the first method, and this is particularly true if the character with which we are concerned is definitely not measurable in a quantitative manner. Thus people may be classified only as dead or alive; and although there may be a theoretical situation existing for a short period in which this classification is uncertain, it is certainly of no practical significance in describing what has happened to two populations as a result, say, of their having received two different treatments.

In this chapter we are concerned mainly with methods of applying tests of significance in examples where the data are in the form of frequencies as in the first class mentioned above. Snedecor (4) has very aptly used the term *enumeration data* to describe data of this type.

2. Tests of Goodness of Fit. In many problems the test that is required is a comparison of a set of actual frequencies with a corresponding set of theoretical frequencies. Thus in experiments in genetics an F_2 population may be classified into two groups, as in a wheat experiment in which the F_2 population of 131 plants is classified as 106 that are resistant to rust and 25 that are susceptible. The predominance of resistant plants can be explained by the well-known theory of dominance of the genes for rust resistance coupled with the supposition that rust reaction is determined by only one pair of genes, one parent having contributed the gene for rust resistance and the other parent the gene for susceptibility. This is plainly an hypothesis which gives a general explanation of the results, and as such may be subject to testing in the same manner as the familiar null hypothesis of Chapter I. The procedure of this test follows from the following considerations.

In a population for which the hypothesis is true, if a large number of samples of 131 plants each are taken, these will be found to vary around a mean value for the frequencies of resistant and susceptible plants which will be directly calculable from the hypothesis. Thus in the present example it is easily demonstrated that the mean of such a population will be 98.25 resistant plants and 32.75 susceptible plants. In taking samples from this population, it is to be expected that owing to random variation some of these samples will exhibit quite wide variations from the mean of the population, but a large proportion of them will, of course, be fairly close to the mean of the population. If we knew the theoretical distribution of such samples around the mean, we could calculate for samples the same size as ours the numbers of resistant and susceptible plants which would occur as the result of random variations in only 5% of the trials. This would establish for us the 5% level of significance—that is, if our actual sample fell outside of the range of this 5% level we would say that the data did not substantiate the hypothesis, in fact it is fairly convincing evidence that the hypothesis is not true. If our sample fell well within the 5% level we would then say that there was good agreement between the data and the hypothesis, but the hypothesis would not necessarily be proved. Now the distribution of the samples can be calculated directly by methods similar to those used in Chapter I, and we shall see in Chapter X that if the sample is small it may be advantageous to proceed on this basis. However, for general application a much easier method is available. This method involves the calculation for the data of the sample a statistic known as χ^2 (chi square) which is distributed in a known manner depending on the number of degrees of freedom available for its estimation. For the general case χ^2 is given by:

$$\chi^2 = \Sigma\left[\frac{(a - t)^2}{t}\right] \tag{1}$$

where a represents the actual frequencies and t the corresponding theoretical frequencies. Thus in the present example the actual frequencies are 106 and 25, and the corresponding theoretical frequencies are 98.25 and 32.75. The two values of $a - t$ are therefore both equal to 7.75, and $\chi^2 = 7.75^2/98.25 + 7.75^2/32.75 = 2.445$.[1] The number of degrees of freedom available for the estimation of χ^2 is 1. In this respect the problem is similar to the t test for the differences between paired values. Here we have two pairs of differences as represented by the two values of $a - t$, and consequently there is only one degree of freedom. Another concept of the degrees of freedom arises from the fact that there are only two classes, resistant and susceptible. The total number in the sample being fixed, if the number in any one class is fixed the number in the other class must also be fixed. There is therefore only one class

---

[1] For simple ratios a direct formula suggested by F. R. Immer for calculating χ^2 may be used. This formula is:

$$\chi^2 = \frac{(a_1 - a_2 x)^2}{xN}$$

where the theoretical ratio is $x : 1$, a_1 is the actual frequency corresponding to x and a_2 is the actual frequency corresponding to 1. N is the total frequency.

which can be arbitrarily assigned a given frequency, and this means that there is only one degree of freedom.

The next step in the test is to examine the tables that give the distribution of χ^2 and find the value at the 5% level for one degree of freedom. We enter Table 95 and find that the value of χ^2 at the 5% point is 3.84. Our conclusion is that the data do not disagree significantly with the hypothesis. Of course, we can if necessary go further and determine approximately in what proportion of cases such a result as ours would be obtained. The χ^2 value of 2.445 falls between the two values of χ^2 that correspond to the 10 and 20% levels of P. By interpolation our value is found to correspond to the 13% point, and consequently we can say that a sample showing a deviation from the theoretical as great as or greater than the one observed would be expected to occur in 13% of the trials. The observed deviation is therefore not very important and does not in any sense disprove the hypothesis.

It should be noted at this point that the possible deviations from the theoretical may occur in both directions, and that in the test of significance both these possibilities have been taken into account. Since there is very often a good deal of confusion on this point, it may be just as well to emphasize here that it is absolutely necessary, in testing the hypothesis set up, to take into account possible deviations in both directions. Our hypothesis involves picturing a population deviating about a mean of 98.25 resistant to 32.75 susceptible plants. According to the theory, deviations of 7.75 in either direction are equally likely, and in our sample the deviation happened to be positive for the resistant group and negative for the susceptible group. If we should determine the proportion of the trials in which a positive deviation as great as or greater than the one observed would occur, it is clear that this proportion would be exactly half of the proportion determined above, or about $6\frac{1}{2}\%$. But this would not be a test of agreement with the hypothesis, any more than it would be to determine the proportion of the trials, say, in which a deviation of $+7.75$ to $+8.00$ would occur. The proportion would be very small, but it would in no way indicate disagreement with the hypothesis. Another way to consider this problem is to examine the possible consequences of accepting as a test of significance the 5% level, taking into account positive deviations only. On a large series of samples the investigator would expect to classify 5% of the samples as giving a significant disagreement with the hypothesis, even when the hypothesis is true. If positive deviations only are considered he would classify only $2\frac{1}{2}\%$ of the samples in this way, and consequently would not be setting up the level of significance at the 5% but at the $2\frac{1}{2}\%$ point. In certain cases, as we shall see later in the next chapter, it is legitimate as a test of significance to take into consideration the deviations at one end of the distribution only; but these are special cases and not comparable to the example given above.

Example 17. In a cross of two wheat varieties, Reward and Hope, the following results were obtained for the frequencies of resistant, semi-resistant, and susceptible plants in the F_2 generation.

Resistant   111

Semi-Resistant   232

Susceptible   1181

The theoretical frequencies according to two hypotheses are as follows:

	Single Factor Difference	Two Complementary Factors and an Inhibitor
Resistant	381	119
Semi-resistant	762	238
Susceptible	381	1167

If we wish to test the two hypotheses by comparing the actual with the expected frequencies in each case, the work may be set up and carried through as follows:

Single Factor Hypothesis			Complementary and Inhibiting Factor Hypothesis		
Actual	Theoretical	$(a - t)^2/t$	Actual	Theoretical	$(a - t)^2/t$
111	381	191.3	111	119	0.5378
232	762	368.6	232	238	0.1513
1181	381	1679.8	1181	1167	0.1680

$x^2 = 2239.7$ $n = 2$ $P = 0.0000$ $x^2 = 0.857$ $n = 2$ $P = 0.65$

We have two degrees of freedom in each case, and we find for the first case that such a large value of x^2 is not given in the table. The largest value under $n = 2$ is 9.21, which corresponds to a P of 0.01. We can conclude, therefore, that the probability of obtaining deviations, due to chance variation, as great as or greater than those observed is too remote to be considered. In the second case, $x^2 = 0.857$ and this corresponds approximately to $P = 0.65$. The fit here is very good since deviations as great as or greater than those observed may be expected in at least 50% of the cases. The final conclusion is that the single factor hypothesis is quite inadequate to explain the type of segregation observed, but there is good evidence to support the second hypothesis based on a pair of complementary factors and an inhibiting factor.

Example 18. In an assumed cross between parents of the constitution $BBcc$ and $bbCC$, the F_2 population is classified as follows:

BC	Bc	Cb	cb	Total
1260	625	610	5	2500

According to a theoretical $9 : 3 : 3 : 1$ ratio, the theoretical frequencies would be:

BC	Bc	Cb	cb	Total
1406	469	469	156	2500

The actual results differ very widely from the expected as indicated by calculating χ^2. In this case we find $\chi^2 = 255.60$ and referring to Table 95 and entering at $n = 3$ we note that 11.34 is the highest value given. It is clear that the fit is very poor; so we proceed to analyze the data for the source of the disturbance, and develop a hypothesis more in accordance with the facts. In the first place the assumption is made when the $9 : 3 : 3 : 1$ ratio is built up that the ratio of B to b is $3 : 1$, and that of C to c is also $3 : 1$. A discrepancy in either one of these ratios will result in a poor fit to the $9 : 3 : 3 : 1$ for the whole set. Consequently we set up the two actual ratios and calculate χ^2 for each.

B	b		C	c
1885	615		1870	630

$$\chi^2 = (1885 - 3 \times 615)^2/3 \times 2500 \qquad \chi^2 = (1870 - 3 \times 630)^2/3 \times 2500$$

$$= 0.2133 \qquad\qquad\qquad\qquad = 0.0533$$

Now χ^2 *values may be added together or separated into components.* In this case we can add the two χ^2 values, obtaining a new χ^2 of 0.2666. Similarly we add the degrees of freedom, obtaining $n = 2$. On looking up the tables we find that the P value is between 0.95 and 0.50 but closer to the latter, hence the fit is good and the discrepancy of the actual from the theoretical $9 : 3 : 3 : 1$ ratio is not due to the segregation of the individual pairs of factors, but to the behavior of the factor pairs in relation to each other. In other words, there must be a tendency for the factors to be linked in inheritance. It is a common procedure in such cases to calculate the linkage intensity. An approved method (1) for examples of this type gives 9% of crossing over, and on that basis we can determine a new set of expected frequencies. These are set up below with the actual frequencies and another value of χ^2 determined.

Classes	Actual Frequencies	Theoretical Frequencies	$(a - t)^2/t$
BC	1260	1255	0.0199
Bc	625	620	0.0403
cB	610	620	0.1613
cb	5	5	0.0000
			$\chi^2 = 0.2215$

The theoretical frequencies in this table have been calculated on the basis of 9% crossing over, a value which was determined from the sample itself. Therefore, we lose one degree of freedom and must enter the table under $n = 2$. In this case we find P = approximately 0.90. There is a very close agreement between the two sets of frequencies, but it would not be correct to consider this a very satisfactory fit. Such close agreement could only occur by chance on the basis of the hypothesis being tested in 10% of the cases. However, the agreement is not sufficiently close to prove that the original data were selected to give a good fit. If we had obtained a P of 0.95, it would have been worth while investigating the data to determine the reason for the very unusual agreement.

Example 19. The goodness of fit test may be useful in determining the agreement between actual and theoretical normal frequency distributions. In Chapter III, Example 1, we calculated the normal frequencies corresponding to the actual frequencies for the transparencies of 400 red blood cells. In Table 21, these two distributions are repeated, and the third column gives the calculation of χ^2.

TABLE 21

ACTUAL AND NORMAL FREQUENCIES FOR TRANSPARENCIES
OF 400 RED BLOOD CELLS, AND CALCULATION OF χ^2

Actual	Theoretical Normal	$(a - t)^2/t$
4	4.64	.0883
11	7.92	1.1978
17	16.84	.0015
29	30.28	.0541
43	44.76	.0692
56	59.16	.1688
58	64.96	.7457
63	60.40	.1119
61	47.56	3.7980
25	31.16	1.2178
20	18.24	.1698
9	8.80	.0045
4	5.28	.3103
400	400.00	$\chi^2 = 7.9377$

In connection with a test of this kind, two important points should be noted. (1) At the tails of the distribution the theoretical frequencies and corresponding actual frequencies are grouped. The object is to avoid very small theoretical values which, if present, to some extent invalidate the χ^2 test. The general rule is to avoid having theoretical frequencies less than 5. This point is discussed in greater detail in the following chapter on tests of goodness of fit and independence with small samples. (2) The theoretical frequencies are determined from the total frequency and the mean and standard deviation of the sample, so we must deduct one degree of freedom for each. Thus three degrees of freedom are absorbed in fitting, and since there are 13 classes we have 10 degrees of freedom for the estimation of χ^2.

In the present example we enter the χ^2 table therefore under $n = 10$, and note that a χ^2 of 7.9377 corresponds approximately to a P value of 0.65. Consequently the fit may be considered a very good one.

3. Tests of Independence and Association. From a cross of two wheat varieties 82 strains were developed and tested for their agronomic characters. One set of data for these strains is given in Table 22. On

TABLE 22

CLASSIFICATION OF 82 STRAINS OF WHEAT FOR
YIELD AND CHARACTER OF AWNS

	Yield Classes—weight in grains			
	151–200	201–250	251–325	Total
Awned	6	7	21	34
Awnless	18	21	9	48
Total	24	28	30	82

examining the frequencies in the 3×2 table, we note that there seems to be a tendency for the awned types to give higher yields than the awnless ones. To test the significance of such a result, we have to determine the probability of its occurrence if the two characters are entirely independent. For this particular problem we have to find the percentage of cases in which the above distribution, or one emphasizing still more the difference in yield of the two classes of varieties, would be obtained if there were no tendency whatever for awned varieties to yield higher or lower than awnless ones. Such a test could be applied by calculating χ^2 if we could obtain the theoretical frequencies for each cell representing complete independence of the two characters. A reasonable basis for the calculation of these theoretical frequencies is to assume that, if the distributions are independent, they will be distributed within the table in the same proportion as they are in the totals. Thus in the cell in Table 22 containing 6 strains, we should have, on the basis of complete independence, x strains where $x : 24 : : 34 : 82$. Hence $x = (24 \times 34)/82$. In the cell below, $x = (24 \times 48)/82$. In the same manner all the theoretical frequencies can be calculated, and then we can proceed to the calculation of χ^2. This is the direct method of calculating χ^2, but a shorter method for general use is given below under Section 5.

4. Degrees of Freedom in χ^2 Tables. In goodness of fit tests where the theoretical frequencies are determined according to some chosen hypothesis, the degrees of freedom can usually be equated to $(N-1)$ where N is the number of cells in the table. In certain cases, however, as in Example 19 above, additional statistics calculated from the sample are utilized to determine the theoretical frequencies, and one degree of freedom must be subtracted for each of such statistics.

In tests of independence or association, the subtotals of the classes into which the variates are distributed are used to determine the theoretical frequencies, and obviously these must be treated as statistics, so far as they themselves absorb degrees of freedom. Examining Table 22, we note that originally we have 5 degrees of freedom in the table, but 1 of these is absorbed by the awning subtotals and 2 for the yield subtotals. Therefore we have finally only 2 degrees of freedom left for the estimation of χ^2. Another method of determining the degrees of freedom is to make an actual count of the number of cells that can be filled up arbitrarily. To do this we must assume that the subtotals are chosen first. Then, as in Table 22, any two cells such as those containing 6 and 7 may be filled up arbitrarily but all the rest are fixed. The two cells that can be filled arbitrarily represent 2 degrees of freedom.

In $m \times n$ fold tables the degrees of freedom can be equated to $(m-1)(n-1)$ for the general case with which we are dealing. Special cases will of course arise where this rule will not hold, but usually it is easy in such cases to arrive at the correct number by some such method as that described above.

5. Methods of Calculation for Independence and Association Tests. (a) *For $(m \times n)$ fold tables.* The generalized χ^2 table may be represented as follows:

		C				
	1	2	3 $\cdots\cdots\cdots$ n			
1	11	12	13		$1n$	T_{B1}
2	21	22				T_{B2}
B 3						T_{B3}
.			etc.			.
.						.
.						.
m						T_{Bm}
	T_{C1}	T_{C2}	$T_{C3}\cdots\cdots\cdots T_{Cn}$			T

In order to determine χ^2 we must calculate the theoretical frequency for each cell. For cell 11 we find $t = (T_{C1} \cdot T_{B1})/T$, and for cell 12, $t = (T_{C2} \cdot T_{B1})/T$, and so forth for all the cells. We then set up the theoretical frequencies with the corresponding actual frequencies and calculate $\chi^2 = \Sigma[(a - t)^2/t]$.

(b) *For (2 × n) fold tables.* A table of this type may be represented as follows:

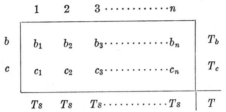

We can calculate χ^2 for this table in exactly the same manner as for the $(m \times n)$ fold table above, but a short-cut method giving χ^2 directly without calculating the theoretical frequencies is given by Brandt and Snedecor, as follows:

$$\chi^2 = \frac{T^2}{T_b T_c} \left\{ \Sigma \left(\frac{b^2}{T_s} \right) - \frac{T_b^2}{T} \right\} \tag{2}$$

Each frequency in either of the rows is squared and divided by the corresponding subtotal. These are summated and the correction term subtracted as shown in the formula. The remainder is multiplied by the quotient of the square of the total frequency by the product of the two subtotals on the right. This formula shows as each value of b^2/T_s is calculated the contribution of each pair to the value of χ^2.

(c) *For (2 × 2) fold tables.* Representing the (2 × 2) fold table as follows:

b_1	b_2	T_b
c_1	c_2	T_c
T_1	T_2	T

χ^2 is given by $\dfrac{(b_1 c_2 - c_1 b_2)^2 T}{T_1 \cdot T_2 \cdot T_b \cdot T_c}$ (3)

We multiply diagonal frequencies and find the difference between the two products. The difference is squared and multiplied by the grand total, and the result is divided by the product of the subtotals.

6. Coefficient of Contingency. It will have been noted that the methods employed in tests of independence and association are comparable to the method of correlation, with this essential difference, that in the former the categories are either *descriptive* or *numerical*. If the categories are numerical and of *equal magnitude*, we can calculate a correlation coefficient for any of the tables to which we usually apply χ^2 with the reservation that if the categories are very broad we will get only an approximation to the true value of the correlation coefficient even if corrections are made for grouping. The necessity for the use of χ^2 arises, therefore, from material which can be classified, at least for one character, only in *descriptive* categories, or in numerical categories that are not of *equal* magnitude. For tables to which only χ^2 methods can be applied, some investigators feel that in addition to the χ^2 test, which is essentially a test of significance, they should have some measure of *association* comparable to the correlation coefficient. A measure of this type is Pearson's coefficient of contingency (C) given by:

$$C = \sqrt{\frac{\chi^2}{N + \chi^2}}$$

where N is the total number of observations (not the number of classes).

Since it is a function of χ^2, the significance of the coefficient of contingency must be the same as for χ^2. It is not necessary, therefore, to have a standard error of C in order to test its significance.

7. Exercises.

1. Test the goodness of fit of observation to theory for the following ratios:

	Observed Values		Theoretical Ratio	
	A	a	A	a
(1)	134	36	3	1
(2)	240	120	3	1
(3)	76	56	1	1
(4)	240	13	15	1

The χ^2 values you should obtain are: (1)   1.32
                                                       (2)   13.33
                                                       (3)   3.03
                                                       (4)   0.53

2. In an F_2 family of 200 plants segregating for resistance to rust, if resistance is dominant and susceptibility recessive, find the ratio that gives a P value of exactly 0.05 when fitted to a 3 : 1 ratio.

The are two possibilities, the ratios being 138 : 62 or 162 : 38.

3. In a certain cross the types represented by BC, Bc, bC, and bc are expected to occur in a $9 : 3 : 3 : 1$ ratio. The actual frequencies obtained were:

BC	Bc	bC	bc
102	16	35	7

Determine the goodness of fit, and if the fit is poor analyze the data further to disclose the source of the discrepancy.

$\chi^2 = 9.86$; P is less than 0.01. Hence the fit is poor.

In further analysis, test the segregation for each factor separately.

4. Test the goodness of fit of the actual to the theoretical normal frequencies for either of the distributions from Chapter II, Exercise 2, or Chapter II, Exercise 3. Watch the grouping of the classes at the tails of the distributions in order that the theoretical frequency in any one class is not less than 5.

For Exercise 2, $\chi^2 = $ approximately 10.

For Exercise 3, $\chi^2 = $ approximately 2.6.

5. Table 23 gives the data obtained during an epidemic of cholera (3) on the effectiveness of inoculation as a means of preventing the disease. Test the hypothesis that in the inoculated group the number of persons attacked is not significantly less than in the not inoculated group, and the number not attacked is not significantly greater. Note carefully how this hypothesis is worded.

TABLE 23

FREQUENCIES OF ATTACKED AND NOT ATTACKED
IN INOCULATED AND NOT INOCULATED GROUPS

	Not attacked	Attacked
Inoculated	192	4
Not inoculated	113	34

6. Calculate χ^2 and locate the approximate P value for Table 22 given in Section 3 above. $\chi^2 = 15.87$.

7. The data in Table 24 were obtained in a cross between a rust-resistant and a susceptible variety of oats. The F_3 families were compared for reaction to rust in the seedling stage, and in the field under ordinary epidemic conditions.

TABLE 24

CLASSIFICATION OF SEEDLING AND FIELD REACTIONS
OF 810 F_3 FAMILIES OF OATS

		Seedling Reaction		
		Resistant	Segregating	Susceptible
Field Reaction	Resistant	142	51	3
	Segregating	13	404	2
	Susceptible	2	17	176

Test the significance of the association in this table, and calculate the coefficient of contingency.

$\chi^2 = 1127.87$. (This result will vary according to the accuracy with which the t values are calculated. To check approximately with the value given here calculate the t values to at least two decimal figures.)

REFERENCES

1. R. A. FISHER and BHAI BALMUKAND. *Journ. Gen.*, **20**: 79–92, 1928.
2. R. A. FISHER. Statistical Methods for Research Workers, Oliver and Boyd, London, 1936. Reading: Chapter IV.
3. M. GREENWOOD and G. U. YULE. *Proc. Roy. Soc. Med.*, **8**: 113, 1915.
4. G. W. SNEDECOR. Statistical Methods. Collegiate Press, Inc., Ames, Iowa, 1937. Reading: Chapters 1, 9.
5. L. H. C. TIPPETT. The Methods of Statistics. Williams and Norgate, Ltd., London, 1931. Reading: Chapter IV.

CHAPTER X

TESTS OF GOODNESS OF FIT AND INDEPENDENCE WITH SMALL SAMPLES

1. Inadequacy of the χ^2 Criterion and the Correction for Continuity. The method of χ^2 is based on the smooth curve of a continuous distribution and, when the numbers are large, gives probability results that are very close to the true values. When the numbers are small, and especially when only one degree of freedom is involved, the χ^2 method is quite inaccurate. One reason for this will be clear from an examination of Fig. 10, representing the distribution obtained by expanding the

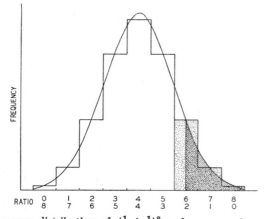

| RATIO | 0 8 | 1 7 | 2 6 | 3 5 | 4 4 | 5 3 | 6 2 | 7 1 | 8 0 |

Fig. 10.—Frequency distribution of $(\frac{1}{2} + \frac{1}{2})^8$ and corresponding smooth curve. Shaded areas indicate the need for a correction to χ^2 for small samples.

binomial $(\frac{1}{2} + \frac{1}{2})^8$. Given a theoretical ratio of 1 : 1, say, for the success or failure of an event, the binomial distribution as in Fig. 10 would give the theoretical frequency of the successes through the total range from 0 to 8. If we wished to determine the probability of obtaining 6 or more successes in 1 trial of 8 events, we would find the ratio of the dotted area of the figure to that of the whole. A χ^2 test of the 6 : 2 ratio, however, would be based on the smooth curve shown in Fig. 10, and the probability would be the ratio of the cross-hatched area to the whole. The cross-hatched area is obviously less than the dotted area,

101

by an amount equal approximately to one-half the area of the 6 : 2 ratio column.   Consequently the χ^2 test will give a probability result that is too low.

In order to correct for the above-mentioned discrepancy in the χ^2 test, Yates (8) has suggested a correction which he proposes to call the *correction for continuity*.   In the ordinary case χ^2 is given by $\Sigma(a - t)^2/t$, where a represents the actual and t the theoretical frequencies.   Yates's correction is applied by subtracting $\frac{1}{2}$ from each value of $(a - t)$, but it must always be subtracted in the direction that reduces the numerical value of $(a - t)$.   In Fig. 10 the application of the correction would result in extending the cross-hatched area to the line bordering the columns representing the 5 : 3 and 6 : 2 ratios, and must obviously bring about an improvement in the estimate of probability.

It should be noted in connection with tests of significance applied to ratios that the χ^2 method is exactly equivalent to the use of the standard deviation to determine the significance of a deviation from the mean.   Likewise the correction for continuity must be made when the numbers are small.   As will be evident from Fig. 10, the correction is simply a matter of subtracting $\frac{1}{2}$ from the deviation from the mean. To test the significance of a 6 : 2 ratio when the theoretical is 1 : 1 or 4 : 4, we would take the deviation equal to $(6 - 4 - \frac{1}{2}) = 1.5$.   The standard deviation of a binomial distribution is $\sqrt{pqn} = \sqrt{\frac{1}{2} \times \frac{1}{2} \times 8} = 1.4142$, and we can test in the usual way, using tables of the probability integral.

The χ^2 test for ratios is also inaccurate when applied to samples from populations having a definitely skewed distribution.   In the case of ratios of successes to failures where the theoretical ratio is not 1 : 1, this inadequacy of the χ^2 test becomes obvious.   Table 25 gives the true probabilities calculated from the binomial distribution of obtaining from 16 to 0 successes when each trial consists of 16 events.   These are worked out for two cases: (1) when the theoretical ratio is 1 : 1, and (2) when the theoretical ratio is 3 : 1.   The corresponding $\frac{1}{2}P$ [1] values obtained by calculating χ^2 with and without Yates's correction are given in the same table.   For the symmetrical binomial distribution it will be noted that the $\frac{1}{2}P$ values for χ'^2 with Yates's correction agree very well with the correct values except at the extreme tails of the distribution where χ'^2 tends to overestimate the probability.   For the asymmetrical distribution the agreement is not good anywhere in the range.   In both cases it

---

[1] $\frac{1}{2}P$ is used here to indicate that the probability is calculated from the area of only one tail of the distribution.   As the problem is stated in terms of "15 or more successes," etc., it is obvious that only one tail of the distribution must be considered.

will be observed that χ^2 uncorrected gives a very decided underestimate of the probability through practically the whole range.

TABLE 25

PROBABILITY OF n SUCCESSES IN A SAMPLE OF 16 EVENTS

	Distribution = $(\frac{1}{2} + \frac{1}{2})^{16}$			Distribution = $(\frac{3}{4} + \frac{1}{4})^{16}$		
		Corrected	Uncorrected		Corrected	Uncorrected
Successes	$\frac{1}{2} P$ (Bin)	$\frac{1}{2} P (\chi'^2)$	$\frac{1}{2} P (\chi^2)$	$\frac{1}{2} P$ (Bin)	$\frac{1}{2} P (\chi'^2)$	$\frac{1}{2} P (\chi^2)$
16	0.000,015	0.000,088	0.000,032	0.010,023	0.021,656	0.010,461
15	0.000,259	0.000,577	0.000,233	0.063,477	0.074,457	0.041,638
14	0.002,090	0.002,980	0.001,350	0.197,112	0.193,248	0.124,109
13	0.010,635	0.012,224	0.006,210	0.404,988	0.386,406	0.281,837
12	0.038,406	0.040,059	0.022,750			
11	0.105,056	0.105,650	0.066,807	0.369,812	0.386,406	0.281,837
10	0.227,248	0.226,627	0.158,655	0.189,653	0.193,248	0.124,109
9	0.401,809	0.401,294	0.308,538	0.079,556	0.074,457	0.041,638
8				0.027,129	0.021,656	0.010,461
7	0.401,809	0.401,294	0.308,538	0.007,469	0.004,687	0.001,946
6	0.227,248	0.226,627	0.158,655	0.001,644	0.000,748	0.000,266
5	0.105,056	0.105,650	0.066,807	0.000,285	0.000,087	0.000,027
4	0.038,406	0.040,059	0.022,750	0.000,038	0.000,008	0.000,002
3	0.010,635	0.012.224	0.006,210	0.000,004	0.000,001	0.000,000
2	0.002,090	0.002,980	0.001,350	0.000,000	0.000,000	0.000,000
1	0.000,259	0.000,577	0.000,233	0.000,000	0.000,000	0.000,000
0	0.000,015	0.000,088	0.000,032	0.000,000	0.000,000	0.000,000

In probability tests applied to 2×2 frequency tables, the same difficulties arise with regard to the application of χ^2 as for testing the goodness of fit of simple ratios. Since only one degree of freedom is involved, the number of possible combinations of the frequencies of unlike probability is relatively small and the theoretical distribution is, therefore, definitely discontinuous. The error is not significant when the frequencies are large, but with small frequencies it is very decided. The skewness factor is not so important for 2×2 tables as for simple ratios, as the χ^2 curve adopts itself within certain limits to the shape of the theoretical distribution. After correction for continuity the remaining discrepancy may be regarded as due to the comparison between a histogram and a smooth curve which gives an approximate fit.

The method of making the correction for continuity is to determine the larger of the two products b_1c_2 and b_2c_1, and for the larger subtracting 0.5 from the two factors, and for the smaller adding 0.5 to the two factors.   After making these corrections the usual formula may be applied.

Table 26 has been prepared to show the relation between the values of $\frac{1}{2}P$ calculated for the 2×2 table:

using (a) a direct method for determining the exact probability, (b) χ^2 without correction, and (c) χ'^2, or that obtained by using the correction for continuity.   The direct method was devised by R. A. Fisher (1) and will be described below under "Methods of Calculation."   The probability value for the modal frequency has been omitted since it may be considered as belonging to either tail of the distribution.

It will be noted that at the extreme tails of the distribution χ^2 tends to overestimate the probability, but that in the range where significance may be in doubt the agreement is fairly good.   On the other hand, as indicated by the $\frac{1}{2}P$ values for χ^2, unless the correction for continuity is made there is a very decided underestimation of the probability throughout the whole range.

For 2×3 frequency tables, the correction for continuity is not so important as for 2×2 tables.   With 2 degrees of freedom the number of possible combinations is much greater than for 1 degree of freedom, and the agreement between the smooth curve and the histogram must be much better.   With more than 2 degrees of freedom the correction for continuity would hardly be necessary in any case.   It must be remembered, however, that the tendency, especially when the numbers are small, is to underestimate the probability; and it may be necessary in certain cases to check the probability by direct calculation, or if this is impractical, by an analytical study of the larger table made by breaking it up into parts or condensing it into a single 2×2 table.   The direct calculation of probabilities, even in a 2×3 table, is slightly complicated; so that in most cases the best practice is to endeavor to make an application of χ^2 such that we are reasonably sure of a fair approximation to the true probability.

TABLE 26

PROBABILITIES FOR ALL THE COMBINATIONS OF A 2×2 TABLE

| Combination | $\frac{1}{2} P$ Calculated by | | |
	Direct Method	χ^2	χ'^2
12 0 6 8	0.00192	0.00082	0.00325
11 1 7 7	0.02828	0.01087	0.03084
10 2 8 6	0.15585	0.07460	0.15475
9 3 9 5	0.43707	0.27756	0.49346
8 4 10 4			
7 5 11 3	0.24577	0.13251	0.24557
6 6 12 2	0.06124	0.02459	0.06188
5 7 13 1	0.00741	0.00241	0.00835
4 8 14 0	0.00032	0.00012	0.00059

2. Methods of Calculation.   Example 20.   In a study of the blood groups of some North American Indians, Grant (2) obtained the results given in the following table:

| Band of Indians | Blood Groups | | | | |
	O	A	B	AB	
Fond du lac	18	6	5	0	29
Chipewyan	13	0	1	0	14
	31	6	6	0	43

It appears that pure Indians tend towards a very high percentage of individuals having the blood group O, but the group at Fond du lac had an obviously larger percentage of white blood as indicated by other characteristics. The essential problem in this case is to test the significance of the distribution of the two bands into two main groups, O and not O. We form, therefore, a 2 × 2 table, as below:

	O	not O	
Fond du lac	18	11	29
Chipewyan	13	1	14
	31	12	43

Either the χ^2 test with the correction for continuity or the direct probability method would be applicable to this table. In order to indicate the methods of calculation we shall apply the test in both ways.

(a) χ^2 corrected for continuity. If a 2 × 2 table is represented as follows:

b_1	b_2	T_b
c_1	c_2	T_c
T_1	T_2	T

the corrected value of χ^2 is given by

$$\chi^2 = \frac{\left(b_1 c_2 - c_1 b_2 - \frac{T}{2}\right)^2 T}{T_1 \cdot T_2 \cdot T_b \cdot T_c} \tag{1}$$

where $T/2$ always reduces the numerical value of $(b_1 c_2 - c_1 b_2)$. This is of course equivalent to the method described on page 103.

Applying the corrected formula to our example, we have

$$\chi^2 = \frac{(13 \times 11 - 18 - \frac{43}{2})^2 \, 43}{31 \times 12 \times 14 \times 29} = 3.0499$$

Using Yules table of "P for divergence from independence in the fourfold table" (9), we look up

$$\chi^2 = 3.0 \qquad P = 0.08326$$
$$\chi^2 = 3.1 \qquad P = 0.07829$$
$$\text{Difference} = 0.00497$$

and by direct interpolation $P = 0.08077$ and $\frac{1}{2} P = \mathbf{0.0404}$.

In order to obtain P more accurately we can make use of the fact that the distribution of χ^2 is normal for one degree of freedom, and $\sqrt{\chi^2} = t$ the value for entering tables of the probability integral. Here $\sqrt{\chi^2} = \sqrt{3.0499} = \mathbf{1.7464}$, and in Sheppard's table of the probability integral we look up

$$t = 1.74 \quad \tfrac{1}{2}(1 + \alpha) = 0.9590705$$
$$t = 1.75 \quad \tfrac{1}{2}(1 + \alpha) = 0.9599408$$

Difference $= 0.0008703$

and interpolating directly for $t = 1.7464$ we have $\tfrac{1}{2}(1 + \alpha) = 0.959,6275$. Since we want $\tfrac{1}{2}P$ we take $\tfrac{1}{2}P = 1 - \tfrac{1}{2}(1 + \alpha) = 0.04037$.

(b) Direct probability method for a 2×2 table. Representing a 2×2 table as above, R. A. Fisher (1) has shown that, for any particular combination of b_1, b_2, c_1, c_2, the direct probability of its occurrence is given by

$$\left(\frac{T_1! \, T_2! \, T_b! \, T_c!}{T!}\right)\left(\frac{1}{b_1! \, b_2! \, c_1! \, c_2!}\right) \tag{2}$$

The easiest method of performing the calculations is by means of a table of logarithms of factorials. The different combinations that can occur are as follows:

17	12	18	11	19	10	20	9
14	0	13	1	12	2	11	3

and so forth

all other combinations having the same probability and occurring with equal frequency with one of the above. In this case, therefore, we require the sum of the separate probabilities of the first two combinations. These are given by:

$$\left[\frac{31! \times 12! \times 29! \times 14!}{43!} \times \frac{1}{18! \times 11! \times 13!}\right]$$

$$\left[\frac{31! \times 12! \times 29! \times 14!}{43!} \times \frac{1}{17! \times 14! \times 12!}\right]$$

When a series of such terms are to be calculated, labor is saved by first calculating the logarithm of the constant factor. The logarithms of the terms are then obtained by subtracting the logarithms of the factorials in the numerator of each term.

In this example, log constant factor $= 31.701,1593$

The logs to be subtracted are $33.201,7770$ and $34.171,8139$, giving:

$$\log \text{ term } 1 = \bar{2}.499,3823 \quad \text{Term } 1 = 0.031,578$$
$$\log \text{ term } 2 = \bar{3}.529,3454 \quad \text{Term } 2 = 0.003,338$$

Total $= \tfrac{1}{2}P = 0.0349$

The values of $\tfrac{1}{2}P$ obtained by the two methods are in fairly close agreement.[1]

[1] The student may use this example in order to straighten out in his mind the reason why for certain tests it is correct to base the decision on the value of $\tfrac{1}{2}P$ instead of P. Actually the hypothesis being tested here is that Indians having an admixture of white blood do not contain a greater percentage of individuals with the blood group O than Indians that are relatively pure. If the hypothesis is stated differently—for example, that the two groups of Indians are random samples drawn from the same population with respect to the distribution of the blood group O—then it would be necessary to use the full value of P in order to make the test. The test based on the value of $\tfrac{1}{2}P$ arises from the knowledge that the Fond du lac group had an obviously larger percentage of white blood than the Chipewyans.

Example 21.   For a certain disease we will assume that it has been shown that recovery or death is a certainty and that without treatment about half of the patients recover. A new treatment tried out in 16 cases gives 12 recoveries and 4 deaths. Is this a significant demonstration of the efficacy of the treatment?

This problem can be solved by the direct calculation of probabilities according to the binomial distribution, or since the theoretical distribution is symmetrical the χ^2 test corrected for continuity will give a fairly close approximation. Both methods will be used in order to demonstrate methods of calculation.

(a) χ^2 corrected for continuity.   For ratios the short formula for determining χ^2 as in Chapter IX, Section 2, is modified as follows to correct for continuity.

$$\chi^2 = \frac{\left(a_1 - a_2 x - \dfrac{x+1}{2}\right)^2}{xN} \tag{3}$$

where the theoretical ratio is $x : 1$, a_1 is the actual frequency corresponding to x, and a_2 is the actual frequency corresponding to 1. N is the total frequency or $(a_1 + a_2)$, and $\dfrac{x+1}{2}$ always reduces the numerical value of $(a_1 - a_2 x)$.   In the present example:

$$\chi^2 = \frac{(12 - 4 - 1)^2}{16} = \frac{49}{16} = 3.0625$$

From Yule's table of P we find $\frac{1}{2} P = 0.0401$. The odds are about $25 : 1$ against the occurrence of a $12 : 4$ ratio due to chance alone.

(b) Direct probability from the binomial.   Let p represent the probability of recovery and q the probability of death. We know that $p = q = \frac{1}{2}$, and we require the first five terms of the expansion of $(p + q)^n$ where $n = 16$. The expansion of $(p + q)^n$ is given by:

$$(p + q)^n = p^n + {}_nC_1 p^{n-1}q + {}_nC_2 p^{n-2}q^2 + \cdots + {}_nC_n q^n \tag{4}$$

where $\qquad {}_nC_r = \dfrac{n(n - 1)(n - 2) \cdots (n - r + 1)}{1 \cdot 2 \cdot 3 \cdots r} = \dfrac{n!}{r! \, (n - r)!}$

In our example we have:

$$\left(\frac{1}{2} + \frac{1}{2}\right)^{16} = \left(\frac{1}{2}\right)^{16} + \frac{16!}{15!}\left(\frac{1}{2}\right)^{16} + \frac{16!}{2! \, 14!}\left(\frac{1}{2}\right)^{16} + \frac{16!}{3! \, 13!}\left(\frac{1}{2}\right)^{16} + \cdots + \left(\frac{1}{2}\right)^{16}$$

In each term we have the constant factor $(\frac{1}{2})^{16}$. We determine the logarithm of this factor in the ordinary way and proceed to determine the logarithms of the coefficients by means of a table of the logarithms of factorials. The work is as shown in Table 27, which is self-explanatory with the possible exception of the last column. The term values give the probabilities of obtaining in one trial the number of recoveries (or deaths) shown in the same line. In general, however, we do not ask that question. We inquire, for example, as to the probability of obtaining 12 or *more* recoveries in a sample of 16, and hence we must add the probabilities for 12, 13, 14, 15, and 16 recoveries. These summations have been performed and are given in the last column under the heading $\frac{1}{2}P$. Again, since we have summated for one tail of the distribution only, we represent the probability by $\frac{1}{2}P$.

The answer to our problem is given in the line representing 12 recoveries. The corresponding value of $\frac{1}{2}P$ is 0.0384, and this compares reasonably well with $\frac{1}{2}P = 0.0401$, obtained by the χ^2 method.

TABLE 27

CALCULATION OF PROBABILITIES FROM THE BINOMIAL $(\frac{1}{2} + \frac{1}{2})^{16}$

Recoveries	Log $_nC_r$	Log $p^{n-r}q^r$	Log Term	Term	$\frac{1}{2}P$
16		$\bar{5}.183,5200$	$\bar{5}.183,5200$	0.000,015	0.000,015
15	1.204,1200	"	$\bar{4}.387,6400$	0.000,244	0.000,259
14	2.079,1812	"	$\bar{3}.262,7012$	0.001,831	0.002,090
13	2.748,1880	"	$\bar{3}.931,7080$	0.008,545	0.010,635
12	3.260,0714	"	$\bar{2}.443,5914$	0.027,771	0.038,406

Example 22. In the example above, let us assume that without treatment the ratio of recoveries to deaths is 3 : 1 instead of 1 : 1, and in the group of 16 patients receiving treatment the actual ratio is 14 : 2. Test the significance of the treatment.

This problem differs from the first, in that the theoretical distribution is skewed, and what has been said about the χ^2 method being remembered, it may be taken for granted that χ^2 will not give a good approximation to the true probability. We must solve this problem, therefore, by a direct calculation of the probability from the binomial distribution.

Since the ratio of recoveries to deaths is 3 : 1, $p = \frac{3}{4}$ and $q = \frac{1}{4}$, and we must calculate the first three terms of the expansion of $(\frac{3}{4} + \frac{1}{4})^{16}$. Using the formula given we have:

$$\left(\frac{3}{4} + \frac{1}{4}\right)^{16} = \left(\frac{3}{4}\right)^{16} + \frac{16!}{15!}\left(\frac{3}{4}\right)^{15}\left(\frac{1}{4}\right) + \frac{16!}{2!\,14!}\left(\frac{3}{4}\right)^{14}\left(\frac{1}{4}\right)^2$$

Noting for convenience in calculation that:

$$\left(\frac{3}{4}\right)^{15}\left(\frac{1}{4}\right) = \left(\frac{1}{4}\right)^{16} 3^{15} \quad \text{and} \quad \left(\frac{3}{4}\right)^{14}\left(\frac{1}{4}\right)^2 = \left(\frac{1}{4}\right)^{16} 3^{14}$$

The factor $(\frac{1}{4})^{16}$ is constant, and when several terms are to be calculated this transformation results in a saving of labor.

The calculations are given in Table 28. In the $\frac{1}{2}P$ column representing 14 recoveries we have $\frac{1}{2}P = 0.1971$, or the odds are only about 5 : 1 that the treatment is beneficial. This is an indication of a beneficial effect but it cannot in any sense be

TABLE 28

CALCULATION OF PROBABILITIES FROM THE BINOMIAL $(\frac{3}{4} + \frac{1}{4})^{16}$

Recoveries	Log $_nC_r$	Log $p^{n-r}q^r$	Log Term	Term	$\frac{1}{2}P$
16		$\bar{2}.000,9808$	$\bar{2}.000,9808$	0.010,023	0.010,023
15	1.204,1200	$\bar{3}.523,8595$	$\bar{2}.727,9795$	0.053,454	0.063,477
14	2.079,1812	$\bar{3}.046,7382$	$\bar{1}.125,9194$	0.133,635	0.197,112

considered a proof.   It would be sufficient evidence to warrant further investigation, but the practical aspect of such a problem must not be lost sight of, in that the actual gain in recoveries is very small and further investigation might best be directed along the line of trials with other treatments.

3. Selection of Method for Tests of Significance. Some confusion may arise as to when to apply χ^2 and when to apply the direct method of calculating probabilities.   Also when applying χ^2 the question arises whether or not the correction should be applied.   In general these points can be made clear by the consideration of some hypothetical examples.

Example 23.   The following is a 2 × 4 fold table of frequencies

	A	B	C	D
I	28	46	83	126
II	68	43	12	1

The numbers are large, and the theoretical frequencies in each cell are large. The χ^2 criterion may be applied to the whole table, and no correction is required.
Example 24.   If some of the numbers in a 2 × 4 fold table are small, as in the table below, the table must be rearranged.

	A	B	C	D
I	26	84	2	1
II	94	18	1	4

Obviously the classification of the I and II frequencies into C and D is meaningless, and the rearrangement is either a matter of adding these frequencies to B or eliminating them altogether.   Assuming that they can be eliminated we have a 2 × 2 table

	A	B
I	26	84
II	94	18

To this table it is perfectly legitimate to apply the χ^2 test, and, although the numbers are fairly large, the correction for continuity will improve the results slightly.   Obviously it would be very laborious to make a direct calculation of the probability, so we would not even consider the method in this case.

Example 25. We have a 2 × 2 table in which the numbers are small:

	A	B
I	8	2
II	4	12

For this case the direct method is the most accurate and is not difficult.

Example 26. Given a theoretical ratio of 1 : 1 for the occurrence of A and B in a series of events, we obtain in 100 trials 60 A's and 40 B's. What is the significance of this result?

The numbers are large so that the direct calculation of the probability will be very cumbersome. Therefore, we use χ^2 with the correction for continuity, or we calculate the ratio of the deviation (also corrected for continuity) to its standard deviation and get the probability from tables of the probability integral. The correction for continuity is not important, but it is bound to give a slight improvement.

Example 27. In a test of the goodness of fit of a ratio, we have a very skew distribution. For example, the theoretical ratio of successes to failures is 15 : 1, and the actual results are 5 failures out of 160 events. The direct method is the only one that will give an accurate probability result in this case, and we must calculate the *last* six terms of the expansion of $(15/16 + 1/16)^{160}$. When the numbers are large, the calculations are somewhat laborious, but in most cases it is sufficient to determine whether the result is or is not significant; and it will only be necessary in working from one end of the distribution to calculate enough terms such that their sum $(\frac{1}{2}P)$ is 0.05. If the observed deviation is within that range it is not significant. If the deviations in both directions are to be considered, we work from both ends of the distribution until the sum of the terms at each end is equal to 0.025.

Example 28. The theoretical ratio gives a skew distribution, but the numbers are small. Calculate the probability by the direct method as in Example 27.

4. Exercises.

1. (a) Expand the binomials $(\frac{1}{2} + \frac{1}{2})^8$ and $(\frac{3}{4} + \frac{1}{4})^{12}$, and calculate the value of each term.

(b) If there is an equal probability of the birth of male and female rabbits determine the probability in a litter of 8 of the occurrence of 2 females and 6 males.

(c) Plot the histogram for the expansion of $(\frac{3}{4} + \frac{1}{4})^{12}$. A bag contains white and black balls in the ratio of 3 white to 1 black. Show that, if a sample of 12 balls is taken at random, the probability of obtaining 12 white balls is different from that of obtaining 6 or more black balls, although both cases represent an equal deviation from the expected 9 white to 3 black.

(a) In order to check the work add all the terms and the sum should be very close to 1.000.

(b) $P = 0.1094$. (Note that this is not a test of significance. It is merely a question of determining the probability of the occurrence of one particular ratio.)

(c) Illustrates the problem of making tests of significance in skew distributions.

2. Koltzoff (3) performed an experiment on the control of sex in rabbits. Sperms were placed in a physiological solution in a tube and an electrical current passed through the tube. A female impregnated with sperms taken from the anode produced 6 females and 0 males, and another female impregnated with sperms from the cathode produced 1 female and 4 males. Test the significance of this result.

Using the direct method P is 0.0152.

3. From a study of the position of the polar bodies in the ova of the ferret, Mainland (4) gives the frequencies in the following table:

	Similar	Different
10μ apart..............	5	1
More than 10μ apart....	1	6

Test the significance of the apparent association between similarity and position of the polar bodies. $\frac{1}{2}P = 0.025$ calculated by the direct method.

4. Neatby (6) studied the association, in a random sample of lines from a wheat cross, of resistance to different physiologic forms of the stem rust organism. Two tables from his results are given below. Test the significance of the association in each case.

		Form 21					Form 21	
		SR	S				SR	S
Form	R........	28	41		Form	R........	46	40
27	SR........	17	15		57	S........	0	16

R (resistant) SR(semi-resistant) S (susceptible)

$$\chi^2 = 0.93 \qquad\qquad \chi^2 = 13.50$$

5. Twenty-two animals are suffering from the same disease, and the severity of the disease is about the same in each case. In order to test the therapeutic value of a serum it is administered to 10 of the animals and 12 remain uninoculated as a control. The results are as follows:

	Recovered	Died
Inoculated........	7	3
Not inoculated....	3	9

Determine the probability in such an experiment of obtaining this or a result more favorable to the treatment.   By the direct method $\frac{1}{2}P = 0.0456$.

6. An experiment is conducted similar to that in Exercise 5 but no uninoculated animals are available for a control. Previous results, however, indicate very strongly that the proportion of recoveries to deaths without treatment is 1 to 3. Again, the result is 7 recoveries to 3 deaths when 10 animals are treated. Test the significance of this result, and explain why it differs from that obtained in Exercise 5.

$$\frac{1}{2}P = 0.0035.$$

In the problem of Exercise 5 the theoretical ratio is itself estimated from the sample.

REFERENCES

1. R. A. FISHER. Statistical Methods for Research Workers. Oliver and Boyd, London, 1936. Reading: Chapter IV, Sections 21.01, 21.03.
2. J. C. B. GRANT. National Museum of Canada, Bull. 64, 1930.
3. N. K. KOLTZOFF and V. N. SCHROEDER. *Nature*, **131**, No. 3305, 1933.
4. DONALD MAINLAND. *Am. Jour. Anat.*, **47**, No. 2, 1931.
5. DONALD MAINLAND. The Treatment of Clinical and Laboratory Data. Oliver and Boyd, London, 1938. Reading: Chapter III.
6. K. W. NEATBY. *Sci. Agr.*, **12**: 130–154, 1931.
7. L. H. C. TIPPETT. The Methods of Statistics. Williams and Norgate, Ltd., London, 1931. Reading: Chapter III, Section 3.8.
8. F. YATES. *Journ. Roy. Stat. Soc.*, Suppl. i., No. 2, 1934.
9. G. U. YULE. The Theory of Statistics. Charles Griffin and Co., London, 1924.

CHAPTER XI

THE ANALYSIS OF VARIANCE

1. The Heterogeneity and Analysis of Variation. If we consider the variation in such a character as stature in man, it is obvious that this variation in general is not homogeneous. Two races may differ decidedly in their average stature, and the individuals of each race will vary around a common mean. Also, with reference to the variation within each race, there are regional and genetic differences between certain groups so that even within the race the variation is not strictly homogeneous. In actual fact we can conclude with a reasonable degree of certainty that variation cannot be strictly homogeneous unless it is purely random, i.e., caused by a multiplicity of minor factors that cannot be distinguished one from another. In experimental work the heterogeneity of variation is usually predetermined by the plan of the experiment. One set of results is obtained, for example, under a given set of conditions and another under distinctly different conditions, the object being to compare the two groups of results. Here the heterogeneity of the variation is the factor that is being tested, and the degree of its expression determines the significance of the findings of the experiment. It would seem to be a necessity, therefore, in studies of variation, to be able to differentiate the variation according to causes or groups of causes, especially in experimental work where such differentiation is an essential part of the analysis of the results. The analysis of variance supplies the mechanism for this procedure and in addition sets out the results in a form to which tests of significance can be applied.

The points mentioned above may be made more obvious by the consideration of a theoretical example. Suppose that, for two races of men that we shall designate as A and B, the mean stature of race A is 66 inches and that of race B is 68 inches. Histograms are prepared for the frequency distributions of stature for the two races, and one histogram is superimposed on the other. The two distributions will undoubtedly overlap, but are very likely to show two distinct peaks at the means of the two populations. The variation over all the individuals comprising the two races could then be fairly definitely described as heterogeneous. We might now endeavor to picture what the situation might be if we were dealing with several races instead of only two. There might be a number of peaks, perhaps as many peaks as there are races;

114

but it is more likely that some of the groups will so nearly coincide as to be indistinguishable. Now that we have in mind several races, however, it is probably easier to think in terms of the total variability of all the individuals concerned being divided up into two portions. One portion is that which occurs within all the races. To get a mental picture of this, we might suppose the frequency distributions for all the races superimposed on one another in such a way that the means of the different races would coincide. The resulting distribution would be a sort of average of all the separate distributions. The second portion of the variability would be that resulting from the differences between the means, and if we had a sufficient number of these means we could make up another frequency distribution for them. For each type of distribution a standard deviation or a variance could be calculated, and it becomes clear at once that a comparison of two such statistics would be valuable in coming to a conclusion as to the degree of heterogeneity. To make this point still more obvious, let us imagine a series of samples being taken from a homogeneous population. As we have already learned, these samples will have different means, but these differences will result merely from random sampling. They will be large or small according to the magnitude of the variation in the population from which they are drawn. This is a very important generalization and one which is fundamental to an understanding of the analysis of variance. If the original population has a very small variation, the means of the samples drawn from it will also have a small variation. If the population has a large variation, it is to be expected that this will be reflected in the variations of the means of the samples. In fact, without going into the intricacies of an algebraic proof it seems reasonable to assume that, on the average, the variance of the means of the samples will be equal to that in the original population, provided of course that we multiply this variance by the number in the samples. Thus, if the variance of the population is v, the variance of the sample means is expected to be v/n, where n is the number of individual determinations entering into each mean.

The next step in the development of these ideas is to consider what the situation would be if, in taking a series of samples, we did not know that they were being taken from a homogeneous population. The variance of the population is unknown; hence it must be estimated from the values in the samples. The most logical estimate is that arising from the variations within each sample, from its own mean. Suppose that this estimate is v_1 and the estimate of the variance of the sample means is v_2/n. Multiplying the latter by n we have v_2, which we shall expect to be very close to v_1 if the population is homogeneous, but which may be very much larger than v_1 if the population is heterogeneous and this heterogeneity has corresponded with the method of taking the samples.   This suggests to us that there may be a technique here for making a test of significance.   The null hypothesis is that all the samples have been drawn from the same population, and therefore that v_2 does not differ significantly from v_1.   For example, if we take the ratio v_2/v_1, a test of significance could be made if, for a given example, we could determine the proportion of the trials in which a value as large as or larger than v_2/v_1 would be obtained owing entirely to random sampling fluctuations.   We are indebted to Dr. R. A. Fisher for many of the recent developments in statistical methods, but especially for the solution of this particular problem.   If there are only two samples it will be noted that we have already discussed a solution, in that we may apply the t test to the significance of the difference between the means.   However, if there are more than two samples the t test does not apply, and we must use the technique of the analysis of variance as developed by R. A. Fisher (3).   The details of this technique are best learned by the consideration of actual data.

2. Division of "Sums of Squares"[1] and Degrees of Freedom.   As pointed out in previous chapters the variance is a measure of variation, and it consists of a sum of squares of deviations from the mean divided by the corresponding degrees of freedom.   In a set of observations, if the total sum of squares of the deviations from the mean can be divided up according to some scheme suggested by the data, and the degrees of freedom can be divided correspondingly, it is clear that a variance can be calculated for each group as well as for the total.   It is through the comparison of such variance values that we obtain a true picture of the variation in the entire set of observations.

With respect to the division of sums of squares, the best way to observe this and to follow the method is to deal with actual data.   The figures given below are yields in bushels per acre of 6 plots of wheat. Three of these plots are of variety A and three of variety B.

| A | 27.6 | 32.4 | 23.4 |
| B | 19.2 | 18.6 | 16.5 |

The total sum of squares is made up of the sum of the deviations of the 6 plots from the general mean.   A logical division of this total is to separate it into one part due to variation within the varieties, and another

---

[1] "Sums of squares" written thus is an abbreviation for (sums of squares of deviations from the mean), but in general throughout this book the quotation marks are omitted.

part due to variation between the varieties. Let the general mean be $\bar{x}$, which in this case is $137.7/6 = 22.95$. And the mean of A is $\bar{x}_a = 27.8$, and the mean of B is $\bar{x}_b = 18.1$. Then subtracting 22.95 from each value, squaring and summating, we have:

$$\sum_1^6 (x - \bar{x})^2 = 185.715$$

where $\sum_1^6$ indicates that 6 deviations are summated. Now, to obtain the sum of squares for within the varieties, we must repeat the above operation for each variety and add the two sums of squares together. Thus for A we subtract 27.8 from each of the A values and square and summate. This gives:

$$\sum_1^3 (x - \bar{x}_a)^2 = 40.560$$

and for B we have

$$\sum_1^3 (x - \bar{x}_b)^2 = 4.020$$

Then $\sum_1^2 \sum_1^3 (x - \bar{x}_i)^2 = 40.560 + 4.020 = 44.580$, where the double summation indicates the process of adding together the two sums of squares, and $\bar{x}_i$ represents the mean of one group.

The next step is to calculate the sum of squares for between the varieties. This is given by

$$3 \times [(27.8 - 22.95)^2 + (18.1 - 22.95)^2] = 141.135$$

Note that we obtain the deviations of the *means* of A and B from the general mean and then square and summate, but we *multiply the whole sum by* 3 because each value such as 27.8 represents the *mean* of 3 single plots.

The formula for this sum of squares will be $3 \sum_1^2 (\bar{x}_i - \bar{x})^2$.

Now if we add the sums of squares

Within		Between		Total
44.580	$+$	141.135	$=$	185.715

$$\sum_1^2 \sum_1^3 (x - \bar{x}_i)^2 + 3 \sum_1^2 (\bar{x}_i - \bar{x})^2 = \sum_1^6 (x - \bar{x})^2$$

we note that the within and between sums are exactly equal to the total. That the sums of squares can always be divided in this way is very easily proved for the general case. A set of observations classified in one direction may be represented as follows

$$
\begin{array}{c|l}
1 & x_{11} \quad x_{12} \quad x_{13}\cdots\cdots x_{1n} \\
2 & x_{21} \quad x_{22} \quad x_{23}\cdots\cdots x_{2n} \\
\text{Groups } 3 & x_{31} \quad x_{32} \quad x_{33}\cdots\cdots x_{3n} \\
\cdot & \quad\cdot \quad\quad \cdot \quad\quad \cdot \quad\quad\quad \cdot \\
\cdot & \quad\cdot \quad\quad \cdot \quad\quad \cdot \quad\quad\quad \cdot \\
\cdot & \quad\cdot \quad\quad \cdot \quad\quad \cdot \quad\quad\quad \cdot \\
k & x_{k1} \quad x_{k2} \quad x_{k3}\cdots\cdots x_{kn}
\end{array}
$$

where there are k groups and n single observations in each group.

For any one observation, say x_{11}, we can write

$$(x_{11} - \bar{x}) = (x_{11} - \bar{x}_1) + (\bar{x}_1 - \bar{x})$$

where $\bar{x}_1$ is the mean of group 1. Then

$$(x_{11} - \bar{x})^2 = (x_{11} - \bar{x}_1)^2 + (\bar{x}_1 - \bar{x})^2 + 2(x_{11} - \bar{x}_1)(\bar{x}_1 - \bar{x})$$

And summating for all the values in group 1 we have

$$\sum_1^n (x - \bar{x})^2 = \sum_1^n (x - \bar{x}_1)^2 + n(\bar{x}_1 - \bar{x})^2 + 2(\bar{x}_1 - \bar{x})\sum_1^n (x - \bar{x}_1)$$

The last term is zero because the sum of the deviations from the mean must be zero and each deviation is multiplied by a constant factor. The second last term is written $n(\bar{x}_1 - \bar{x})^2$ because the factor $(\bar{x}_1 - \bar{x})^2$ is constant and we merely summate it n times. Finally we have

$$\sum_1^n (x - \bar{x})^2 = \sum_1^n (x - \bar{x}_1)^2 + n(\bar{x}_1 - \bar{x})^2$$

Now we repeat this for each group, and summating over all the k groups we have

$$\sum_1^{nk} (x - \bar{x})^2 = \sum_1^k \sum_1^n (x - \bar{x}_i)^2 + n\sum_1^k (\bar{x}_i - \bar{x})^2 \tag{1}$$

which is exactly equivalent to the equation given above with the actual sums of squares.

The division of degrees of freedom corresponding to the sums of squares follows easily. In the example for two varieties we have a total of 5 degrees of freedom, for within varieties we have 2 in each group making a total of 4, and for between varieties we have only 1. Thus

$$
\begin{array}{ccc}
\text{Total} & \text{Within} & \text{Between} \\
5 & = \quad 4 & + \quad 1
\end{array}
$$

In the general case as outlined above the degrees of freedom corresponding to the sums of squares of equation (1) are

$$\begin{array}{ccc} \text{Total} & \text{Within} & \text{Between} \\ (nk - 1) = & k(n - 1) + & (k - 1) \end{array}$$

3. Setting up the Analysis of Variance. For the practical example with two varieties we can now set up an analysis of variance as follows:

Source of Sum of Squares	Sum of Squares	Degrees of Freedom	Mean Square or Variance
Within varieties..........	44.580	4	11.14
Between varieties........	141.135	1	141.1
Total...........	185.715	5	

As would be expected from the difference between the means of A and B, the variance for between varieties is very high as compared to that for within varieties. Reference to Chapter IV on tests of significance with small samples will recall that the variance for within varieties is the variance which is converted into a standard error in order to test the significance of the difference between the means. This variance can be termed, therefore, the *error* variance and can be used as a measure of the significance of the variance for between varieties.

4. Tests of Significance. In the typical analysis of variance we have an error variance with which we wish to compare one or more other variances. Strictly speaking, all these variances are *estimates* of the true value, and this is, of course, the reason why to obtain them we must divide the sums of squares by the degrees of freedom. In order to understand the test of significance it is necessary to consider in the first place the condition that would obtain on the average if the variance we are testing is subject to exactly the same source of variability as the error variance. Let the sum of squares for error be represented by S_1 and the sum of squares for the variance to be tested by S_2. The corresponding degrees of freedom are n_1 and n_2, and the estimates of variance are:

$$v_1 = \frac{S_1}{n_1} \qquad\qquad v_2 = \frac{S_2}{n_2}$$

and let $F = v_2/v_1$.

Suppose that v_2 represents the variance for between the varieties A and B as in the actual example above. If there is no real difference between A and B, the differences between the means that occur will be due to soil heterogeneity which is the sole cause contributing to the error variance. On the average, therefore, $v_1 = v_2$, or $F = 1$. But if the experiment, still assuming that A is not different from B, is repeated a number of times, F will be subject to random fluctuations and will be distributed in some regular manner. Thus in any one experiment if $F = 2.6$ we could judge the significance of this value if we could determine the exact percentage of cases in which an F of 2.6 would occur as the result of random sampling fluctuations. The problem is therefore one of determining the distribution of F and tabulating the results in such a way that they can be used to determine probabilities. R. A. Fisher (3) has worked out the distribution of F and in tests of significance replaces it by $z = \frac{1}{2} \log_e F$. The distribution of z depends entirely on the degrees of freedom n_1 and n_2, from which the variances are estimated. Its use therefore does not involve any assumptions regarding the population and is equally applicable for large and small samples. Tables have been prepared giving the values of z at the 5% and the 1 % points for different values of n_1 and n_2. In comparing v_1 and v_2, if we find that z is equal to the value given at the 5% point, this means that the observed F value would occur owing to random sampling fluctuations in only 5% of the cases.

Snedecor (11) has calculated tables of F for the 5% and 1% points, and this enables us to make a test of significance directly without looking up logarithms. Table 96 is a copy of Snedecor's table of F.

5. Multiple Classification of Variates. In the simple example we have considered, the variates were classified according to variety only. They may, however, be classified in several ways, and it is only rarely that they are not classified in two or three ways. We shall consider two-fold classifications first. The general case may be represented as follows:

Classes

	1	2	$3 \cdots n$
1	x_{11}	x_{12}	$x_{13} \cdots x_{1n}$
2	x_{21}	x_{22}	$x_{23} \cdots x_{2n}$
Groups 3	x_{31}	x_{32}	$x_{33} \cdots x_{3n}$
.	.	.	.
.	.	.	.
.	.	.	.
k	x_{k1}	x_{k2}	$x_{k3} \cdots x_{kn}$

in which the variates are in k groups and n classes. The essential difference between this arrangement and that illustrated under Section 2 above is that the variates in any one class have something in common in that they can be logically placed together and recognized as a definite unit.   In field experiments the groups may be varieties and the classes blocks or replicates.   In a chemical experiment the groups may represent formulae and the classes different temperature or moisture conditions under which the formulae are tried.   In medical or nutritional work the groups may be different foods and the classes different quantities or times of feeding.

The equations representing sums of squares and degrees of freedom for the twofold classification are as follows:

$$\begin{array}{ccccc} & \text{Total} & \begin{array}{c}\text{Within Groups}\\\text{and Classes}\end{array} & \begin{array}{c}\text{Between}\\\text{Groups}\end{array} & \begin{array}{c}\text{Between}\\\text{Classes}\end{array} \end{array}$$

$$\text{Sums of Squares}\quad \sum_{1}^{nk}(x - \bar{x})^2 = \sum_{1}^{nk}(x - \bar{x}_q - \bar{x}_c + \bar{x})^2 + n\sum_{1}^{k}(\bar{x}_q - \bar{x})^2 + k\sum_{1}^{n}(\bar{x}_c - \bar{x})^2 \qquad (2)$$

$$\text{Degrees of Freedom}\quad nk - 1 = (n - 1)(k - 1)\quad + (k - 1)\quad + (n - 1)$$

where $\bar{x}_q$ is the mean of a group and $\bar{x}_c$ is the mean of a class.   Note that in this case the sum of squares for within groups and classes is rather complex and in corresponding form to equation (1) should be written with a triple summation.   The form used, however, is more convenient and expresses the idea successfully.   It is customary in analyses of experiments to refer to the within sum of squares as that due to *error* as it gives rise to the variance with which the other estimates of variance can be compared.

In order to picture a threefold classification, we can assume that in the previous example there are m classes and n subclasses.   Graphically the arrangement will be:

1	2	3	. . . .	m
1 2···n	1 2···n	1 2···n		1 2···n

The analysis of data of this type introduces a new factor in the sums of squares, in that we must consider the *interactions* of the three classes with one another.   This is best studied, however, from actual examples, and the same applies to still more complex types of classifications.

6. Selecting a Valid Error. Significance is a relative and not an absolute term. Differences are found to be significant or insignificant in relation to the variability arising from a source which is arbitrarily selected according to the interpretation that is to be put on the result. To make these points clear let us assume that an experiment is being conducted involving chemical determinations. Two kinds of material are being tested; the method is to draw samples from each kind of material, and in the laboratory each sample is being tested in duplicate. obviously here we have two sources of error. The first arises from sampling the material, and the second from differences between the results for duplicate determinations arising purely from errors in the laboratory technique. These two *sources* of error are independent and therefore may be of the same magnitude or widely different. If 20 samples are taken from each kind of material the analysis of variance will be of the following form:

	DF	Variance
Materials (A and B)............	1	m
Between A samples..........	$\left.19\right\}38$	$\left.\begin{array}{c}a\\b\end{array}\right\}s$
Between B samples..........	19	
Between duplicates..........	40	d
Total.................	79	

For the purpose of this discussion it can be assumed that the variances a and b are of the same magnitude and can be considered together, say as variance s. Now we wish to test the significance of the difference between the two kinds of materials, and we will suppose that d is very small in comparison to s. It is not difficult to see that the variance m is contributed to by the variability in the samples, or in other words that on the average if there is no difference between the two materials the variance m will be equal to the variance s. Since d is very small it is clear that to use it to test m is quite erroneous, as even when there is no difference between the materials the ratio of m to d will be quite large. What will the situation be, however, if d is much larger than s? With a little thought it will be plain that this would be a very unlikely situation as s is in itself contributed to by the factors that result in the variance d. Putting it another way, if there is no variation whatever due to sampling, s will on the average be equal to d. The question therefore has no point, and we must consider the only other possibility, and that is that d and s are of about equal magnitude. The inference, then, is that s results largely from the differences between the duplicates, and that the sampling error is in itself insignificant. The obvious course here is to use d in order to test m, and at the same time we take advantage of the greater precision due to d being represented by a larger number of degrees of freedom than s.

Another hypothetical experiment may be considered in which the situation is slightly different. Again two materials are being compared, but it can be assumed that the material is sufficiently homogeneous that the sampling error is negligible. There is a possibility of error in the laboratory technique and also there is a possibility of personal error in that no two operators can be expected to get exactly the same results. In making out the plan of the experiment it is decided that six different operators shall be used, all of whom perform exactly the same test on the same two materials. Also each operator makes his determination in triplicate in order that a measure may be obtained of the error in the technique. The analysis of variance for the results will be as follows:

	DF	Variance
Materials...................	1	m
Operators...................	5	o
Error due to operators........	5	e
Error of determination........	24	d
Total................	35	

The variance e now requires some consideration in order to note its relation to the significance of the results. If we set up the mean results for each operator in a table it will be of the following form:

		Operators					
		1	2	3	4	5	6
Materials	A	a_1	a_2	a_3	a_4	a_5	a_6
	B	b_1	b_2	b_3	b_4	b_5	b_6

where a_1, for example, represents the mean of three determinations made by operator 1 on material A.

Now the variance e results from differences between such values as $(a_1 - b_1)$ and $(a_2 - b_2)$. There being 6 of these values, there are 5 degrees of freedom available for estimating the variance. If each operator gets the same result for the difference between A and B, the variance e will be zero; but if the operators get widely varying differences the variance e will be very high. Suppose now that the experiment is presumed to be a sample of a large population of operators making similar determinations on these same two materials, then the variance m, which represents the difference between the two materials, will be contributed to by the factors that produce e; and hence, if there is no difference between the materials, m will be equal to e. In sampling such a population, therefore, and testing the significance of the results, it will be necessary to use e as an error variance to test the significance of m. This fact may be more obvious if we consider the disastrous results of not using the variance e as a measure of error. The variance d may be quite low owing to extreme care in the standardization of the technique as applied to any one individual operator, and we shall assume that it is much lower than e. Using d as an error we find that, although m is very little greater than e, it is very significant if compared with d. The results are used therefore to prove that, for example, A gives a much larger result than B, and on this basis the two materials are utilized in some industry for manufacturing purposes. The manufacturers, however, in utilizing the material may have to employ a large number of operators; and hence the error that was neglected in the laboratory creeps in and it turns out in actual practice that the two materials give the same result, and the so-called carefully controlled experiment of the laboratory is discredited. This mistake would have been avoided if the investigator had carefully considered the exact nature of the population that was being sampled and made his test of significance accordingly. Of course it might happen that only one operator was used in the experiment, in which case the reader will recall the discussion of Chapter V on the scope of experiments and will realize that this would be another example of an experiment so planned that it did not have sufficient scope to answer the questions that it was supposed to answer.

A point that may now be raised is this. If the error resulting from the determinations made by individual operators is not to be used to test the significance of the difference between the materials, what benefit is to be derived from making the determinations in triplicate and including the variance d in the analysis? The answer to this is that if there is an appreciable error in the determinations, the variance e will be contributed to by this source of variation, and hence, if there is no variation due to the operators, on the average e will be equal to d. The variance d, therefore, enables us to apply a test of significance to e; and, furthermore, if d is appreciable, it reduces the precision of the experiment by making its contribution to e. In the latter case, improvement in the technique of the determination may result in a considerable improvement in the precision of the experiment.

A variance such as e in the hypothetical example given above is usually referred to as an *interaction* variance. It gets this name because if it represents a fairly large effect it may be taken as an indication of an interaction between the two factors that are concerned. In considering operators and materials, for example, we may conclude if e is very large that the materials respond quite differently in the hands of different operators. As a matter of fact, if we are willing to use more than one word to describe such an effect, it might be more appropriate to speak of an interaction as a *differential response*. Let us assume that, in general, material B gives a higher result in the determinations that are being made than material A. This may appear more reasonable if we assume that A and B are not different in quality but in quantity, in which case it is customary to refer to A and B as representing two different levels of one of the interacting factors. The more appropriate symbolism then would be to represent A and B by such symbols as X_1 and X_2, the same letter indicating that there are no qualitative differences between the two, and the subscripts indicating that this factor is at two different levels. Now if X_2 gives a higher value in the determinations than X_1, this is plainly a case of response to quantity, and if there were several levels of X instead of only two the result would recall the phenomena observed in the study of regression. It is now easy to visualize what is meant by a differential response. Some of the operators may be able to obtain the maximum response whereas others may obtain a much smaller response. In certain instances it may easily turn out that with some operators the response will be positive and with other operators it will be negative. This type of effect would be likely to result in a very large interaction variance.

The meaning of interactions will be discussed in further detail in the consideration of actual examples. For the present it will suffice for the student to have a clear conception of the idea of differential responses, and to realize that frequently an interaction variance is in reality a true error variance and therefore must be used to test the significance of the results of the experiment.

Example 29. Simple Classification of Variates. Table 29 given the yields of four plots each of three varieties of wheat. We shall use the analysis of variance to determine the significance of the differences between the varieties.

TABLE 29

YIELDS OF 4 PLOTS EACH OF 3 VARIETIES

	Plot Yields				Totals
A	29.2	36.4	22.4	27.6	115.6
B	32.7	39.3	28.6	29.3	129.9
C	18.7	23.1	21.3	19.6	82.7
				Total	328.2

The first step is to decide on the form of the analysis and to allocate the degrees of freedom to each component according to the scheme decided upon. In this case we are concerned merely with comparing the variety variance with a variance for error, and the most logical error variance is one arising from within the varieties. The form of the analysis is therefore

	Sum of Squares	DF
Between varieties		2
Within varieties (error)		9
Total		11

The second step is to calculate the sums of squares. The best plan is first to obtain the total sum of squares. A formula has been given above, but this is not the best formula for actual calculation. It is much better to make use of the identity

$$\sum_{1}^{nk}(x - \bar{x})^2 = \sum_{1}^{nk}(x^2) - \frac{T_x^2}{nk} \tag{3}$$

where T_x is the total of all the values of x or $\sum_{1}^{nk}(x)$.

Therefore we merely square and summate the actual values and subtract from this sum the square of the grand total divided by the number of variates. The figures are

Total sum of squares $= 9452.50 - 8976.27 = 476.23$

The calculation of the sum of squares for between varieties is carried out with the assistance of a similar identity

$$n\sum_{1}^{k}(\bar{x}_i - \bar{x})^2 = \frac{\sum_{1}^{k}(T_i^2)}{n} - \frac{T_x^2}{nk} \tag{4}$$

where T_i represents the total for a variety. The formula consists therefore of squaring and summating the totals, dividing by the number of variates entering into each total, and then subtracting the same term as for the total sum of squares. The figures are

Between varieties $= 9269.16 - 8976.27 = 292.89$

To determine the sum of squares for within varieties we can perform a separate calculation for each variety:

$$\begin{aligned}
\text{Within } A &= 3441.12 - 115.6^2/4 = 100.28 \\
\text{`` } B &= 4290.23 - 129.9^2/4 = 71.73 \\
\text{`` } C &= 1721.15 - 82.7^2/4 = 11.33
\end{aligned}$$

Total within $\ldots\ldots\ldots\ldots = 183.34$

Actually it was not necessary to calculate the last sum of squares as we could have obtained it by subtracting the sum of squares for between varieties from the total. Thus:

Total   Between   Within
$476.23 - 292.89 = 183.34$

However, when possible it furnishes a very easy check on the calculations to obtain the error sum of squares directly and indirectly.

The third step is to set up the analysis of variance and make the tests of significance. This is performed in Table 30.

TABLE 30
ANALYSIS OF VARIANCE

	Sum of Squares	Degrees Freedom	Variance	F	$z = \frac{1}{2} \log_e F$
Between varieties......	292.89	2	146.4	7.19	0.9863
Error.................	183.34	9	20.37		
Total............	476.23	11			

In Fisher's tables we look up the 5% point of z for $n_1 = 2$ and $n_2 = 9$. The value is 0.7242, so that the variety differences here are quite significant. Using Snedecor's tables of F (Table 96) we find that the 5% point for F is 4.26, and we of course reach exactly the same conclusion.

Example 30. Twofold Classification of Variates. In a swine-feeding experiment Dunlop (2) obtained the results given in Table 31. The three rations, A, B, and C differed in the substances providing the vitamins. The animals were in 4 groups of 3 each, the grouping being on the basis of litter and initial weight. For our purpose we shall assume that the grouping is merely a matter of replication.

TABLE 31
GAINS IN WEIGHT OF SWINE FED ON RATIONS A, B, C

		I	II	III	IV	Totals
	A	7.0	16.0	10.5	13.5	47.0
Ration	B	14.0	15.5	15.0	21.0	65.5
	C	8.5	16.5	9.5	13.5	48.0
		29.5	48.0	35.0	48.0	160.5

The form of the analysis is

	Sum of Squares	DF
Rations......................		2
Groups......................		3
Error.......................		6
Total.....................		11

Calculating the sums of squares we have

Total	$2316.75 - (160.5)^2/12 = 2316.75 - 2146.6875 = 170.0625$	
Rations	$= (47.0^2 + 65.5^2 + 48.0^2)/4 - 2146.6875$	$= 54.1250$
Groups	$= (29.5^2 + \cdots + 48.0^2)/3 - 2146.6875$	$= 87.7292$
Error	$=$ remainder	$= 28.2083$

This gives us an analysis of variance as follows:

	Sum of Squares	Degrees Freedom	Variance	F	5% Point
Rations...	54.1250	2	27.06	5.76	5.14
Groups....	87.7292	3	29.24	6.22	4.76
Error.....	28.2083	6	4.701		
Total...	170.0625	11			

The variance for rations is just significant. The meaning of the significance of the variance for groups depends on the manner in which the classification into groups has been made. We have assumed here that the groups are merely replications, in which case the error variance is a result of variations within groups not due to the rations. It is therefore valid to consider this variance as an error variance with which the others can be compared. The group variance, since it results from the plan of the experiment, is an expression of error control. If the arrangement had been other than in groups we would have had a simple classification into within and between rations. The variance for within rations would have been much larger than it is according to the present arrangement, and consequently the experiment would have been less precise.

Example 31. Selecting a Valid Error. A series of 5 wheat varieties were grown at 4 stations and baking tests made on the flour. A sample of each variety was taken from each station and milled into flour. Two loaves were baked from each sample. The error of determination was given, therefore, by the differences between the loaf volumes of the duplicate loaves. These data were supplied by courtesy of the Associate Committee on Grain Research of the National Research Council of Canada.

TABLE 32

DUPLICATE LOAF VOLUMES FOR 5 VARIETIES OF WHEAT GROWN AT 4 STATIONS
(Loaf volumes in cc. − 500)/10

		Stations								Totals
		I		II		III		IV		
Varieties	1	7.5	4.5	15.5	14.0	16.5	14.5	19.0	18.6	110.0
	2	12.5	13.2	20.0	18.5	15.0	14.0	23.8	24.4	141.4
	3	7.0	1.0	10.0	8.0	15.5	14.0	17.8	18.5	91.8
	4	1.5	2.0	13.0	15.0	8.5	9.0	14.8	16.6	80.4
	5	28.0	29.0	19.5	16.0	10.5	12.0	22.0	24.8	161.8
Totals		106.2		149.5		129.5		200.3		585.5

On examining the form that the analysis of variance will take, we note first that we must have a station variance represented by 3 degrees of freedom, and a variety variance represented by 4 degrees of freedom. There must also be an interaction effect which may be regarded as the differential response of the varieties at the different stations. The rule for finding the degrees of freedom for an interaction is to multiply the degrees of freedom for the interacting factors. The interaction variance must therefore be represented by $3 \times 4 = 12$ degrees of freedom. There is a total of 40 determinations, so that there is a total of 39 degrees of freedom. The remaining 20 degrees of freedom must represent the error of duplicate determinations, and we have a check on this because there are 20 pairs of loaves and since each pair gives us 1 degree of freedom there must be 20 in all. The final form of the analysis is:

Variance	DF
Stations.....................	3
Varieties.....................	4
Interaction...................	12
Error.......................	20
Total.....................	39

To obtain the sums of squares another table as given below is required. This table gives the values of $(x - y)$ and $(x + y)$, where x and y are taken to represent the paired values.

		I	II	III	IV
	1	3.0	1.5	2.0	0.4
	2	0.7	1.5	1.0	0.6
$(x - y)$	3	6.0	2.0	1.5	0.7
	4	0.5	2.0	0.5	1.8
	5	1.0	3.5	1.5	2.8

		I	II	III	IV	Totals
	1	12.0	29.5	31.0	37.6	110.1
	2	25.7	38.5	29.0	48.2	141.4
$(x + y)$	3	8.0	18.0	29.5	36.3	91.8
	4	3.5	28.0	17.5	31.4	80.4
	5	57.0	35.5	22.5	46.8	161.8
Totals		106.2	149.5	129.5	200.3	585.5

The first half of this table may be used for calculating the error sum of squares. A general rule for the sum of squares for differences within paired values is to use the identity

$$\text{Total minus between pairs} = \tfrac{1}{2}\Sigma(x - y)^2$$

The two expressions on the left are $\Sigma(x^2) - T_x^2/N$ and $\Sigma(x + y)^2/2 - T_x^2/N$. On subtracting and simplifying we obtain $\tfrac{1}{2} \Sigma(x - y)^2$. The calculations give

$$\text{Within pairs (error)} = \tfrac{1}{2} (93.33) = \textbf{46.66}$$

From the second half of the calculation table we determine

$$\text{Between pairs} = \frac{20566.13}{2} - \frac{585.5^2}{40}$$

$$= 10283.065 - 8570.256 = 1712.81$$

$$\text{Stations} = \frac{90519.03}{10} - 8570.256 = 481.65$$

$$\text{Varieties} = \frac{73186.61}{8} - 8570.256 = 578.07$$

$$\text{Interaction} = \text{Remainder} = 653.09$$

This procedure gives us a general rule for the calculation of interaction sums of squares. In the table considered we find the total and subtract the sum of squares for the two interacting factors. The remainder is the interaction.

The analysis of variance is as follows

	Sum of Squares	DF	Variance
Stations..........	481.65	3	160.5
Varieties..........	578.07	4	144.5
Interaction........	653.09	12	54.42
Error.............	46.66	20	2.333
Total...........	1759.47		

We now have to decide whether we should use the variance from the duplicate loaf volumes or the interaction variance to test the significance of the differences between stations and varieties. If the purpose of the experiment is to determine which of the varieties will give the highest loaf volume over the whole area that the stations sample, it will be necessary to use the interaction variance because in this light the stations are merely replications of the experiment. The error from duplicate loaf volumes will give an indication merely of the accuracy of the laboratory technique. If it is large it will reduce the significance of the differences, because it raises the value of the interaction variance.

On comparing the variety variance with the interaction variance we get an F value of 2.66; and since the 5% point is 3.26, we must conclude that, considering the whole area being sampled, the differences in loaf volume are not significant. In other words, the variation in the order of the mean loaf volumes of the varieties, from station to station, is so great that the differences between the means for the whole area may easily be accounted for by this variation.

The interaction variance is very much higher than that arising from differences between duplicate loaf volumes. This means that the laboratory error is not an appreciable factor affecting the precision of the results in this experiment.

Since variety tests are conducted in replicated plots at each station, it follows that if loaf volume determinations had been made on each plot another measure of error could have been obtained. This error would have measured the variation due to soil heterogeneity; and, if the variety variance for the whole area was significant when compared to the pooled error due to soil heterogeneity, this would indicate that in general at each station the differences between the means of the varieties were greater than could be accounted for by such sampling variation. This would not, however, alter our conclusion based on the test using the interaction as an error.

Example 32. Threefold Classification of Variates. In testing out a machine for molding the dough in experimental baking, Geddes, et al. (5), used 3 adjustments of the machine, designated A, B, and C, and tried them out on a series of 5 flours baked according to 2 formulae. The loaf volume data are given in Table 33.

TABLE 33

LOAF VOLUME RESULTS IN A TEST OF A MACHINE FOR MOLDING THE DOUGH
(Loaf volume in cc. − 500)/10

Formula	Machine Setting	Flours					Totals
		1	2	3	4	5	
Simple	A	9.4	2.6	12.3	4.6	13.5	42.4
	B	9.6	3.1	13.0	4.3	13.8	43.8
	C	9.6	2.7	12.4	1.8	13.0	39.5
	Flour subtotals	28.6	8.4	37.7	10.7	40.3	125.7
Bromate	A	13.7	21.6	19.4	13.5	24.5	92.7
	B	12.7	22.6	20.6	10.4	24.3	90.6
	C	12.6	21.8	20.9	6.8	23.2	85.3
	Flour subtotals	39.0	66.0	60.9	30.7	72.0	268.6
	Flour totals	67.6	74.4	98.6	41.4	112.3	394.3

On working out the form of the analysis we find that there is an additional complication here as compared to those that have been worked out previously. The 6 rows in Table 33 represent 2 classifications, but for the present we shall consider them as 6 classes giving us a simple twofold classification. The form of the analysis is then:

Flours.....................	4 DF
Classes.....................	5 DF
Interaction (a).............	20 DF
Total.................	29 DF

But the 5 degrees of freedom for classes must be split up into:

Machine settings ABC........	2 DF
Formulae SB................	1 DF
Interaction $ABC \times SB$........	2 DF

Hence interaction (*a*) in the first analysis is an interaction of the above three factors with the flours.   Realizing this, we can then write out the form of the analysis in full:

$$
\begin{aligned}
&\text{Flours (1 ... 5)} \ldots\ldots\ldots\ldots\ldots\ldots\ldots && 4\ DF \\
&\text{Machine settings } (ABC) \ldots\ldots\ldots\ldots && 2\ DF \\
&\text{Formulae } (SB) \ldots\ldots\ldots\ldots\ldots\ldots && 1\ DF \\
&\text{Interaction } (ABC \times SB) \ldots\ldots\ldots\ldots && 2\ DF \\
&\quad\text{``}\qquad (1 \ldots 5 \times ABC) \ldots\ldots\ldots && 8\ DF \\
&\quad\text{``}\qquad (1 \ldots 5 \times SB) \ldots\ldots\ldots && 4\ DF \\
&\quad\text{``}\qquad (1 \ldots 5 \times ABC \times SB) \ldots && 8\ DF \\
\hline
&\text{Total} \ldots\ldots\ldots\ldots\ldots\ldots\ldots\ldots && 29\ DF
\end{aligned}
$$

The last interaction is known as a *triple* interaction.   In this case it represents the degree to which the interaction of $(ABC \times SB)$ is different for the different flours. If the interaction $(ABC \times SB)$ is the same for each flour, the triple interaction will be zero.

To determine the sums of squares for the components set out above it is necessary to set up 3 calculation tables as below:

Machine Settings	Flours					Totals
	1	2	3	4	5	
A	23.1	24.2	31.7	18.1	38.0	135.1
B	22.3	25.7	33.6	14.7	38.1	134.4
C	22.2	24.5	33.3	8.6	36.2	124.8
Totals...	67.6	74.4	98.6	41.4	112.3	394.3

Formulae	Flours					Totals
	1	2	3	4	5	
S	28.6	8.4	37.7	10.7	40.3	125.7
B	39.0	66.0	60.9	30.7	72.0	268.6
S + B	67.6	74.4	98.6	41.4	112.3	394.3
S − B	10.4	57.6	23.2	20.0	31.7	

Formulae	Machine Settings			
	A	B	C	Totals
S	42.4	43.8	39.5	125.7
B	92.7	90.6	85.3	268.6
S + B	135.1	134.4	124.8	394.3
S − B	50.3	46.8	45.8	142.9

The calculations are [1]

Total	$= 6618.43 - \dfrac{394.3^2}{30} = 6618.43 - 5182.42$	$= \mathbf{1436.01}$

Flours $(1\cdots5)$ $= 34{,}152.33/6 - 5182.42 =$ **509.64**

Settings (ABC) $= 51{,}890.41/10 - 5182.42 =$ **6.62**

Formulae SB $= (268.6 - 125.7)^2/30 =$ **680.68**

Interaction $(ABC{\times}SB) = \Sigma(S-B)^2/10 - 680.68 = 6817.97/10 - 680.68 = \mathbf{1.12}$

Interaction $(1\cdots5) \times (ABC)$

Total for table $= 11{,}436.57/2 - 5182.42 = 535.86$

Flours $(1\cdots5) =$ 509.64

Settings $(ABC) =$ 6.62

Remainder $(1\cdots5) \times (ABC) =$ **19.60**

Interaction $(1\cdots5){\times}(SB) = \Sigma(S - B)^2/6 - 680.68 = 5369.05/6 - 680.68 = \mathbf{214.16}$

Interaction $(1\cdots5 \times ABC \times SB) = $ remainder $= \mathbf{4.19}$

The analysis of variance when set up in detail is as follows:

	Sums of Squares	DF	Variance	F	5% Point
Flours $(1\cdots5)$.................	509.64	4	127.4	243.1	3.84
Formulae (SB).................	680.68	1	680.7	1299.0	5.32
Interaction $(1\cdots5 \times SB)$........	214.16	4	53.54	102.2	3.84
Settings (ABC).................	6.62	2	3.31	6.31	4.46
Interaction $(ABC \times SB)$........	1.12	2	0.560	1.07	4.46
" $(1\cdots5 \times ABC)$......	19.60	8	2.450	4.68	3.44
" $(1\cdots5 \times ABC \times SB)$	4.19	8	0.524		
Total.................	1436.01	29			

It is of interest to make a detailed study of Example 32 from the standpoint of the selection of a valid error. We note first that the determinations were not made in duplicate so that we have no real measure of the error in the technique; and, if such an error is the one that should be used throughout for tests of significance, we shall have to select one of the other variances that gives us a close approximation of what the error of duplicate loaf volumes would be. In the second place it must be remembered that the primary object of the experiment is to study the differences in the loaf volumes due to the different settings of the machine and the differential responses due to these same settings. For this reason the analysis of variance has been separated into two

[1] Note the method used to calculate interactions for a series of paired values. This will be explained in more detail in the next example.

portions. The three effects in the first group are of no particular interest, as previous experience would have enabled the cereal chemists to predict that just such results would be obtained. The separation of these three effects into one group is *not a result of the data obtained in the experiment*, but was preconceived, and it was decided before the experiment was operated that this would be done.

Considering the variance due to the settings, the first question to be asked is whether or not it should be tested against a variance representing purely laboratory error or against the interaction of the settings with the flours. The answer follows from the fact that we are concerned not so much with the interaction of the settings with the flours as with attempting to find out the best single setting of the machine for all purposes; and therefore we do not anticipate that, in differentiating a set of flours, all the settings that have been tried here will be used. Actually our measure of significance in this experiment must be based on the usual experimental error of the laboratory, because, if the machine settings cause differences significantly greater than those resulting from experimental error, it is obvious that before the machine is used for general purposes the most desirable setting must be worked out. In other words we ought to see to it that the machine does not introduce a greater error into the determinations than already exists as the result of the ordinary procedures of the laboratory.

On this basis it follows that the triple interaction is the most logical error to use, as it is the least likely to represent a significant effect and is not likely to be lower than the error due to differences between duplicate loaf volumes. The latter statement is the same as saying that, if there is no actual triple interaction effect, the variance will be equal to the error that would have resulted from using duplicate determinations.

The F values with their 5% points are given in the analysis, and with their aid the results may be summarized very quickly. The flour and formula differences as well as the interaction between them are very large in comparison to the experimental error and may be dismissed with that statement. The primary interest in the experiment is in the settings of the machine and the interaction of the settings with the other factors. The settings are significant in relation to experimental error, and glancing at the totals we note that this must be due to the fact that the C setting gives a somewhat lower loaf volume than A or B. The interaction of ABC with the formulae (SB) is not significant, indicating that the differences between the settings are reasonably consistent for both methods of baking. The interaction of the flours with the settings is significant, and we can conclude that the results with the flours are to a certain extent changed by the machine settings. From an inspection of the results this would seem to be due to flour 4, as for this flour the B and C settings depress the loaf volume to a greater extent than for the others.

7. Summary of Methods of Calculating Sums of Squares. After the form of analysis has been worked out, the greatest difficulty that confronts the student of the methods of this chapter is the calculation of the sums of squares. Most of the methods have been dealt with in the above examples, but it would seem to be desirable to summarize them under one heading.

(a) Total for a set of n single variates. $x_1, x_2, \cdots x_n$.

$$\sum_1^n (x - \bar{x})^2 = \sum_1^n (x^2) - \frac{T_x^2}{n}$$

We square each value and summate, then subtract the square of the total divided by the number of variates.

(b) For a set of k groups when each group is made up of n variates. It there are k groups we can represent the totals for the groups as T_1, $T_2, \cdots T_i \cdots T_k$; and the means for the groups by $\bar{x}_1, \bar{x}_2, \cdots \bar{x}_i \cdots \bar{x}_k$.

$$n \sum_1^k (\bar{x}_i - \bar{x})^2 = \frac{\sum_1^k (T_i^2)}{n} - \frac{T^2}{kn}$$

We square each total, summate, and then divide by the number of variates entering into each total. From this we subtract the square of the grand total divided by the number of variates.

(c) For a set of k groups when the number of variates is not the same for each group. If we represent a particular series with the corresponding number of variates in each group as follows:

Group totals $\qquad T_1, T_2, T_3, T_4$

Numbers $\qquad a, \quad b, \quad c, \quad d$

We calculate:

$$\frac{T_1^2}{a} + \frac{T_2^2}{b} + \frac{T_3^2}{c} + \frac{T_4^2}{d} - \frac{T^2}{(a + b + c + d)}$$

In this case we square each total and divide by the number entering into it. The quotients are summated, and from this sum we subtract the square of the grand total divided by the total number of variates.

(d) For within and between pairs. If a set of paired values are represented as follows:

	1	2	3	$4\cdots n$	Totals
x	x_1	x_2	x_3	$x_4\cdots x_n$	T_x
y	y_1	y_2	y_3	$y_4\cdots y_n$	T_y
					T

The sum of squares for between pairs is:

$$\frac{\Sigma(x+y)^2}{2} - \frac{T^2}{2n}$$

And for within pairs it is:

$$\tfrac{1}{2}\Sigma(x-y)^2$$

If each x and y value represents k variates we have:

$$\text{Between} = \frac{\Sigma(x+y)^2}{2k} - \frac{T^2}{2kn}$$

$$\text{Within} = \frac{\Sigma(x-y)^2}{2k}$$

(*e*) For two groups only. The totals for the groups may be T_x and T_y as above in (*d*). The sum of squares is:

$$\frac{(T_x - T_y)^2}{N}$$

where N is the total number of variates.

(*f*) Simple interaction in a $2 \times n$ table. The table is as in (*d*), in which each value of x and y represents k variates. The interaction $(1, 2, 3, \cdots n) \times (xy)$ is given by:

$$\frac{\Sigma(x-y)^2}{2k} - \frac{(T_x - T_y)^2}{2kn}$$

(*g*) Simple interaction for a 2×2 table. The following is a 2×2 table in which each value of x is a total for k variates.

	A	B
I	x_1	x_2
II	x_4	x_3

The interaction $(AB \times \text{I II})$ is given by

$$\frac{[(x_1 + x_3) - (x_2 + x_4)]^2}{4k}$$

(h) Simple interaction for a $k \times n$ fold table. A table of this type is illustrated in Section 5 above, and equation (2) shows how the sums of squares and degrees of freedom are broken up. The sum of squares for within groups and classes is the same as for the interaction and can be calculated by subtracting the two terms on the right from the total. The procedure therefore is as follows:

$$
\begin{aligned}
\text{Total} &= \Sigma(x^2) - T_x^2/kn \\
\text{For } n \text{ classes} &= \Sigma(T_c^2)/k - T_x^2/kn \\
\text{For } k \text{ groups} &= \Sigma(T_g^2)/n - T_x^2/kn \\
\hline
\text{Interaction} &= \text{Difference}
\end{aligned}
$$

(i) Triple interaction. In more complex analyses it is sometimes necessary to calculate triple interactions. We shall illustrate the method for the simple case of 2×2 tables:[1]

	X			Y			Z	
	A	B		A	B		A	B
I	x_1	x_2	I	x_1	x_2	I	x_1	x_2
II	x_4	x_3	II	x_4	x_3	II	x_4	x_3

The interaction to be calculated is $(XYZ \times \text{I II} \times AB)$. Assume each value to be made up of k variates; then for each of the above tables we have:

$$\text{For } X \ (\text{I II} \times AB) = (x_1 + x_3 - x_2 - x_4)^2/4k$$

$$Y \ (\text{I II} \times AB) = (x_1 + x_3 - x_2 - x_4)^2/4k$$

$$Z \ (\text{I II} \times AB) = (x_1 + x_3 - x_2 - x_4)^2/4k$$

Summating these gives us the sum of the interactions of $(\text{I II} \times AB)$, taking each X, Y, and Z group separately. Next we find $(\text{I II} \times AB)$ for X, Y, and Z combined, having set up another 2×2 table.

[1] If the three factors have only two levels the triple interaction is also represented by only one degree of freedom and may therefore be calculated from a difference between two correctly chosen totals. The method of building up these totals will be clear after a study of the methods of the following chapter.

$$X + Y + Z$$

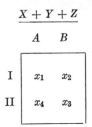

For X, Y, and Z, $(I \; II \times AB) = (x_1 + x_3 - x_2 - x_4)^2/12k$, which, when subtracted from the sum obtained for the three tables above, gives the triple interaction $(XYZ \times I \; II \times AB)$.

According to the same principle, triple interactions may be calculated for any three factors. Note that there are three different ways in which the calculations may be carried out, as repeated calculations of any one of the three simple interactions will finally give the triple interaction. Always examine the three possible methods and decide which one will require the least amount of labor.

8. Exercises.

1. Table 34 taken from data by Crampton and Hopkins (1) gives the gains in weight of pigs in a comparative feeding trial. The 5 lots of pigs represent 5 different treatments, and there were 10 pigs in each lot. Make an analysis of variance for the data, and test the significance of the treatment differences.

TABLE 34

GAINS OF PIGS IN A COMPARATIVE FEEDING TRIAL

Replicate	Lot I	Lot II	Lot III	Lot IV	Lot V
1	165	168	164	185	201
2	156	180	156	195	189
3	159	180	189	186	173
4	167	166	138	201	193
5	170	170	153	165	164
6	146	161	190	175	160
7	130	171	160	187	200
8	151	169	172	177	142
9	164	179	142	166	184
10	158	191	155	165	149

The error variance in this experiment works out to 243.6.

2. In a study of hog prices in Iowa, Schultz and Black (9) have given prices by months, years, and districts. The districts are obtained by dividing the state into 4. A portion of the data is given in Table 35. After completing the analysis of variance for these data, devise graphical means of illustrating the interaction of months with years. It is not necessary in this exercise to make tests of significance of the results, as it is being used here merely to show how the technique of the analysis of variance can be used to separate out the various effects in a set of data.

Sum of squares for months $\times$ *years* $= 83.3413.$

3. In agronomic trials of varieties of cereal crops it is desirable to conduct the trials at various points in the area under consideration and to carry them on for a period of 2 or more years. Immer, et al. (8), have given data on barley yields at several stations in Minnesota over a period of 2 years. Table 36 gives the yields at 3 of the stations for 2 years for 6 varieties. Analyze the results.

Note that the blocks are numbered 1, 2, and 3, but this does not mean that block 1 at University Farm has any relation to block 1 at Waseca or any other station. Consequently the sum of squares and degrees of freedom for blocks are worked out at each station and lumped together in the final analysis. A common error that beginners make in sorting out the degrees of freedom for an experiment of this kind is to regard the blocks as a factor occurring at three levels and thus they have such expressions in their analysis as these:

Blocks $\times$ Stations
" $\times$ Years
" $\times$ Stations $\times$ Years
etc.

These expressions obviously have no meaning as the block numbers do not represent definite levels that are uniform at all stations. The correct procedure is therefore to calculate the block sum of squares for each experiment and add all these sums of squares together in order to show them in the final analysis.

The following values for the sums of squares will assist in checking the calculations.

Total................................. *11,504.61*
Varieties............................ *1,566.58*
Varieties $\times$ Stations $\times$ Years......... *230.52*

TABLE 35

HOG PRICES PAID TO PRODUCERS IN IOWA 1928–29 TO 1930–31

	1928–29 Districts				1929–30 Districts				1930–31 Districts			
	A	B	C	D	A	B	C	D	A	B	C	D
Oct.	9.48	9.46	9.47	9.56	8.79	8.98	8.90	9.15	8.84	8.83	8.80	8.86
Nov.	8.41	8.13	8.43	8.44	8.32	8.30	8.34	8.53	8.04	8.23	8.17	8.45
Dec.	7.91	7.85	7.79	7.96	8.58	8.50	8.44	8.54	7.39	7.31	7.32	7.34
Jan.	8.14	8.28	8.12	8.24	8.79	8.69	8.71	9.02	7.06	7.10	7.11	7.17
Feb.	9.14	9.03	9.00	9.10	9.84	9.59	9.63	9.82	6.44	6.62	6.63	6.65
Mar.	10.57	10.61	10.44	10.49	9.75	9.81	9.78	10.10	6.80	6.87	6.84	6.88
Apr.	10.65	10.53	10.56	10.67	9.20	9.22	9.26	9.42	6.78	6.86	6.92	6.92
May	10.36	10.20	10.07	10.14	9.12	9.10	9.06	9.26	6.03	6.10	6.06	6.30
June	9.95	9.86	9.97	10.03	9.16	9.17	9.14	9.33	5.40	5.39	5.57	5.60
July	10.64	10.47	10.70	10.54	8.24	8.11	8.31	8.60	6.00	5.85	6.16	6.24
Aug.	10.35	10.34	10.34	10.56	8.22	8.52	8.68	8.75	5.91	5.66	6.24	6.36
Sept.	9.37	9.46	9.40	9.51	9.52	9.52	9.64	9.73	5.07	5.20	5.26	5.38

TABLE 36

YIELDS IN BUSHELS PER ACRE OF 6 VARIETIES OF BARLEY GROWN AT 3 STATIONS
IN EACH OF 2 YEARS

Block No.	Man-churia	Gla-bron	Svan-sota	Velvet	Trebi	Peat-land	Station	Year
1	29.2	44.6	33.9	36.7	41.2	38.5		
2	25.0	39.1	39.4	41.0	31.9	29.6	University Farm	1931
3	26.8	45.5	32.1	42.0	36.6	30.2		
1	19.7	28.6	20.1	20.3	19.3	22.3		
2	31.4	38.3	30.8	27.5	22.4	30.8	University Farm	1932
3	29.6	43.5	31.4	32.6	45.5	31.1		
1	47.5	55.4	44.5	56.9	63.9	41.2		
2	52.2	53.4	46.0	40.6	63.8	51.5	Waseca	1931
3	46.9	56.8	51.5	53.2	63.8	53.0		
1	40.8	44.4	41.0	44.6	53.5	39.8		
2	29.4	34.9	41.1	41.4	44.2	39.2	Waseca	1932
3	30.2	33.9	33.4	26.2	50.0	29.1		
1	24.0	27.5	26.5	27.2	42.1	24.7		
2	24.7	25.5	21.5	28.0	42.5	29.5	Morris	1931
3	33.6	33.3	29.3	23.2	46.7	35.4		
1	29.6	36.6	27.1	35.9	40.0	35.7		
2	34.1	34.3	35.7	33.9	46.9	41.9	Morris	1932
3	39.4	34.5	42.3	46.7	53.0	52.0		

4. Find the 5% points of F for the following values of n_1 and n_2:

n_1	n_2
3	51
6	43
4	92
12	195
7	36
11	64
16	39
18	215
17	19
36	28
28	154
53	42

5. Prove: (1) That $\sum_1^n (x^2) - T_x^2/n = \sum_1^n (x - \bar{x})^2$.

(2) That the interaction for a 2×2 table is given by $(x_1 + x_3 - x_2 - x_4)^2/kn$. See Section $7(g)$.

(3) That the sum of squares for the two subtotals T_a and T_b is given by $(T_a - T_b)^2/N$. See Section $7(e)$.

(4) That in a series of pairs the sum of squares for within pairs is given by $\frac{1}{2} \sum (x - y)^2$. See Section $7(d)$.

REFERENCES

1. E. W. Crampton and J. W. Hopkins. *Jour. Nutrition*, **8**: 329–339, 1934.
2. G. Dunlop. *Jour. Agr. Sci.*, **25**: 445–459, 1935.
3. R. A. Fisher. Statistical Methods for Research Workers. Oliver and Boyd, London, 1936. Reading: Chapter VII.
4. R. A. Fisher. The Design of Experiments. Oliver and Boyd, London, 1937. Reading: Chapter X, Section 65.
5. W. F. Geddes, et al. *Can. J. Research*, **4**: 421–482, 1931.
6. C. H. Goulden. Modern Methods of Field Experimentation. *Sci. Agric.*, **11**: 681–701, 1931.
7. C. H. Goulden. Application of the Variance Analysis to Experiments in Cereal Chemistry. *Cereal Chem.*, **9**: 239–260, 1932.
8. F. R. Immer, et al. *Jour. Am. Soc. Agron.*, **26**: 403–419, 1934.
9. T. W. Schultz and A. G. Black. Research Bull. 161, Iowa State Agric. Exp. Station, 1933.
10. G. W. Snedecor. Calculation and Interpretation of the Analysis of Variance and Covariance. Collegiate Press, Inc., Ames, Iowa, 1934. Reading: Parts I, II, and III.
11. G. W. Snedecor. Statistical Methods. Collegiate Press, Inc., Ames, Iowa, 1937. Reading: Chapters X and XI.
12. L. H. C. Tippett. The Methods of Statistics. Williams and Norgate, Ltd., London, 1931. Reading: Chapter VI.

CHAPTER XII

THE FIELD PLOT TEST

GENERAL PRINCIPLES AND STANDARD DESIGNS

1. Soil Heterogeneity. The fact of soil heterogeneity as it affects the yields of crops has been commented on by various writers. In the agronomic test it is the chief source of error in comparing varieties, soil and fertilizer treatments, and factors of a similar type. If soil heterogeneity was practically non-existent a single pair of plots would be sufficient to make a comparison of two varieties, but even then it is doubtful whether that condition would be highly desirable. By a sufficient expenditure we might render a piece of soil completely homogeneous, but by doing so we would partly defeat the purpose of the test which is to determine the behavior of varieties and treatments under a limited range of conditions. We would have selected one particular soil type for our experiment and therefore restricted the area to which our results would apply. The ideal agronomic test is one conducted on a piece of land in which the range in soil type, etc., is the same as that in the district to which the results are to be applied. Usually agronomic tests are on soil that is much less subject to variation than the surrounding district so that in general the results from them are considered as applicable over too wide an area. This is not to argue that more variable soils should be selected, for that might again defeat the purpose of the test by rendering the results insignificant, but rather to point out the limitations of the tests as ordinarily conducted and that the ideal cannot be reached by any method of increasing the uniformity of the soil.

2. Replication. In order to obtain greater accuracy in field experiments, the most effective method is to increase the number of replications. Increasing the plot size is also effective, but increasing replication is much more so. In previous pages it has been pointed out that the standard error of a mean is given by $s/\sqrt{n}$, where s is the standard error of a single determination and n is the number of determinations averaged. It follows, therefore, that, in replicating field plots, the decrease in the standard error of the mean of one variety or treatment is proportional to the *square root of the number of replications*. This rule applies only if the variation due to the replicates themselves is removed from the error, but, as will be pointed out below, this follows naturally from the plan of the test and the use of the analysis of variance.

A most important consideration in the use of replications is that they furnish an estimate of the error of the experiment, and this estimate can be obtained in no other way. The error of the experiment arises from the differences between plots of the same variety or treatment that are not due to the average differences between the replicates. From this it is clear that, if there is only one complete set of plots of all the varieties or treatments, there is no possibility of obtaining a measure of random soil variability that can be used as an error in tests of significance. In terms of the theory which has been emphasized repeatedly in the previous pages, the variance of the variety or treatment means is subject to testing on the hypothesis that it has arisen purely from random variations in the fertility of the field. Since the only way in which we can form a reliable estimate of these random variations is to replicate the experiment, it follows that without replication there is positively no method of making a test of the significance of the variety or treatment differences.

3. Randomization. As pointed out above, the estimate of error is taken from differences between plots that are treated alike. R. A. Fisher states that " an estimate of error so derived will only be valid for its purpose if we make sure that in the plot arrangement, pairs of plots treated alike are not nearer together, or further apart than, or in any other relevant way, distinguished from pairs of plots treated differently." This point is obvious if we consider a simple replicated experiment containing, say, 4 varieties, that we shall designate as A, B, C, and D. Suppose, merely for purposes of argument, that the plots are square and the arrangement of the plots in the field is as follows:

Replicate 1	A	B	C	D
Replicate 2	A	B	C	D
Replicate 3	A	B	C	D
Replicate 4	A	B	C	D

The form of the analysis will be:

	DF	Variance
Replicates..........	3	r
Varieties..........	3	v
Error.............	9	e
Total..........	15	

and now, if there are no variety differences it can be expected that on the average the variance v will be equal to the error e, and unless our experiment is designed to make this true it is unbalanced, or in the usual terminology it is subject to a bias.   On this basis it is possible to picture the situation with respect to bias in this simple experiment, on varying the location of the plots with respect to distances between plots of the same variety and plots with different varieties.   In the first place, suppose that the replicates are only 1 foot apart so that there is for example only a space of 1 foot between the plot of A in the first replicate and the plot of A in the second replicate.   Then between the plots of different varieties there are 6-foot buffer plots of some other crop.   This situation presents a very obvious bias in that the plots of different varieties are farther apart than plots of the same variety. The result is that, if there are no differences between the varieties, the variance v will on the average be larger than e.   This very proposition was recognized by agronomists at an early stage in the development of field plot tests, and as a remedy for it suggestions were made as to the distribution of the plots in a systematic manner over the whole field.   These suggestions, however, did not take into consideration the possibility of a bias in the opposite direction to that of the design outlined above.   That such a bias is a distinct possibility has been shown by Tedin (10), in an extensive study of data from uniformity trials.   A bias in the direction that tends to make the error too large, and the variety or treatment variance too small, is in effect just as disastrous as the opposite type of bias, as it means that, on the average, certain significant effects will be overlooked.

A systematic type of distribution of the plots might be as follows:

A	B	C	D
C	D	A	B
A	B	C	D
C	D	A	B

and it will be noted that the plots of the same variety are scattered widely over the field.   This is the type of arrangement that is likely to result in an error that is too large, but, disregarding that point, there is another type of bias common to all systematic arrangements.   This may be referred to as an intravarietal bias, in that comparisons between different pairs of varieties are not of equal precision.   For example, in both of the systematic arrangements that we have outlined above, the varieties A and B occur on adjacent plots in every replication while the varieties A and D are on the average farther apart.   This is a very undesirable feature of such experiments, for if a single error is used for the whole experiment it means that real differences between the varieties that are close together may be overlooked and other differences that actually do not exist may be judged significant.

From the above discussion it may appear to the reader that the field plot test is extremely complicated and difficult to set up in such a way that there is no bias. Actually, all these difficulties may be very easily overcome by the simple process of arranging the varieties at random in each replication. Thus, instead of either of the arrangements that have been outlined, we would make up one as follows, in which the positions of the varieties are determined entirely at random.

$$
\begin{array}{cccc}
D & C & A & B \\
C & B & A & D \\
B & C & D & A \\
A & D & B & C \\
\end{array}
$$

Then, regardless of the size or shape of the plots, it can be proved either mathematically or by actual trial that, in a series of such tests, using a different random arrangement each time, the variance v will on the average be equal to the variance e. Details of the methods used for randomization are given in Chapter XVI.

4. Error Control. In replicated experiments, the differences between the plots of any one treatment are due in part to experimental error and in part to the average differences between the replicates. The latter is not relevant to the comparisons we wish to make, as each treatment is represented by one plot in each replicate or block. The variance due to blocks is therefore removed from the error, and, the *larger the proportion of the total variability that is removed, the more accurate the experiment.* This has a very important bearing on the plan of an experiment, especially in relation to the shape of the blocks and of the plots. The differences between long narrow plots, when they are placed side by side, are usually less than those between square plots, and similarly for blocks, and since we want the differences between plots as small as possible and the differences between blocks as large as possible, the ideal plan is one which combines long narrow plots with square blocks. Practical considerations limit the shape of the plots, however, and consequently limit also the shape of the blocks; but, if we keep this fundamental principle in mind in drawing up experiments, the greatest possible efficiency will be obtained.

The arrangements for error control by means of replication differ according to the plan of the experiment. There are two fundamental plans, *randomized blocks,* and the *Latin square.* Others that will be described later may be referred to as special types in that they are to a certain extent modifications of the fundamental types, and especially adapted to certain purposes.

5. Randomized Blocks. This plan is the simplest of all the types in which any measure of error control is obtained. It is illustrated in the following diagram, which represents an experiment with 8 treatments in 4 blocks.

I	G	A	H	D	E	D	H	A	**III**
	F	B	C	E	G	C	F	B	
II	B	H	D	F	G	F	C	A	**IV**
	C	E	A	G	E	D	B	H	

In the general case let k represent the number of blocks and n the number of treatments. Then the equation for sums of squares is:

$$\overset{nk}{\underset{1}{\Sigma}}(x - \bar{x})^2 = n \overset{k}{\underset{1}{\Sigma}}(\bar{x}_b - \bar{x})^2 + k \overset{n}{\underset{1}{\Sigma}}(\bar{x}_v - \bar{x})^2 + \overset{nk}{\underset{1}{\Sigma}}(d^2) \qquad (1)$$

$$\quad\;\;(1) \qquad\qquad\qquad (2) \qquad\qquad\quad (3) \qquad (4)$$

where $\bar{x}_b$ is the mean of a block and $\bar{x}_v$ is the mean of a treatment. The last term on the right is actually $\overset{nk}{\underset{1}{\Sigma}}(x - \bar{x}_b - \bar{x}_v + \bar{x})^2$, but is abbreviated for convenience. The corresponding equation for degrees of freedom is:

$$nk - 1 = (k - 1) + (n - 1) + (n - 1)(k - 1) \qquad (2)$$

$$\;\;(1) \qquad\quad (2) \qquad\quad (3) \qquad\qquad (4)$$

In calculating the sums of squares the following formulae are the most convenient.

(1) Total $\quad \overset{nk}{\underset{1}{\Sigma}}(x - \bar{x})^2 = \overset{nk}{\underset{1}{\Sigma}}(x^2) - T^2/nk \qquad\quad T =$ grand total for all plots

(2) Blocks $\quad n \overset{k}{\underset{1}{\Sigma}}(\bar{x}_b - \bar{x})^2 = \overset{k}{\underset{1}{\Sigma}}(T_b^2)/n - T^2/nk \qquad T_b =$ total for one block

(3) Treatments $k \overset{n}{\underset{1}{\Sigma}}(\bar{x}_v - \bar{x})^2 = \overset{n}{\underset{1}{\Sigma}}(T_v^2)/k - T^2/nk \qquad T_v =$ total for one treatment

(4) Error $\quad\quad \overset{nk}{\underset{1}{\Sigma}}(d^2) \quad\quad = (1) - (2) - (3) \qquad$ Subtract blocks and treatments from total.

The analysis of variance is set up in the usual way.
The standard error of the experiment is given by

$$s = \sqrt{\frac{\Sigma(d^2)}{(k-1)(n-1)}} \qquad (3)$$

and for the mean of one treatment

$$s_m = \frac{s}{\sqrt{k}} \qquad (4)$$

6. The Latin Square. The following diagram illustrates a 5×5
Latin square where the letters represent the treatments.

E	B	C	D	A
A	C	D	E	B
D	E	B	A	C
C	D	A	B	E
B	A	E	C	D

Note that the plots are arranged in 5 rows and 5 columns, and that there
must be the same number of treatments as rows and columns. The
treatments are placed at random, subject to the restriction that a treatment can occur only once in any row or column.

Let n represent the number of rows, columns, and treatments, and
the equations for the sums of squares and degrees of freedom are as
follows:

$$\sum_1^{n^2}(x - \bar{x})^2 = n\sum_1^{n}(\bar{x}_r - \bar{x})^2 + n\sum_1^{n}(\bar{x}_c - \bar{x})^2 + n\sum_1^{n}(\bar{x}_v - \bar{x})^2 + \sum_1^{n^2}(d^2) \quad (5)$$

where $\bar{x}_r$ and $\bar{x}_c$ represent the means of rows and columns respectively.

$$(n^2 - 1) = (n-1) + (n-1) + (n-1) + (n-2)(n-1) \quad (6)$$

The calculations for sums of squares are:

(1) Total $\qquad \sum_1^{n^2}(x-\bar{x})^2 = \sum_1^{n^2}(x^2) - T^2/n^2 \qquad T = $ grand total of
$\qquad\qquad\qquad\qquad\qquad\qquad\qquad\qquad\qquad\qquad$ all plots

(2) Rows $\qquad n\sum_1^{n}(\bar{x}_r - \bar{x})^2 = \sum_1^{n}(T_r^2)/n - T^2/n^2 \qquad T_r = $ total for one
$\qquad\qquad\qquad\qquad\qquad\qquad\qquad\qquad\qquad\qquad$ row

(3) Columns $\; n\sum_1^{n}(\bar{x}_c - \bar{x})^2 = \sum_1^{n}(T_c^2)/n - T^2/n^2 \qquad T_c = $ total for one
$\qquad\qquad\qquad\qquad\qquad\qquad\qquad\qquad\qquad\qquad$ column

(4) Treatments $n \sum_1^n (\bar{x}_v - \bar{x})^2 = \sum_1^n (T_v^2)/n - T^2/n^2$　　T_v = total for one treatment

(5) Error　　　　$\sum_1^{nk}(d^2) = (1) - (2) - (3) - (4)$　　Subtract, rows, columns, and treatments from the total.

The standard error in a Latin square is given by

$$s = \sqrt{\frac{\Sigma(d^2)}{(n-2)(n-1)}} \tag{7}$$

And for the mean of one treatment

$$s_m = \frac{s}{\sqrt{n}} \tag{8}$$

The Latin square gives error control in two directions across the field, so that soil gradients are always taken care of. For a few treatments it is a very efficient type of experiment, and it is very doubtful that a better one can be devised. When the number of treatments are more than 8 the Latin square is cumbersome and a point is soon reached where the increase in accuracy does not warrant the added labor. Moreover, as the number of treatments are increased the rows and columns become longer in proportion to their width and a point is reached finally where further accuracy through error control is not obtained.

Example 33. Randomized Blocks. Table 37 gives the yields of 6 wheat varieties obtained in an experiment consisting of 4 randomized blocks. The marginal totals are given in the table so as to facilitate calculation.

TABLE 37

YIELDS IN BUSHELS PER ACRE BY BLOCKS
OF 6 WHEAT VARIETIES

		Blocks 1	2	3	4	Variety Totals
	A	27.8	27.3	28.5	38.5	122.1
	B	30.6	28.8	31.0	39.5	129.9
	C	27.7	22.7	34.9	36.8	122.1
Varieties	D	16.2	15.0	14.1	19.6	64.9
	E	16.2	17.0	17.7	15.4	66.3
	F	24.9	22.5	22.7	26.3	96.4
Block Totals		143.4	133.3	148.9	176.1	601.7

Calculating the sums of squares we have:

Total $\quad \Sigma(x^2) \quad - T^2/nk = 16,460.05 - 15,085.12 \qquad = 1374.93$

Blocks $\quad \Sigma(T_b^2)/n - T^2/nk = 15,252.48 - 15,085.12 \qquad = 167.36$

Varieties $\Sigma(T_v^2)/k - T^2/nk = 16,147.87 - 15,085.12 \qquad = 1062.75$

Error $\qquad\qquad\qquad = 1,374.93 - 167.36 - 1062.75 = 144.82$

The analysis of variance is then as follows:

	Sum of Squares	DF	Variance	F	5% Point of F
Blocks............	167.36	3	55.79	5.78	3.29
Varieties.........	1062.75	5	212.50	22.0	2.90
Error............	144.82	15	9.655		
Total.........	1374.93	23			

The block and variety differences are seen to be significant, and if we wish to compare any two varieties we make use of the standard error.

$$s = \sqrt{9.655} = 3.122 \qquad s_m = \frac{3.122}{\sqrt{4}} = 1.561$$

The standard error of a difference between the means of any 2 varieties is then $1.561 \times \sqrt{2} = 2.21$. Now suppose that we wished to compare varieties D and F for which the means are 16.2 and 24.1 respectively. The difference is 7.9 and we have

$$t = \frac{7.9}{2.21} = 3.57$$

From Table 94 we note that for 15 degrees of freedom $t = 2.95$ at the 1% point, so that the difference between the 2 varieties is very significant. We take t for 15 degrees of freedom corresponding to the number of degrees of freedom available for estimating the error variance. Unless the degrees of freedom are decidedly limited a short cut can be employed for testing significance. From Table 94 we note that t at the 5% point is approximately 2. Therefore a significant difference will be $2 \times \sqrt{2} \times s_m = 2.82\, s_m$. Roughly a significant difference is 3 s_m.

Example 34. The Latin Square. The following is a plan of a Latin square which was used to test the efficiency of different methods of dusting with sulphur in order to control stem rust of wheat. The key to the treatments is given with the plan.

	Columns						KEY TO TREATMENTS
	1	2	3	4	5		

Columns   KEY TO TREATMENTS

     1   2   3   4   5 A = Dusted before rains.

	1	2	3	4	5
I	B	D	E	A	C
II	C	A	B	E	D
Rows III	D	C	A	B	E
IV	E	B	C	D	A
V	A	E	D	C	B

A = Dusted before rains.

B = Dusted after rains.

C = Dusted once each week.

D = Drifting once each week.

E = Check (undusted).

All applications were 30 pounds to the acre at each treatment. Drifting means that the dust was allowed to settle down over the plants from above. In the ordinary procedure the sulphur is forced down among the plants by a blast of air.

The plot yields in bushels per acre are given in Table 38. The figures in the table correspond with the position of the plots in the above plan.

TABLE 38

PLOT YIELDS IN BUSHELS PER ACRE

		Columns				Row Totals	TREATMENT TOTALS
	1	2	3	4	5		
I	4.9	6.4	3.3	9.5	11.8	35.9	A　34.2
II	9.3	4.0	6.2	5.1	5.4	30.0	B　32.3
Rows III	7.6	15.4	6.5	6.0	4.6	40.1	C　65.6
IV	6.3	7.6	13.2	8.6	4.9	39.6	D　39.8
V	9.3	6.3	11.8	15.9	7.6	50.9	E　24.6
Column Totals	36.4	39.7	41.0	45.1	34.3	196.5	

In order to obtain the treatment totals we must select the yields according to the position of the treatments in the plan. Thus for treatment B we have $4.9 + 7.6 + 6.2 + 6.0 + 7.6 = 32.3$. Finally we have all the treatment totals as given in Table 38.

The calculations are as given below:

(1) Total $\quad \sum_1^{n^2}(x^2) \quad - T^2/n^2 = 1829.83 - 1544.49 = 285.34$

(2) Rows $\quad \sum_1^{n}(T_r^2)/n - T^2/n^2 = 1591.16 - 1544.49 = 46.67$

(3) Columns $\quad \sum_1^{n}(T_c^2)/n - T^2/n^2 = 1558.51 - 1544.49 = 14.02$

(4) Treatments $\quad \sum_1^{n}(T_v^2)/n - T^2/n^2 = 1741.10 - 1544.49 = 196.61$

(5) Error $\quad = (1) - (2) - (3) - (4) = 28.04$

Then the analysis of variance is:

	Sum of Squares	DF	Variance	F	5% Point of F
Rows.............	46.67	4	11.67	4.99	3.26
Columns..........	14.02	4	3.50	1.50	3.26
Treatments........	196.61	4	48.62	20.8	3.26
Error.............	28.04	12	2.34		
Total...........	285.34				

7. Factorial Experiments. As the name denotes, in factorial experiments, an attempt is made to study the various treatment factors. Thus an experiment designed to study, at the same time, rate and depth of seeding of a cereal crop would be a factorial experiment in which the 2 factors, rate and depth of seeding, are represented at 2 or more levels. We may use, for example, 3 rates and 3 depths, giving us in all 9 treatment combinations. Usually, there are more than 2 factors, as it is easily seen that the greater the number of factors the greater the scope and inductive value of the experiment. The experiment on rates and depths, for example, might well be conducted with more than 1 variety, as it is conceivable that results obtained with 1 variety might not apply to others. In factorial experimentation, therefore, the study of the interactions is a very important consideration and, until the advent of the development of a suitable technique, was very frequently completely overlooked.

The introduction of factors is of course limited by space and the cost of experimentation, and, in addition, it is easy to add so many factors that the analysis becomes rather complex. If we have to study all the possible combinations in an experiment with 4 factors at 3 levels each, we must have 81 different combinations. The addition of another factor at 3 levels would increase the number of combinations to 243, at which point the experiment would become extremely unwieldy, and since the blocks would be very large, error control would not be highly efficient.

If all the factors are of equal importance, the obvious method is to make up the total number of combinations and randomize them indiscriminately in each block. We shall see later that with this plan considerable increases in precision can be obtained by a process of splitting up the replicates into smaller units and confounding with these smaller blocks certain relatively unimportant degrees of freedom. In many cases the factors are not of equal importance and very efficient use can be made of the *split plot* design, in which more than one error variance is obtained, each one appropriate for testing certain comparisons.

8. Split Plot Experiments. An experiment was conducted in 1932 on the experimental field of the Dominion Rust Research Laboratory, which is a good example of the split plot type. This particular study was designed to determine the effect on the incidence of root rot, of variety of wheat, kinds of dust for seed treatment, method of application of the dust, and efficacy of soil inoculation with the root-rot organism.

The plan of the experiment with the key to the treatments is given below and is sufficient to indicate how the experiment was worked out. Two varieties of wheat, Marquis and Mindum, were used. These varieties were planted in 4 blocks, half of each block being sown to one variety

and half to the other.   The strips were then divided into 10 plots each.
With 5 different kinds of dust and 2 methods of application, dry and wet,
there were 10 different treatments, and one of these was assigned at
random to each plot in each strip.   The plots were then divided length-
wise and on one half the seed was sown with inoculated soil and on the
other half with uninoculated soil.   The final result was as shown in the
plan of the experiment.   It will be noted that the disposition of varieties,
dust treatments, and soil treatments is purely at random throughout
the experiment.

In order to analyze this experiment it is necessary to sort out the
degrees of freedom corresponding to the various components of the test.
In the first place, for the 160 plots there is a total of 159 degrees of freedom.   The 160 plots are in pairs, one of each pair being inoculated (I),
and one uninoculated (U).   A convenient initial classification of the
degrees of freedom (DF) is to consider the field as made up of 80 pairs
of plots, and since there is one DF within each pair, we have

$$
\begin{array}{lll}
\text{Between} & \text{80 pairs} & 79\ DF \\
\text{Within} & \text{``} & 80\ DF \\
\hline
& \text{Total} & 159\ DF
\end{array}
\tag{9}
$$

Then, proceeding to the splitting up of the DF of these two components,
and dealing first with the 79 DF for between pairs, we note that the units
now are plots exactly twice the size of the original plots, and the DF can
be analyzed out without any reference whatsoever to the fact that the
plots are divided into I and U portions.   If the experiment is considered
first as a test of 10 treatments replicated 8 times, the analysis would be as
follows:

$$
\left.
\begin{array}{ll}
\text{Blocks} & 7\ DF \\
\text{Treatments} & 9\ DF \\
\text{Error} & 63\ DF
\end{array}
\right\}
\tag{10}
$$

But the experiment is not actually replicated 8 times, as 4 of these blocks

PLAN OF A SPLIT PLOT EXPERIMENT

	1	2	3	4	5	6	7	8	9	10	
Marquis	5 U I	4 U I	3 U I	8 U I	7 I U	1 U I	9 I U	10 U I	2 I U	6 I U	I
Mindum	6 I U	2 U I	8 U I	10 I U	3 U I	4 I U	1 I U	7 U I	5 I U	9 U I	

PLAN OF A SPLIT PLOT EXPERIMENT—*Continued*

	1	2	3	4	5	6	7	8	9	10	
Marquis	9 I U	10 I U	4 I U	2 I U	1 U I	5 I U	7 I U	6 U I	3 I U	8 I U	II
Mindum	6 U I	9 U I	2 I U	5 I U	1 U I	8 I U	10 U I	4 U I	3 I U	7 U I	
Mindum	10 I U	6 I U	9 U I	1 U I	7 U I	5 U I	2 U I	3 I U	4 U I	8 U I	III
Marquis	4 U I	5 I U	1 I U	2 U I	3 I U	6 I U	7 U I	9 U I	10 U I	8 I U	
Mindum	4 U I	8 U I	9 I U	5 U I	1 I U	3 I U	10 U I	2 I U	6 I U	7 U I	IV
Marquis	8 U I	10 U I	3 I U	2 I U	4 U I	5 I U	7 U I	1 I U	6 U I	9 U I	

Key to Treatments

I = Inoculated soil.
U = Uninoculated soil.

1. Dry, Ceresan.	2. Wet, Ceresan.
3. " Semesan.	4. " Semesan.
5. " DuBay.	6. " DuBay.
7. " Check.	8. " Check.
9. " CaCo₃.	10. " CaCo₃.

are sown to Marquis wheat and 4 to Mindum wheat. The 7 *DF* for blocks contain, therefore, 1 *DF* for varieties and 3 *DF* for the interaction of varieties with blocks, where the blocks consist now of two sets of all the treatments, one set with Marquis wheat and one set with Mindum wheat. The 3 *DF* for the interaction of varieties with blocks obviously represent the error for determining the significance of the differences between the varieties. The final disposition of the 7 *DF* as given in (10) is therefore:

$$\left.\begin{array}{lr}\text{Blocks} & 3\ DF \\ \text{Varieties} & 1\ DF \\ \text{Error (1)} & 3\ DF\end{array}\right\} \qquad (11)$$

We take next the 9 *DF* as given in (10) for treatments. The key to treatments shows that there are 4 different dusts and 1 check, so that we have 4 *DF* for treatments.   Then each dust is applied dry (D) and applied wet (W), so that we must have 1 *DF* for D W.   The remaining 4 *DF* represent the interaction of dusts with D W, so that the 9 *DF* are finally split up as follows:

$$\left.\begin{array}{ll} \text{Dusts} & 4\ DF \\ \text{D W} & 1\ DF \\ \text{Interaction} & 4\ DF \end{array}\right\} \tag{12}$$

The effect of the varieties (V) on the factors given in (12) must also be considered; therefore we must have in the 63 *DF* for error given in (10):

$$\left.\begin{array}{ll} \text{V} \times \text{Dusts} & 4\ DF \\ \text{V} \times \text{D W} & 1\ DF \\ \text{V} \times \text{Dusts} \times \text{D W} & 4\ DF \end{array}\right\} \tag{13}$$

The 9 *DF* represented in (13) must obviously come out of the 63 *DF* for error as given in (10), so that there are actually only 54 *DF* representing true error.   Finally the complete disposition of the 79 *DF* for between pairs of plots can be shown as follows:

$$\left.\begin{array}{ll} \text{Blocks} & 3\ DF \\ \text{Varieties} & 1\ DF \\ \text{Error (1)} & 3\ DF \end{array}\right\} \text{Group (1)}$$

$$\left.\begin{array}{ll} \text{Dusts} & 4\ DF \\ \text{D W} & 1\ DF \\ \text{Dusts} \times \text{D W} & 4\ DF \\ \text{V} \times \text{Dusts} & 4\ DF \\ \text{V} \times \text{D W} & 1\ DF \\ \text{V} \times \text{Dusts} \times \text{D W} & 4\ DF \\ \text{Error (2)} & 54\ DF \end{array}\right\} \text{Group (2)}$$

$$\begin{array}{ll} \text{Total} & \overline{79\ DF} \end{array}$$

Error (2) is applicable to all the factors in the second group.

TABLE 39

PLOT YIELDS IN A SPLIT PLOT EXPERIMENT

1		2		3		4		5		6		7		8		9		10	
64	68	68	71	62	73	56	67	78	69	67	66	71	64	64	75	70	66	67	65
76	69	66	72	75	81	72	71	70	72	73	67	72	70	72	85	76	70	71	74

PLOT YIELDS IN A SPLIT PLOT EXPERIMENT—*Continued*

1		2		3		4		5		6		7		8		9		10	
66	63	63	51	58	64	60	57	55	60	53	61	73	56	59	55	47	58	64	55
54	74	73	72	73	64	79	68	68	72	76	69	66	78	67	63	69	74	73	76
83	73	68	60	82	79	73	81	84	94	77	76	74	77	76	73	69	70	75	88
51	59	57	57	63	60	57	61	63	65	64	61	60	65	56	67	61	74	73	55
63	72	72	83	78	69	70	66	60	66	68	70	63	68	64	61	59	63	65	77
60	69	60	67	67	52	61	56	61	69	58	62	60	72	57	54	58	58	64	65

Considering now the 80 DF for within pairs, the first point to note is that, since these 80 DF represent only differences between members of pairs of adjacent plots, they do not contain any direct effects due to blocks, varieties, or dust treatments. The differences between such plots do represent, however, the effect of I and U corresponding to 1 DF. The first split up of the 80 DF is therefore:

$$
\begin{array}{lr}
\text{I U} & 1\ DF \\
\text{Remainder} & 79\ DF \\ \hline
\text{Total} & 80\ DF
\end{array} \qquad (14)
$$

The 79 DF for the remainder must contain the DF representing the interaction of I U with all the other factors as given in Groups (1) and (2); hence we can set these down in order.

$$
\begin{array}{lr}
\text{I U} \times \text{V} & 1\ DF \\
\text{I U} \times \text{Dusts} & 4\ DF \\
\text{I U} \times \text{D W} & 1\ DF \\
\text{I U} \times \text{Dusts} \times \text{D W} & 4\ DF \\
\text{I U} \times \text{V} \times \text{Dusts} & 4\ DF \\
\text{I U} \times \text{V} \times \text{D W} & 1\ DF \\ \hline
\text{Total} & 15\ DF
\end{array} \qquad (15)
$$

Note that we have left out (I U × Blocks) and the quadruple interaction (I U × V × Dusts × D W). The former belongs to error, and the latter is very unlikely to be significant, and even if it might turn out significant, its interpretation would probably be too complex to have any practical

bearing on the use of the treatments.   The final analysis of the 80 *DF*
for within pairs can now be written down:

I U	1 *DF*
I U × V	1 *DF*
I U × Dusts	4 *DF*
I U × D W	1 *DF*
I U × Dusts × D W	4 *DF*
I U × V × Dusts	4 *DF*
I U × V × D W	1 *DF*
Error (3)	64 *DF*
Total	80 *DF*

(Group (3)

The three groups may be placed together as one complete analysis or
dealt with separately.   It will usually be found most convenient in
checking calculations to consider the three groups together in one complete analysis.

After completing the sorting out of the *DF* the next step is to draw
up the tables from the actual data that are necessary for calculation of
the sums of squares.   In the first place a table such as Table 39 is
required, giving the data for the individual plots in a plan corresponding
to the plan of the experiment.   Comparing the table and the plan we
can then draw up Table 40, which is a series of small tables required for
calculating the sums of squares.

The following is an outline of the analysis of variance for the whole
experiment, with figures in the fifth column indicating the calculation
tables from which the corresponding sums of squares are obtained.

From Table 39 we calculate the total sum of squares for all the plots.
Then from the calculation Table 12, for the differences within pairs of
plots, we determine the sum of squares for the 80 *DF* representing within
pairs.   Subtracting this from the total sum of squares gives the sum of
squares for 79 *DF* representing Groups (1) and (2).

We proceed next to calculate, from the tables, the sums of squares as
indicated in the outline of the analysis of variance, leaving items error
(2) and error (3) to the last.   From the sum of squares representing
within pairs for 80 *DF*, we subtract the first seven items in Group (3).
The remainder is the sum of squares for error (3).   From the sum of
squares for between pairs (79 *DF*) we subtract the total for group (1)
and the first six items in Group (2).   The remainder is the sum of
squares for error (2).

The method of calculation of triple interactions has been described in
a previous chapter.

	Sums of Squares	DF	Variance or Mean Square	Calculation Table
Blocks.........................	989.6	3	329.9	1
Varieties (V)...................	3638.6	1	3638.6	1
Error (1).......................	647.6	3	215.9	1
Dusts..........................	987.6	4	246.9	2
Dry vs. Wet (D W)..............	117.3	1	117.3	2
Dusts × D W...................	46.2	4	11.6	2
V × Dusts.....................	146.7	4	36.7	3
V × D W.......................	91.5	1	91.5	4
V × Dusts × D W..............	148.1	4	37.0	5
Error (2).......................	1059.1	54	19.6	
Inoculated vs. Uninoculated (I U)..	965.3	1	965.3	6
I U × V.......................	0.3	1	0.3	6
I U × Dusts...................	379.8	4	95.0	7
I U × D W.....................	68.9	1	68.9	8
I U × Dusts × D W............	25.8	4	6.4	9
I U × V × Dusts..............	119.4	4	29.8	10
I U × V × D W................	3.9	1	3.9	11
Error (3).......................	931.1	64	14.5	
Total.......................	10,366.8	159		

TABLE 40

SERIES OF SUBTABLES FOR CALCULATING SUMS OF SQUARES

Number		Blocks				
		I	II	III	IV	
(1)	Ma	1351	1178	1229		
	Mi	1454	1408			
	Ma + Mi	2805	2586			10,739
	Ma − Mi	−103	−230			

		Ce	Se	Du	Ch	Ca
(2)	D	1044	1059	1062		
	W	1039	1045			
	D + W	2083	2104			10,739
	D − W	5	14			

		Ce	Se	Du	Ch	Ca
(3)	Ma	970	988	967		
	Mi	1113	1116			
	Ma + Mi	2083	2104			10,739
	Ma − Mi	−143	−128			

TABLE 40—(*Continued*)

SERIES OF SUBTABLES FOR CALCULATING SUMS OF SQUARES

Number Blocks

(4)

	D	W	
Ma	2498		
Mi	2940		
Ma + Mi	5438		10,739

(5)

		Ce	Se	Du	Ch	Ca	
Ma	D	482	487	480			
	W	488	501				
	D + W	970	988				4,988
	D − W	−6	−14				
Mi	D	562	572	582			
	W	551	544				
	D + W	1113	1116				5,751
	D − W	11	28				

(6)

	Ma	Mi	
I	2594		
U	2394		
I + U	4988		10,739

(7)

	Ce	Se	Du	Ch	Ca	
I	1069	1070	1054			
U	1014	1034				
I + U	2083	2104				10,739
I − U	55	36				

(8)

	D	W	
I	2791		
U	2647		
I + U	5438		10,739

(9)

		Ce	Se	Du	Ch	Ca	
D	I	531	535	533			
	U	513	524				
	I + U	1044	1059				5,438
	I − U	18	11				
W	I	538	535	521			
	U	501	510				
	I + U	1039	1045				5,301
	I − U	37	25				

TABLE 40—*(Continued)*

SERIES OF SUBTABLES FOR CALCULATING SUMS OF SQUARES

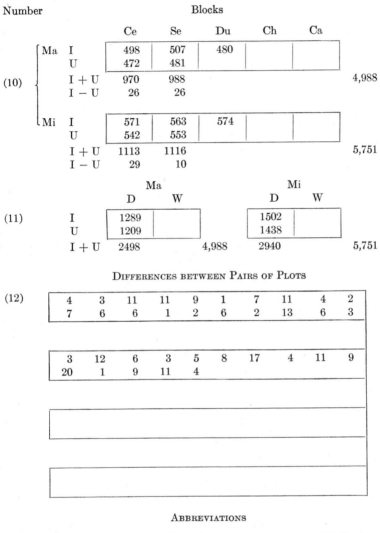

Number			Blocks				
			Ce	Se	Du	Ch	Ca
(10)	Ma	I	498	507	480		
		U	472	481			
		I + U	970	988			4,988
		I − U	26	26			
	Mi	I	571	563	574		
		U	542	553			
		I + U	1113	1116			5,751
		I − U	29	10			

| | | Ma | | | Mi | |
		D	W		D	W
(11)	I	1289			1502	
	U	1209			1438	
	I + U	2498	4,988		2940	5,751

DIFFERENCES BETWEEN PAIRS OF PLOTS

(12)

4	3	11	11	9	1	7	11	4	2
7	6	6	1	2	6	2	13	6	3

3	12	6	3	5	8	17	4	11	9
20	1	9	11	4					

ABBREVIATIONS

Dusts:
Ce (Ceresan)
Se (Semesan)
Du (DuBay)
Ch (Check)
Ca (Calcium carbonate)

Varieties
Ma (Marquis)
Mi (Mindum)

Method of Applying Dust
D (Dry)
W (Wet)

Soil Treatment
I (Inoculated)
U (Uninoculated)

9. Orthogonality and Confounding. F. Yates (16) has given the following definition of orthogonality. It is " that property of the design which ensures that the different classes of effects shall be capable of direct and separate estimation without any entanglement." Thus, in a randomized block experiment, the treatments are orthogonal with blocks in that the effects of each are capable of direct and separate estimation. This orthogonality is accomplished in the design by seeing to it that each block contains the same kind and number of treatments. If by any chance some of the plots in one or more of the blocks are lost, non-orthogonality is introduced, and special methods may be required in order to separate the treatment and block effects. These methods, which have been worked out and described in some detail by Yates, require additional computation, and sometimes the whole procedure may be rather laborious. Consequently in designing an experiment we make every effort to keep within the requirements of orthogonality. In simple experiments this presents no difficulty, but in more complex ones for which a new design is being worked out it is quite easy unwittingly to introduce an element of non-orthogonality. New designs, therefore, require careful scrutiny before they are put into practice.

In factorial experiments involving a fairly large number of combinations, non-orthogonality is sometimes introduced deliberately, and this process is now referred to as confounding. The purpose of confounding in general, as we shall see later in more detail, is to increase the accuracy of the more important comparisons at the expense of the comparisons of lesser importance. In many instances, however, although a certain portion of the information concerning the comparisons of lesser importance is sacrificed, the precision with which all the effects are estimated is increased to a point such that even the partially confounded comparisons are more accurately estimated.

The student should at this point make quite certain of the meaning of confounding, and a few elementary illustrations may be of assistance. Suppose that three fertilizers N, P, and K are being compared at 2 levels of each, so that we have 8 different combinations that we shall designate by $N_0P_0K_0$, $N_0P_0K_1$, $N_0P_1K_0$, $N_1P_0K_0$, $N_0P_1K_1$, $N_1P_0K_1$, $N_1P_1K_0$, and $N_1P_1K_1$, where the subscript numbers refer to the amounts or dosage of each kind of fertilizer. Since $N_0P_0K_0$ means that no fertilizer is applied, and $N_0P_0K_1$ means that only K is applied, these terms may be abbreviated to O, K, P, N, PK, NK, NP, and NPK. In these 8 combinations it will be noted that we have 4 without N and 4 with N. If now we divide the blocks ordinarily containing 8 plots into halves such that one half contains the treatments O, K, P, PK and the other half N, NK, NP, NPK, then the effect of N which may be represented algebraically by $(N_1 - N_0)$ is completely confounded with block effects. The other main effects are still orthogonal with the blocks. For example, in each block we have 2 plots containing P and 2 plots that do not contain P. We would not consider a design of this type in actual practice, as it defeats what is obviously one of the main purposes of the experiment. Assuming, however, that accuracy can be gained by reducing the size of the blocks, it may be worth while to examine all the comparisons to see whether certain of these may be deemed sufficiently unimportant to be sacrificed in order to increase the precision of the remaining comparisons.

The treatment effects may be set out as follows with the corresponding degrees of freedom.

N	1 DF	
P	1 DF	Main effects, 3 DF
K	1 DF	
$N \times P$	1 DF	
$N \times K$	1 DF	Simple interactions, 3 DF
$P \times K$	1 DF	
$N \times P \times K$	1 DF	Triple interaction, 1 DF

To the best of our judgment the triple interaction $N \times P \times K$ would seem to be the least important. At least, even if significant in effect it is the most difficult to interpret in terms of actual fertilizer practice. We shall decide, therefore, to confound this one degree of freedom with blocks, and it remains only to determine the distribution of the treatments in the blocks in a manner which will confound this one comparison and leave all the others intact. Algebraically, all the treatment effects can be represented as follows—

$$N = (N_1 - N_0)(K_1 + K_0)(P_1 + P_0)$$
$$P = (N_1 + N_0)(K_1 + K_0)(P_1 - P_0)$$
$$K = (N_1 + N_0)(K_1 - K_0)(P_1 + P_0)$$

$$N \times P = (N_1 - N_0)(K_1 + K_0)(P_1 - P_0)$$
$$N \times K = (N_1 - N_0)(K_1 - K_0)(P_1 + P_0)$$
$$P \times K = (N_1 + N_0)(K_1 - K_0)(P_1 - P_0)$$

$$N \times P \times K = (N_1 - N_0)(K_1 - K_0)(P_1 - P_0)$$

and on expanding the last expression we have—

$$N \times P \times K = \begin{Bmatrix} +N_0P_0K_1 + N_1P_1K_1 + N_0P_1K_0 + N_1P_0K_0 \\ -N_0P_0K_0 - N_1P_1K_0 - N_0P_1K_1 - N_1P_0K_1 \end{Bmatrix}$$

or
$$\begin{Bmatrix} +K + NPK + P + N \\ -O - NP - PK - NK \end{Bmatrix}$$

This means simply that, if we let the symbols represent the actual yields from the corresponding plots, the sum of squares for the triple interaction will be given by

$$\frac{1}{2k}[(N + P + K + NPK) - (O + NP + PK + NK)]^2$$

where k is the number of plots represented in each total such as $(O + NP + PK + NK)$. Now if we divide each replication into 2 blocks and in one of these put the treatments O, NP, PK, NK, and in the other, N, P, K, NPK, then the above sum of squares will contain not only the triple interaction effect but also the effect of the blocks. The 1 degree of freedom for triple interaction will have been completely confounded with blocks. The analysis of variance for the experiment, assuming 4 replications, will be of the form

Blocks......................	7 *DF*
Main effects.................	3 *DF*
Simple interactions...........	3 *DF*
Error......................	18 *DF*
Total..................	31 *DF*

Since 7 *DF* have been utilized for error control instead of 3 as in an ordinary randomized block experiment, with a moderate degree of soil heterogeneity, it may be expected that the remaining effects will be estimated more accurately by the confounded experiment than by the randomized blocks.

10. Partial Confounding and Recovery of Information. The procedure illustrated above resulted in the complete sacrifice of the information on the triple interaction, and it may be argued that, regardless of the apparent unimportance of the information sacrificed, this is not good experimental procedure in that the experimenter is taking too much for granted in attempting to forecast a result on which he has no previous information, and using this as a basis for the experimental design. The difficulty can be overcome by a process known as partial confounding, which amounts to confounding different degrees of freedom in different replications and using the results from the blocks in which the particular effects are not confounded to recover a portion of the information desired. In order to partially confound the experiment described above and at the same time recover a portion of the information on all the comparisons, we shall require at least 4 replications. In each replication we can confound with blocks a degree of freedom from one of the interactions. The method of laying out the treatments in the blocks is obvious if we expand algebraically each of the expressions for the interactions. Thus

$$\text{I} \quad (N \times P \times K) = (N_1 - N_0)(P_1 - P_0)(K_1 - K_0) = \begin{pmatrix} +K + NPK + & P + & N \\ -O - & NP - PK - & NK \end{pmatrix}$$

$$\text{II} \quad (N \times P) \quad = (N_1 - N_0)(P_1 - P_0)(K_1 + K_0) = \begin{pmatrix} +O + & NP + & K + NPK \\ -N - & P - NK - & PK \end{pmatrix}$$

$$\text{III} \quad (N \times K) \quad = (N_1 - N_0)(P_1 + P_0)(K_1 - K_0) = \begin{pmatrix} +O + & NK + & P + NPK \\ -N - & K - NP - & PK \end{pmatrix}$$

$$\text{IV} \quad (P \times K) \quad = (N_1 + N_0)(P_1 - P_0)(K_1 - K_0) = \begin{pmatrix} +O + & PK + & N + NPK \\ -P - & K - NP - & NK \end{pmatrix}$$

Then in the first replication we can confound the triple interaction and conserve it in all the remaining replications. In the second replication we can confound the simple interaction $N \times P$ and conserve it in all the remaining replications. With 4 replications we can confound each interaction in 1 replication and conserve it in all the others.

In recovering information with respect to the interactions it will, of course, be necessary to make the desired comparisons only in those replications in which the particular interaction is not confounded. Thus if we are computing the sum of squares for $N \times P$ we omit replication II entirely and make up our totals from the other three. The final analysis will be of the form:

Blocks........................	7 DF
Main effects...................	3 DF
Simple interactions............	3 DF
Triple interactions............	1 DF
Error........................	17 DF
Total....................	31 DF

The result of this procedure is to sacrifice one-quarter of the information on each interaction, but the main effects and that portion of the information with respect to the interactions that is recovered may be estimated with greater accuracy.

Using a set of figures from uniformity data the procedure for designing and analyzing a partially confounded $2 \times 2 \times 2$ experiment is illustrated in Example 35.

Example 35.   Partial Confounding in a 2 × 2 × 2 Experiment.

TABLE 41

PLAN OF FIELD SHOWING LOCATION OF TREATMENTS AND CORRESPONDING YIELDS,
FOR A PARTIALLY CONFOUNDED 2 × 2 × 2 EXPERIMENT

Replication No.	Treatment	Yield	Treatment	Yield	Treatment	Yield	Treatment	Yield	
	NK	159	P	153	O	145	K	189	
	O	179	NPK	202	PK	191	P	272	
I	PK	135	N	153	NK	300	N	160	
	NP	130	K	182	NP	240	NPK	305	
		603		690		876		926	3,095
	NPK	155	N	191	O	226	P	266	
	NP	129	NK	138	K	159	NK	300	
II	K	151	P	188	NPK	240	PK	233	
	O	159	PK	210	NP	182	N	278	
		594		727		807		1077	3,205
	P	154	K	143	P	186	N	209	
	NK	77	NP	119	NPK	173	K	93	
III	O	92	N	115	O	170	PK	224	
	NPK	128	PK	179	NK	213	NP	245	
		451		556		742		771	2,520
	N	113	P	136	PK	182	K	293	
	PK	127	NK	197	O	175	NK	226	
IV	NPK	185	K	182	NPK	156	NP	248	
	O	148	NP	212	N	183	P	269	
		573		727		696		1036	3,032
									11,852

Table 41 gives the location of the treatments in the field and the corresponding yields. The latter were taken from uniformity data as the results from an actual experiment were not available. Note that the replicate numbers (actually two replicates) correspond with the numbers given opposite the expansion of the interactions on page 163. Thus in replicate I the triple interaction $N \times P \times K$ is confounded with blocks, and so forth for the other interactions in the remaining replications. Within each block the treatments are assigned to the plots at random.

In Table 42 the treatment totals are arranged in a convenient form for the calculation of sums of squares. For example, in calculating the triple interaction

TABLE 42

TREATMENT TOTALS REQUIRED FOR CALCULATION
OF SUMS OF SQUARES

Treatment	All Replications	Minus Replication I	Minus Replication II	Minus Replication III	Minus Replication IV
O	1294	970	909	1032	971
N	1402	1089	933	1078	1106
P	1624	1199	1170	1284	1219
K	1392	1021	1082	1156	917
NP	1505	1135	1194	1141	1045
NK	1610	1151	1172	1320	1187
PK	1481	1155	1038	1078	1172
NPK	1544	1037	1149	1243	1203

$N \times P \times K$ we must use the totals from the replicates in which this interaction is not confounded. These are given in the third column, and we find

$$N \times P \times K = (1021 + 1037 + 1199 + 1089 - 970 - 1135 - 1155 - 1151)^2/48 = 88$$

Similarly the interaction $P \times K$ is calculated from the totals in the sixth column

$$P \times K = (1219 + 917 + 1045 + 1187 - 971 - 1172 - 1106 - 1203)^2/48 = 147$$

The main effects are of course calculated from all the replicates, so we make use of the totals in the second column.

TABLE 43

COMPLETE ANALYSIS FOR PARTIALLY CONFOUNDED
$2 \times 2 \times 2$ EXPERIMENT

	Sums of Squares	DF	Mean Square
Blocks..............	112,462	15	7,497
N..................	1,139	1	1,139
P..................	3,249	1	3,249
K..................	638	1	638
$N \times P$.............	9	1	9
$N \times K$.............	3,781	1	3,781
$P \times K$.............	147	1	147
$N \times P \times K$.........	88	1	88
Error..............	61,895	41	1,510
Total.............	183,408	63	

11. Splitting up Degrees of Freedom into Orthogonal Components.
Before considering the problem of confounding in experiments of a more
complex type, the student should acquaint himself with the methods
of separating effects representing more than 1 degree of freedom into
component parts that are mutually independent and therefore may be
separately estimated from the data.   Thus if we have 3 levels of nitrogen
in a fertilizer experiment, there are 2 degrees of freedom representing
the effect of nitrogen.   These 2 degrees of freedom may be separated
with their appropriate sums of squares in an infinite number of ways,
but unless the separation is a purely formal one we will probably wish
to separate them in some way such that they will represent definite facts
relative to the interpretation of the experiment.   In the case of the 3
levels of nitrogen N_1, N_2, and N_3, the 2 degrees of freedom can be
expressed by

(a) $N_3 - N_1$

(b) $2N_2 - N_1 - N_3$

and in this form (a) represents the linear effect of N on yield, and (b) the
quadratic effect.   If the yields are represented graphically, (b) will be
zero if the 3 points lie exactly on a straight line.   These two expressions
merely bring out the fact that any 2 points can be fitted by a straight line
function, and any 3 points by a quadratic function.   Any other division
of the degrees of freedom that we might make would probably not have
as valuable a meaning as this one, although if one felt quite certain that
N_3 was a decided overdose of nitrogen one might wish to measure the
linear effect by $N_2 - N_1$, and the quadratic effect by $2N_3 - N_1 - N_2$.
In general, however, the expressions such as (a) and (b) are the most
useful.

If we have 4 levels of nitrogen the 3 degrees of freedom may be
divided:

(c) $3N_4 + N_3 - N_2 - 3N_1$ Linear term

(d) $N_4 - N_3 - N_2 + N_1$ Quadratic term

(e) $N_4 - 3N_3 + 3N_2 - N_1$ Cubic term

The rule for writing out the expressions for the division of degrees of
freedom is to see to it that in each expression the sum of the coefficients is
zero, and for any pair of expressions the sum of the products of the

corresponding coefficients is zero. Thus, in the set immediately above, the sums of the coefficients are

(c) $\qquad$ $3 + 1 - 1 - 3 = 0$

(d) $\qquad$ $1 - 1 - 1 + 1 = 0$

(e) $\qquad$ $1 - 3 + 3 - 1 = 0$

Then multiplying the coefficients:

$(c \times d)$ $\qquad$ $3 - 1 + 1 - 3 = 0$

$(c \times e)$ $\qquad$ $3 - 3 - 3 + 3 = 0$

$(d \times e)$ $\qquad$ $1 + 3 - 3 - 1 = 0$

We must remember, however, that if we wish to write the polynomial expressions as has been done here there is only one set that can be written.

The sum of squares for any one of the above expressions may be calculated by means of a simple rule. For example, if we have the expressions (a) and (b) the sums of squares are

(a) $\dfrac{1}{2k} (N_3 - N_1)^2$ $\qquad\qquad$ (b) $\dfrac{1}{6k} (2N_2 - N_1 - N_3)^2$

where the numerical portion of the divisor comes from summing the squares of the coefficients within the bracket. The value of k comes from the number of units entering into each subtotal. For example, in (b), N_1, N_2, and N_3 may represent subtotals from 8 plots, whence the complete divisor is 48.

An actual example of the division of 3 degrees of freedom according to the scheme outlined above is given by Yates (17). The figures are for response to nitrogen, and the results of the analysis are reproduced below:

	DF	SS
Linear term.............	1	19,536.4
Quadratic term..........	1	480.5
Cubic term.............	1	3.6
Total...............	3	20,020.5

When compared with the error of the experiment, the quadratic term turned out to be insignificant, and the cubic term was below expectation. Undoubtedly, this type of result is quite usual in agricultural experiments, and since we can separate out not only main effects in the above manner but also interaction effects, it follows that if a portion of the degrees of freedom for an interaction effect is to be sacrificed by confounding it is desirable in general to sacrifice that portion that is least likely to be significant. At any rate, it may be wise to ensure that at least the interaction between linear effects may be partially recovered from the confounded experiment.

If the interaction between nitrogen at 2 levels and potash at 2 levels can be represented by $(N_2 - N_1)(K_2 - K_1)$ it follows that, if there are 3 levels of nitrogen, the interaction $N \times K$ can be broken up into two parts:

$$(K_2 - K_1)(N_3 - N_1) \quad \text{and} \quad (K_2 - K_1)(2N_2 - N_1 - N_3)$$

where the second expression represents the interaction of the quadratic effect of nitrogen with potash. This point may be more obvious if we consider $(2N_2 - N_1 - N_3)$ as representing deviations from linear regression instead of the quadratic response, and hence the interaction may be written as K regression $\times$ N deviation or $K_r \times N_d$. Now if we have 3 levels of potash as well as 3 levels of nitrogen the 4 degrees of freedom for the interaction $N \times K$ may be broken up as follows:

$N_r \times K_r$	$(N_3 - N_1)(K_3 - K_1)$	1 DF
$N_r \times K_d$	$(N_3 - N_1)(2K_2 - K_1 - K_3)$	1 DF
$N_d \times K_r$	$(2N_2 - N_1 - N_3)(K_3 - K_1)$	1 DF
$N_d \times K_d$	$(2N_2 - N_1 - N_3)(2K_2 - K_1 - K_3)$	1 DF
$N \times K$		4 DF

and it may be of interest to do this from the standpoint of obtaining complete information with respect to the interaction. Yates (17) has given a useful table for calculating the sums of squares, which is reproduced below in Table 44.

TABLE 44

GUIDE FOR CALCULATING SUMS OF SQUARES FOR THE
INTERACTIONS IN A 3 $\times$ 3 TABLE

$N_r \times K_r$			$N_r \times K_d$			$N_d \times K_r$			$N_d \times K_d$		
K_1	K_2	K_3	K_1	K_2	K_3	K_1	K_2	K_3	K_1	K_2	K_3
N_1 +1		−1	N_1 −1	+2	−1	N_1 −1		+1	N_1 +1	−2	+1
N_2			N_2			N_2 +2		−2	N_2 −2	+4	−2
N_3 −1		+1	N_3 +1	−2	+1	N_3 −1		+1	N_3 +1	−2	+1

Divisor $4k$ $12k$ $12k$ $36k$

k = Number of units in each cell.

To use the table it is necessary to set up a table of subtotals in the same form as the above squares. The subtotals are added or subtracted according to the signs in the appropriate table. Thus if the subtotals are represented by

$$x_1 \qquad x_2 \qquad x_3$$
$$y_1 \qquad y_2 \qquad y_3$$
$$z_1 \qquad z_2 \qquad z_3$$

we get the sum of squares for $N_d \times K_r$ by

$$\frac{1}{12k} (2y_1 + x_3 + z_3 - x_1 - z_1 - 2y_3)^2$$

In certain cases it may not be necessary to divide up the degrees of freedom into orthogonal components that have any definite meaning, in which case we refer to the division as a purely formal one. A 3×3 table, for example, may be represented as follows:

	P_1	P_2	P_3
N_1	11	12	13
N_2	21	22	23
N_3	31	32	33

and from knowledge that has been derived from a study of the properties of the Latin square, Fisher, (2), it can be shown that the 4 degrees of freedom representing the interaction $N \times P$ can be split up into two orthogonal components by making up totals from the diagonals of the above square. Thus 2 degrees of freedom of the interaction is represented by the differences between the totals $(11 + 22 + 33)$, $(21 + 32 + 13)$, $(31 + 12 + 23)$, and the other 2 by the differences between the totals $(11 + 32 + 23)$, $(21 + 12 + 33)$, $(31 + 22 + 13)$. As a matter of fact this provides a very useful method of calculating the interaction in a 3×3 table as it is a direct method and the total sum of squares calculated independently from the same table may be used to obtain a perfect check on all the calculations.[1] The division of the 4 degrees of freedom is, however, purely formal. In other words, we would expect that on the average the two components would give us equal estimates of the interaction variance.

[1] Note that the second set of totals can be obtained most easily by setting up the numbers in the first three totals in the form of another square, and taking from this square the same diagonals as were used in the first instance.

12. Confounding in a 3 × 3 × 3 Experiment. We shall now consider the possibilities of confounding in a 3 × 3 × 3 experiment. The 3 main factors can be represented by N, K, and P, and since each of these occurs at 3 levels there are 27 different combinations. The 26 degrees of freedom for treatments can be subdivided at first as follows:

$$
\left.\begin{array}{ll}
N & 2\ DF \\
K & 2\ DF \\
P & 2\ DF
\end{array}\right\}\text{Main effects 6 }DF
$$

$$
\left.\begin{array}{ll}
N \times K & 4\ DF \\
N \times P & 4\ DF \\
K \times P & 4\ DF
\end{array}\right\}\text{Simple interactions 12 }DF
$$

$$
N \times K \times P \qquad 8\ DF \quad \text{Triple interaction 8 }DF
$$

Now if we wish to conserve the main effects and the simple interactions we must have at least 9 plots in each block. That is, the 3 levels of each fertilizer must each be represented by 3 plots, and the 9 combinations of each pair of fertilizers must each be represented by 1 plot. The required combinations to fulfill these conditions are given by a 3 × 3 Latin square in which the rows may be taken to represent the 3 levels of nitrogen, the columns the 3 levels of potash, and the Latin letters (here replaced by numbers) the 3 levels of phosphate. R. A. Fisher, in introducing this solution, points out that there are only 12 solutions of this 3 × 3 square and that these 12 fall into 4 sets such that in any one set the other 2 may be generated by cyclic substitution of the numbers in the square. The entire 12 solutions are reproduced below.

	a			b			c		
I	1 2 3			2 3 1			3 1 2		
	2 3 1			3 1 2			1 2 3		
	3 1 2			1 2 3			2 3 1		
II	1 3 2			2 1 3			3 2 1		
	3 2 1			1 3 2			2 1 3		
	2 1 3			3 2 1			1 3 2		
III	1 2 3			2 3 1			3 1 2		
	3 1 2			1 2 3			2 3 1		
	2 3 1			3 1 2			1 2 3		
IV	1 3 2			2 1 3			3 2 1		
	2 1 3			3 2 1			1 3 2		
	3 2 1			1 3 2			2 1 3		

To make the meaning of these squares perfectly clear, suppose that we consider the treatments represented by the square I (a). These are, $N_1K_1P_1$, $N_1K_2P_2$, $N_1K_3P_3$, $N_2K_1P_2$, $N_2K_2P_3$, etc. In any one replication we must have all the treatments of one complete set such as I, II, III, or IV, and within the replication the division of the treatments into blocks is according to the division of the sets into (a), (b), and (c).   In a single replication we have 2 degrees of freedom for blocks, and these must represent 2 degrees of freedom of the triple interaction that have been confounded, as we have seen to it that the main effects and the simple interactions have all been conserved.   It follows also that it is impossible, if the main effects and the simple interactions are conserved, to confound more than 2 out of the 8 degrees of freedom of the triple interaction.   Such being the case, we shall still have, after confounding, 6 degrees of freedom for the triple interaction, which we may use to test the significance of the residual portion of this effect.

The actual procedure of confounding in an experiment of this kind is to set up the treatments and divide them into blocks according to one of the cyclic sets.   The same division of the treatments into blocks is retained throughout the remaining replications.   In analyzing the results, if set I has been used for confounding, then sets II, III, and IV are used to build up the treatment totals from which the sum of squares for the triple interaction is calculated.   The details of this are given in Example 36.

13. Partial Confounding in a 3 × 3 × 3 Experiment.   By the methods described above we are able to divide the 8 degrees of freedom for the triple interaction into 4 sets of 2 that are mutually independent and therefore may be separately estimated from the data.   But these sets represent purely formal differences, and although we confound only 2 of them and conserve 6, we are not able to separate out particular effects such as that represented by $N_r \times K_r \times P_r$ for particular study. To do this we must adopt the method of partial confounding which results from using each of the cyclic sets once, one for each replication. We require therefore a minimum of 4 replications.   Space is inadequate here to go into detail regarding the method of separating out the particular components, but the student interested in these further aspects of confounding will be able to obtain further information from R. A. Fisher's "The Design of Experiments," and from the monograph by F. Yates, "Factorial Experimentation."

Example 36.   A Confounded 3 × 3 × 3 Experiment.   In the preparation of this example, data from a uniformity trial have been used.   It serves therefore merely to show the technique of setting up and analyzing a 3 × 3 × 3 experiment in which 2 degrees of freedom from the triple interaction have been confounded with blocks.

As indicated in Table 45 giving the treatment numbers and the corresponding yields, the distribution of the treatments into the 3 blocks of each replication is according to cyclic set I as described above.   In order to abbreviate, only the subscript numbers of the treatments are given, it being assumed that the three ingredients such as NKP are in the same order in each case. Within the blocks the treatments are, of course, randomized.

Table 46 is obtained by collecting the plot yields from Table 45. It is used for calculating the main effects and the simple interactions. At the foot of this table are given the treatment totals from which the sum of squares for the 6 degrees of freedom for the triple interaction is calculated. These treatment totals may be obtained very quickly by the combined use of the cyclic sets as given on page 170 and the 3×3 tables for N and K, one for each level of P. Knowing that set I has been used for confounding, we obtain our treatment totals for calculating the triple interaction, from the application of sets II, III, and IV, to the data given in Table 46. For example, taking set II we note that the 1's in group (a) correspond in Table 46 (a) with 1604, 1523, and 1912; the 2's correspond in Table 46 (b) with 1893, 2030, and 1845; and the 3's in Table 46 (c) with 1741, 1838, and 1917. Adding all these values, we obtain 16,303. Then to obtain the next total the same process is repeated, using the square indicated by II (b), and finally the third square, II (c), gives the third total. The sets III and IV are then used in a similar manner to obtain the remaining totals. The sum of squares is calculated for each set of 3 totals and these are added to give the sum of squares for the 6 degrees of freedom of the triple interaction.

Mainly as an exercise, the sums of squares for the individual degrees of freedom as represented by the regression and deviation from regression effects have all been calculated and are shown in the analysis of variance Table 47. These calculations are very simple if one makes use of Yates's diagram as given on page 168. A few of the calculations are reproduced below for further guidance:

$$N_r \qquad (15{,}393 - 16{,}900)^2/144 \qquad\qquad\qquad = 15{,}771.17$$
$$N_r \times K_r \; (5403 + 5706 - 5376 - 4894)^2/96 \qquad = 7{,}332.51$$
$$N_d \times P_r \; (2 \times 5244 + 5057 + 5596 - 4812 - 5667 - 2 \times 5297)^2/288 = \quad 16.06$$
$$N_d \times K_d \; (5403 + 5376 + 4 \times 5436 + 4894 + 5706 - 2 \times 5520$$
$$- 2 \times 5096 - 2 \times 5818 - 2 \times 5074)^2/864 = \quad 13.25$$

METHODS FOR TESTING A LARGE NUMBER OF VARIETIES

14. General Principles. In factorial experiments, when the total number of combinations is fairly large, we have seen that greater accuracy can be obtained by confounding with blocks certain of the degrees of freedom for the higher-order interactions. In variety experiments the numbers are frequently quite large and we again meet with the problem of insufficient accuracy owing to the large size of the blocks. In order to overcome this difficulty Yates has developed methods that, by a procedure analogous to confounding in factorial experiments, enables us to divide up the replications into much smaller blocks, and these are used as error control units. Since the small blocks contain only a fraction of the total number of varieties, they are referred to as *incomplete blocks*. Yates (20) in a preliminary examination of uniformity data concluded that incomplete block experiments would give increases in efficiency over randomized blocks of 20 to 50%. Goulden (6) arrived at practically the same conclusion after a fairly extensive study.

TABLE 45

TREATMENT NUMBERS AND CORRESPONDING PLOT YIELDS FOR 3 × 3 × 3 EXPERIMENT. THE SAME TWO DEGREES OF FREEDOM FROM THE TRIPLE INTERACTION CONFOUNDED IN ALL REPLICATES

Treatment No.	Yield	Treatment No.	Yield	Treatment No.	Yield	Treatment No.	Yield	Treatment No.	Yield	Treatment No.	Yield
212	159	131	153	121	145	111	189	232	153	233	210
321	179	311	202	233	191	122	272	112	226	132	225
231	135	232	153	323	300	212	160	131	122	121	290
133	130	333	182	331	240	313	305	311	281	312	262
313	155	213	191	211	226	223	266	213	334	211	369
111	129	112	138	312	159	321	300	333	208	331	150
223	151	221	188	222	240	231	233	221	276	113	267
332	159	123	210	113	182	332	278	322	355	222	338
122	154	322	143	132	186	133	209	123	247	323	323
Block totals	1351		1560		1869		2212		2202		2434
122	77	213	119	233	173	133	93	131	303	132	271
313	92	112	115	132	170	321	224	221	221	331	251
133	128	333	179	113	213	332	245	213	216	211	199
321	113	123	136	323	182	313	293	232	319	121	129
231	127	311	197	312	175	122	226	311	269	323	237
111	185	131	182	121	156	231	248	123	221	113	282
212	148	322	212	211	183	223	269	333	359.	312	303
332	215	221	120	222	138	111	228	322	319	233	300
223	132	232	162	331	192	212	326	112	314	222	247
Block totals	1217		1422		1582		2152		2541		2219
231	102	131	105	121	154	223	154	112	233	132	269
212	143	333	227	233	145	133	197	311	297	323	283
313	171	123	218	312	214	332	197	232	318	312	179
321	190	112	180	331	219	321	227	131	250	233	191
111	159	213	165	211	186	212	222	221	227	121	137
122	279	232	173	132	187	111	230	123	197	331	179
223	125	311	156	323	148	231	204	322	161	211	162
332	150	322	212	222	309	122	201	213	228	113	202
133	104	221	234	113	246	313	251	333	247	222	250
Block totals	1423		1670		1808		1883		2158		1852
313	124	213	276	323	276	212	228	221	260	233	388
133	136	333	269	132	225	313	295	311	166	222	228
122	297	131	255	331	343	111	304	213	309	323	244
212	265	221	164	233	145	231	212	333	246	121	324
223	209	112	264	113	258	122	320	131	309	211	421
111	180	311	277	121	194	133	325	322	252	113	344
332	259	232	283	222	280	321	464	112	335	331	336
321	215	322	259	312	304	332	376	232	247	312	249
231	262	123	243	211	285	223	410	123	269	132	360
Block totals	1947		2290		2310		2934		2393		2894

TABLE 46

TREATMENT TOTALS COLLECTED FROM TABLE 45 FOR CALCULATION
OF SUMS OF SQUARES

		K_1	K_2	K_3		
(a)	P_1 $\begin{matrix} N_1 \\ N_2 \\ N_3 \end{matrix}$	1,604	1,529	1,679	4,812	
		2,031	1,690	1,523	5,244	$k = 8$
		1,845	1,912	1,910	5,667	
		5,480	5,131	5,112	15,723	

		K_1	K_2	K_3		
(b)	P_2 $\begin{matrix} N_1 \\ N_2 \\ N_3 \end{matrix}$	1,805	1,826	1,893	5,524	
		1,651	2,030	1,808	5,489	$k = 8$
		1,845	1,913	1,879	5,637	
		5,301	5,769	5,580	16,650	

		K_1	K_2	K_3		
(c)	P_3 $\begin{matrix} N_1 \\ N_2 \\ N_3 \end{matrix}$	1,994	1,741	1,322	5,057	
		1,838	1,716	1,743	5,297	$k = 8$
		1,686	1,993	1,917	5,596	
		5,518	5,450	4,982	15,950	

		K_1	K_2	K_3		
$(P_1 + P_2 + P_3)$	$\begin{matrix} N_1 \\ N_2 \\ N_3 \end{matrix}$	5,403	5,096	4,894	15,393	
		5,520	5,436	5,074	16,030	$k = 24$
		5,376	5,818	5,706	16,900	
		16,299	16,350	15,674	48,323	

		K_1	K_2	K_3		
$(N_1 + N_2 + N_3)$	$\begin{matrix} P_1 \\ P_2 \\ P_3 \end{matrix}$	5,480	5,131	5,112	15,723	
		5,301	5,769	5,580	16,650	$k = 24$
		5,518	5,450	4,982	15,950	
		16,299	16,350	15,674	48,323	

		P_1	P_2	P_3		
$(K_1 + K_2 + K_3)$	$\begin{matrix} N_1 \\ N_2 \\ N_3 \end{matrix}$	4,812	5,524	5,057	15,393	
		5,244	5,489	5,297	16,030	$k = 24$
		5,667	5,637	5,596	16,900	
		15,723	16,650	15,950	48,323	

		P_1	P_2	P_3		
$(N_1 + N_2 + N_3)$	$\begin{matrix} K_1 \\ K_2 \\ K_3 \end{matrix}$	5,480	5,301	5,518	16,299	
		5,131	5,769	5,450	16,350	$k = 24$
		5,112	5,580	4,982	15,674	
		15,723	16,650	15,950	48,323	

	II	III	IV	
(a)	16,303	15,836	15,831	
(b)	15,720	16,506	15,764	$k = 72$
(c)	16,300	15,981	16,728	
	48,323	48,323	48,323	

TABLE 47

ANALYSIS OF VARIANCE FOR $3 \times 3 \times 3$ EXPERIMENT SHOWING SUMS OF SQUARES FOR INDIVIDUAL TREATMENT DEGREES OF FREEDOM

	DF	SS	SS	DF	MS	F	5% Point
Blocks........	23	548,407	548,407	23	23,844	8.83	1.59
N_r...........	1	15,771 }	15,897	2	7,948	2.94	3.05
N_d...........	1	126 }					
P_r...........	1	358 }	6,485	2	3,243	1.20	3.05
P_d...........	1	6,128 }					
K_r...........	1	2,713 }	3,936	2	1,968	0.73	3.05
K_d...........	1	1,223 }					
$N_r \times P_r$.......	1	1,040 }					
$N_r \times P_d$.....	1	4,737 }	5,909	4	1,477	0.55	2.43
$N_d \times P_r$......	1	16 }					
$N_d \times P_d$.....	1	116 }					
$N_r \times K_r$.....	1	7,332 }					
$N_r \times K_d$.....	1	1,508 }	10,619	4	2,655	0.98	2.43
$N_d \times K_r$......	1	1,765 }					
$N_d \times K_d$......	1	13 }					
$P_r \times K_r$.......	1	294 }					
$P_r \times K_d$.....	1	1,850 }	11,357	4	2,839	1.05	2.43
$P_d \times K_r$......	1	7,422 }					
$P_d \times K_d$......	1	1,791 }					
$N \times P \times K$...	2	3,131 }					
	2	3,452 }	14,631	6	2,438	0.90	2.15
	2	8,048 }					
Error........	168	453,509	453,509	168	2,699		
	215	1,070,750					

15. Incomplete Block Experiments. There are a number of different types of incomplete block experiments, and only those are described here that would seem to be of the greatest practical value in agronomic tests. The type which can probably be regarded as the most elementary is known as the *two-dimensional quasi-factorial* with *two groups of sets*. By extending this type to three groups of sets we have a somewhat greater degree of complexity, and this complexity continues to increase with the number of groups of sets until we reach the point of using *all possible* groups of sets, wherein the entire process of analysis suddenly becomes very much simplified. The latter type may be referred to as a *symmetrical incomplete block* experiment. Quasi-factorial experiments of the *three-dimensional* type are also possible, and one of the simplest of these will be described.

In discussing the general principles involved in incomplete block experiments we shall consider an hypothetical experiment with only 9 varieties. With such a small number of varieties it would probably not be worth while to use these methods, but a small example of this kind will be quite sufficient to illustrate the general principles. First, we take 9 numbers to represent the varieties and write them down in the form of a square. These are two-figure numbers, the first figure representing the row and the second the column of the square.

$$
\begin{array}{ccc}
11 & 12 & 13 \\
21 & 22 & 23 \\
31 & 32 & 33
\end{array}
$$

If we suppose now that this square represents, instead of 9 different varieties, 9 combinations of 2 factors at 3 levels as in a simple 3×3 factorial experiment, the degrees of freedom can be divided as follows:

A (factor for which levels are indicated by first figure of two-figure numbers) 2 *DF*
B (factor for which levels are indicated by second figure of two-figure numbers) 2 *DF*
$A \times B$ (interaction)   4 *DF*

Furthermore, since the 4 *DF* for the interaction can be separated into two orthogonal components, each represented by 2 *DF*, the total of 8 *DF* can be split up into 4 pairs. Then if the 9 combinations making up a complete replication are divided into 3 blocks, either one of the above pairs of degrees of freedom may be confounded with blocks. If we should decide to confound the A factor with blocks, the degrees of freedom for one replication will be apportioned as follows:

$$
\begin{array}{ll}
\text{Blocks} \dots \dots \dots \dots \dots & 2\ DF \\
B \dots \dots \dots \dots \dots \dots & 2\ DF \\
A \times B \dots \dots \dots \dots \dots & 4\ DF
\end{array}
$$

and the method of confounding would be merely to put the treatments together in the same block that occur in the rows of the square given above. Similarly the B factor may be confounded by putting the treatments in the same block that occur in the columns of the square. Then from our knowledge of the properties of a Latin square it is clear that if the interaction $A \times B$ is to be confounded it is only necessary to put the treatments together in the same block that occur in the diagonals of the square. In one replication we can confound only 2 out of the 4 degrees of freedom. For example, in one replication the arrangement of the treatments in the blocks might be as follows:

Block 1	11	22	33
Block 2	21	32	13
Block 3	31	12	23

and the degrees of freedom will be divided in the following manner:

Blocks	2 *DF*
A	2 *DF*
B	2 *DF*
A × *B*	2 *DF*

Alternative to the above scheme 2 degrees of freedom from the interaction may be confounded with blocks by this arrangement:

Block 1	11	32	23
Block 2	21	12	33
Block 3	31	22	13

Finally, it works out that in each replication a different pair of degrees of freedom may be confounded with blocks, in which case the analysis of variance will be of the following form:

Blocks	11 *DF*
A	2 *DF*
B	2 *DF*
A × *B*	4 *DF*
Error	16 *DF*

By a process of partial confounding all the degrees of freedom for the 9 treatment combinations can be recovered, and at the same time error control has been improved by the use of smaller blocks. The loss of information due to partial confounding is seen to be exactly $\frac{1}{4}$, since each pair of degrees of freedom has been confounded in 1 replication and conserved in 3. In other words, both the main factors and the interaction are determined with $\frac{3}{4}$ of the precision that would have resulted if there had not been any confounding. The presumption, of course, is that the error will be sufficiently reduced by confounding to more than make up for the loss in precision.

Returning now to the testing of 9 different varieties, it should be obvious that, if the varieties are designated by numbers and arranged in a square as above, we can go through the same procedure of partial confounding as has been outlined above for a 3 × 3 factorial experiment, and theoretically the same increase in accuracy due to confounding will be obtained. The method of analysis will also be clear from these considerations, as we work it out in the first place as though it is a factorial experiment and, after finding the sums of squares for the imaginary factors and their interaction, we combine these to form the variety sum of squares.

The fact that the variety numbers are first arranged in the form of a square simulating a two-factor experiment is the basis of the term " two-dimensional." The number of groups of sets is based on the number of groups of degrees of freedom that are confounded with blocks. In the quasi-factorial 3 × 3 experiment, for example, the 8 DF for the 9 treatments can be divided orthogonally into 4 pairs, and if we confound only 2 of these pairs, the experiment is said to consist of " two groups of sets." With 9 varieties we have seen that 4 pairs of degrees of freedom can be confounded, in which case we might refer to the experiment as one with "four groups of sets," but as pointed out above it is usual to refer to experiments of this type as symmetrical incomplete block experiments.

In a quasi-factorial experiment with only two groups of sets it will be obvious that all comparisons are not made with the same precision. Suppose, for example, that the blocks are made up out of the rows and columns of the square, in which case the analogous factorial experiment would be outlined as follows:

$$
\begin{array}{ll}
\text{Blocks} \dots\dots\dots & 5\ DF \text{ (assuming 2 replicates only)} \\
A \dots\dots\dots\dots & 2\ DF \\
B \dots\dots\dots\dots & 2\ DF \\
A \times B \dots\dots\dots & 4\ DF \\
\text{Error} \dots\dots\dots & 4\ DF \\
\end{array}
$$

In which the imaginary factors A and B are confounded in one replicate and conserved in the other, while the interaction $A \times B$ is conserved in both replicates. The main factors A and B are determined with only $\frac{1}{2}$ the precision with which the interaction is determined, and transferring these ideas to a variety experiment it becomes clear that the varieties that occur in the same row and in the same column are compared more accurately than those that do not occur at all in the same block.

Another point that we should note here is that in estimating the result for any one treatment combination of the partially confounded factorial experiment, or of one variety in the quasi-factorial experiment, it will be necessary to make a correction for the blocks in which they occur. The actual totals are partially confounded with blocks. One variety may occur mainly in low-yielding blocks and another one in high-yielding blocks, and therefore the actual yield of the first variety must be increased and the yield of the second variety lowered, in order to make the two variety yields comparable. The details of this method of correction are given below.

16. Two-Dimensional Quasi-Factorials with Two Groups of Sets.
Assuming that only 9 varieties are to be tested, the first step is to take
9 numbers to represent the varieties, as pointed out above, and arrange
them in the form of a square. The next step is to arrange the varieties
in sets according to the rows and columns of the square. These are
given below and the first group of sets is referred to as group X and the
second group of sets as group Y.

Group X				Group Y		
11	12	13		11	21	31
21	22	23		12	22	32
31	32	33		13	23	33

The varieties in the sets are those that are assigned to the incomplete
blocks, and each group makes up a complete replication. The varieties
occurring in the same block are, of course, those that are between the
same set of parallel lines in the above figure. The groups can now be
repeated as many times as we wish in order to bring up the replicates
to the required number. The varieties are randomized within each
block, but the blocks themselves may be placed in any order.[1]

Figure 11 illustrates diagrammatically the set up of the experiment
assuming 4 complete replications. The yields may be arranged in a
form somewhat similar to this for convenience in calculation. After
setting up the original yields they must be combined for each group and
then for both groups. The marginal totals are then obtained for each
group and for both groups combined, and we are ready to proceed with
the calculation of the sums of squares and the corrected variety means.

The calculation of the variety sum of squares follows from the analogy
to a factorial experiment.

DF

In Group Y	$A = \Sigma(Y_{u.}^2)/np - Y_{..}^2/np^2$	$p-1$
In Group X	$B = \Sigma(X_{.v}^2)/np - X_{..}^2/np^2$	$p-1$

$$\text{Group } X + \text{Group } Y(A \times B) = \Sigma(T_{uv}^2)/2n - \Sigma(T_{u.}^2)/2np$$
$$- \Sigma(T_{.v}^2)/2np + T_{...}^2/2np^2 \qquad (p-1)^2$$

---

[1] In certain cases the experimenter may decide, even after conducting the experiment as a quasi-factorial, to use the actual yields or some other character of the
varieties, without correction. For example, he may wish to make quality or other
tests on composite samples made up from all the replicates. For this purpose it is
somewhat better to have the incomplete blocks randomized within each replication.

Group X

11	12	13		11	12	13
21	22	23		21	22	23
31	32	33		31	32	33

Group Y

11	12	13		11	12	13
21	22	23		21	22	23
31	32	33		31	32	33

$X_u.$

x_{11}	x_{12}	x_{13}	$X_1.$
x_{21}	x_{22}	x_{23}	$X_2.$
x_{31}	x_{32}	x_{33}	$X_3.$
$X_{.v}$	$X_{.1}$ $X_{.2}$ $X_{.3}$		$X_{..}$

$Y_u.$

y_{11}	y_{12}	y_{13}	$Y_1.$
y_{21}	y_{22}	y_{23}	$Y_2.$
y_{31}	y_{32}	y_{33}	$Y_3.$
$Y_{.v}$	$Y_{.1}$ $Y_{.2}$ $Y_{.3}$		$Y_{..}$

$T_u.$

T_{11}	T_{12}	T_{13}	$T_1.$
T_{21}	T_{22}	T_{23}	$T_2.$
T_{31}	T_{32}	T_{33}	$T_3.$
$T_{.v}$	$T_{.1}$ $T_{.2}$ $T_{.3}$		$T_{..}$

Fig. 11.   Representation of a miniature example of a two-dimensional quasi-factorial experiment with two groups of sets.

where p is the number of varieties in one set and n is the number of repetitions of each group.

Yates (20) gives a direct method of calculating the sum of squares for varieties which is probably quicker than the one used above.   Yates's formula is

$$\text{Varieties } (SS) = \Sigma(T_{uv}^2)/2n + \Sigma(X_u. - Y_u.)^2/2np + \Sigma(X_{.v} - Y_{.v})^2/2np$$
$$- (X.. - Y..)^2/2np^2 - [\Sigma(X_u^2.) + \Sigma(Y_{.v}^2)]/np$$

We next calculate the total sum of squares for all the plots and for the blocks, and obtain the error sum of squares by subtraction.   The summarized analysis is of the form

	DF
Blocks.............	$2np - 1$
Varieties...........	$p^2 - 1$
Error..............	$(p - 1)(2np - p - 1)$
Total..........	$2np^2 - 1$

Just as in the factorial experiments that have been confounded all comparisons must be made within blocks.   This means that to compare 2 varieties directly we cannot use the actual variety totals but must prepare for these varieties ratings based on their behavior as compared to other varieties in the same blocks.   The least squares method gives us as the best rating for any variety uv, the following expression which we shall refer to as a corrected variety mean.

$$t_{uv} = \frac{T_{uv}}{2n} + \frac{1}{2np}\,(X_{.v} - Y_{.v}) + \frac{1}{2np}\,(Y_{u.} - X_{u.})$$

If a large table of yields is to be corrected it may save time to set up the corresponding portions of the correction in the margins of the table.   If

we let $C_{.v} = \dfrac{1}{2np}\,(X_{.v} - Y_{.v})$ and $C_{u.} = \dfrac{1}{2np}\,(Y_{u.} - X_{u.})$, then $C_{.1}$ will be

the portion to be added to all the variety means in the first column, and $C_{1.}$ will be the portion to be added to all the variety means in the first row.

In this as in all other quasi-factorial arrangements the error variance must be multiplied by a factor depending on the type of experiment, to give the variance for comparing 2 varieties by their corrected means. If s^2 is the error variance, the variance of the difference between the corrected means of 2 varieties that occur in the same set is

$$V(t_{21} - t_{11}) = \frac{s^2}{n}\left(\frac{p+1}{p}\right)$$

For 2 varieties not having a set in common the variance of the difference is

$$V(t_{22} - t_{11}) = \frac{s^2}{n}\left(\frac{p+2}{p}\right)$$

The mean variance of all comparisons is

$$V_m = \frac{s^2}{n}\left(\frac{p+3}{p+1}\right)$$

and when p is not too small we may use the latter variance for all comparisons without appreciable error.

Example 37.   **Two-Dimensional Quasi-Factorial with Two Groups of Sets.** Using uniformity data and assuming a test of 25 varieties in 4 replications this example has been worked through in detail in order to show the methods of calculation. Setting up first the specifications of the test:

Varieties in each set (p)........................ $= 5$
Varieties $(v) = p^2$............................ $= 25$
Sets $(s) = 2p$................................. $= 10$
Replications of each group (n).................. $= 2$
Replications $(r) = 2n$......................... $= 4$
Blocks $(b) = 2np$............................. $= 20$
Total number of plots $(N) = 2np^2$............. $= 100$

The variety numbers are first written down in the form of a square:

$$
\begin{array}{ccccc}
11 & 12 & 13 & 14 & 15 \\
21 & 22 & 23 & 24 & 25 \\
31 & 32 & 33 & 34 & 35 \\
41 & 42 & 43 & 44 & 45 \\
51 & 52 & 53 & 54 & 55
\end{array}
$$

and the 10 sets in 2 groups of 5 taken from the rows and columns of the square. The varieties in these sets are then randomized in the blocks as indicated in Table 49. Here the groups are repeated twice so that $(n = 2)$ and $(r = 4)$, and the groups are separated in the field. It might be wise if there is a marked difference in variability in different parts of the field to randomize the blocks over the whole field instead of keeping them together as complete replications, but in general this would seem to be unnecessary and it is a decided convenience from the standpoint of making observations on the plots to have all the plots in one replication together.

After obtaining the block totals and the grand total the next step is to set up Table 50, the construction of which should present no difficulty. Note that the marginal totals $X_{u.}$ and $Y_{.v}$ are those in which variety and block effects are confounded.

By the shortest method the sum of squares for varieties is calculated as follows—

$\Sigma(T_{uv}^2)/2n$...................... $=$ 1,961,637.50
$\Sigma(X_{u.} - Y_{u.})^2/2np$.............. $=$ 81,162.50
$\Sigma(X_{.v} - Y_{.v})^2/2np$.............. $=$ 117,817.50
$-(X_{..} - Y_{..})^2/2np^2$................ $= -$ 51,076.50
$-\{\Sigma(X_{u.}^2) + \Sigma(Y_{.v}^2)\}/np$........... $= -$2,058,800.00 (Groups + Sets + Mean)

Total = Varieties (SS)......... $=$ 50,741.50

The total sum of squares for all plots is 630,266.00 and for blocks is 467,586.00. Having obtained these, we can set up the analysis of variance.

TABLE 48

ANALYSIS OF VARIANCE

TWO DIMENSIONAL QUASI-FACTORIAL—TWO GROUPS OF SETS

	SS	DF	MS	F	5% Point
Blocks.........	467,586.00	19	24,609.8	12.3	1.78
Varieties.......	50,741.50	24	2,114.2	1.06	1.72
Error.........	111,938.50	56	1,998.9		
Total........	630,266.00	99			

In order to obtain the corrected variety yields we calculate

$$C_{.v} = \frac{1}{2np} (X_{.v} - Y_{.v}) \text{ for } v = 1, 2, 3, 4, 5$$

$$C_{u.} = \frac{1}{2np} (Y_{u.} - X_{u.}) \text{ for } u = 1, 2, 3, 4, 5$$

These are entered in the margins of a (5×5) table as in Table 51 and added to the actual means of corresponding cells in the table.

To obtain a further check on the sums of squares for varieties we can now calculate it in another way using the formula

$$\text{Varieties } (SS) = \Sigma(t_{uv} \cdot T_{uv}) - \Sigma(t_{u.} \cdot X_{u.}) - \Sigma(t_{.v} \cdot Y_{.v})$$

where $t_{1.}$, for example, is the mean of all the t_{uv} values in the first row of Table 51 and $t_{.1}$ is the mean of the first column.

To make comparisons between the corrected means we may if we wish to be exact take into consideration whether or not the varieties being compared occur in the same set. To compare varieties 21 and 22, for example, we calculate the variance according to the formula

$$V(t_{21} - t_{22}) = \frac{s^2}{n} \left(\frac{p+1}{p} \right) = \left(\frac{1998.9}{2} \times \frac{6}{5} \right) = 1199.3$$

$$SE(t_{21} - t_{22}) = \sqrt{1199.3} = 34.63$$

$$t^* \qquad = \frac{161.50 - 123.75}{34.63} = 1.09$$

To compare varieties 11 and 54 we would have

$$V(t_{11} - t_{54}) = \frac{s^2}{n} \left(\frac{p+2}{p} \right) = \left(\frac{1998.9}{2} \times \frac{7}{5} \right) = 1399.23$$

$$SE(t_{11} - t_{54}) = \sqrt{1399.23} = 37.41$$

$$t^* \qquad = \frac{135.25 - 170.25}{37.41} = 0.94$$

We would obviously not be very far wrong, even with a p value as low as 5, to use for all comparisons the *mean* variance for the difference between 2 varieties. This would be

$$V_m = \frac{s^2}{n} \left(\frac{p+3}{p+1} \right) = \left(\frac{1998.9}{2} \times \frac{8}{6} \right) = 1332.6$$

$$SE_m = \sqrt{1332.6} = 36.50$$

* The t used here is, of course, the statistic defined by R. A. Fisher in "Statistical Methods for Research Workers."

TABLE 49

POSITION OF VARIETIES IN THE FIELD AND CORRESPONDING PLOT YIELDS.
TWO-DIMENSIONAL QUASI-FACTORIAL EXPERIMENT
WITH TWO GROUPS OF SETS

Set No.	Variety No.	Yield	Variety No.	Yield	Variety No.	Yield	Variety No.	Yield	Variety No.	Yield	Block Totals
1y	31	215	21	300	51	255	41	185	11	145	1,100
2y	22	150	12	50	52	45	32	105	42	155	505
5y	55	125	35	30	15	65	25	130	45	55	405
4y	14	85	34	55	54	110	24	130	44	40	420
3y	53	45	43	45	13	60	23	15	33	−5	160
1y	11	210	21	290	41	325	31	230	51	220	1,275
2y	12	310	32	230	22	155	52	195	42	245	1,135
5y	15	315	45	215	55	160	25	285	35	230	1,205
3y	53	185	43	220	33	175	13	275	23	185	1,040
4y	14	130	24	190	34	160	44	110	54	155	745
1x	14	140	15	165	11	265	13	150	12	180	900
4x	41	190	42	135	45	100	43	145	44	205	775
3x	33	250	31	150	35	150	34	195	32	155	900
2x	22	75	21	105	25	130	23	180	24	90	580
5x	55	40	54	155	53	65	52	60	51	40	360
5x	55	115	54	185	53	240	51	120	52	125	785
1x	11	145	13	105	14	50	15	130	12	135	565
3x	32	150	33	115	34	60	35	110	31	25	460
2x	21	5	24	65	25	70	23	60	22	20	220
4x	41	30	42	50	43	35	45	20	44	50	185
									Grand Total =		13,720

TABLE 50

YIELDS OF VARIETIES BY GROUPS, AND TOTAL YIELDS FOR BOTH GROUPS

Values of x_{uv}

	v	1	2	3	4	5	$Xu.$
	u						
Group X	1	410	315	255	190	295	1,465
	2	110	95	240	155	200	800
	3	175	305	365	255	260	1,360
	4	220	185	180	255	120	960
	5	160	185	305	340	155	1,145
	$X._v$	1075	1085	1345	1195	1030	$5,730 = X..$

TABLE 50—*Continued*

Values of y_{uv}

u \ v	1	2	3	4	5	Y_u
1	355	360	335	215	380	1,645
2	590	305	200	320	415	1,830
Group Y 3	445	335	170	215	260	1,425
4	510	400	265	150	270	1,595
5	475	240	230	265	285	1,495
$Y_{.v}$ 2375	1640	1200	1165	1610		7,990 = $Y_{..}$

Values of T_{uv}

u \ v	1	2	3	4	5	$T_{u.}$
1	765	675	590	405	675	3,110
Group X 2	700	400	440	475	615	2,630
+ 3	620	640	535	470	520	2,785
Group Y 4	730	585	445	405	390	2,555
5	635	425	535	605	440	2,640
$T_{.v}$ 3450	2725	2545	2360	2640		13,720 = $T_{..}$

v	$X_{.v} - Y_{.v}$	u	$Y_{u.} - X_{u.}$
1	−1300	1	180
2	− 555	2	1030
3	145	3	65
4	30	4	635
5	− 580	5	350
$(X_{..} - Y_{..}) = -2260$		$(Y_{..} - X_{..}) = 2260$	

TABLE 51

CALCULATION OF CORRECTED VARIETY MEANS (t_{uv})

u \ v	1	2	3	4	5	$C_{u.}$
1	135.25	150.00	163.75	111.75	148.75	9.00
2	161.50	123.75	168.75	171.75	176.25	51.50
3	93.25	135.50	144.25	122.25	104.25	3.25
4	149.25	150.25	150.25	134.50	100.25	31.75
5	111.25	96.00	158.50	170.25	98.50	17.50
$C_{.v}$	−65.00	−27.75	7.25	1.50	−29.00	0

$$C_{.1} = -1300/20 = -65.00$$
$$C_{1.} = 180/20 = 9.00$$

17. Two-Dimensional Quasi-Factorials with Three Groups of Sets.

A possible criticism of the quasi-factorial method with two groups of sets as described above is that there is too great a discrepancy between the estimates of the error variance for comparing varieties in the same and in different sets. This can be partly overcome by increasing the

number of groups, and hence the type with three groups of sets is theoretically an improvement over the previous type. It requires, however,
more computation, and the number of replications must be a multiple
of 3. Details for setting up and analyzing such experiments may be
found in the reference of Yates (20).

18. Three-Dimensional Quasi-Factorials with Three Groups of Sets.
In the two-dimensional types the varieties were represented by two-
figure numbers corresponding to the two dimensions of a square. In
the three-dimensional types the varieties are represented by three-figure
numbers (uvw) corresponding to the three dimensions of a cube. Thus
in a cube with p numbers on a side we can represent p^3 varieties, and
taking these numbers in sets of p by slicing in three directions we can
make up $3p^2$ sets. There will be three groups of p^2 sets, each one corresponding to a direction in which the cube is sliced. At this point
the student should draw up a cube, put in the numbers, and practice
writing out the sets. It will then be noted that the sets can be written
out directly for any value of p by expanding the sets given below for
$p = 3$.

When the number of varieties is very large, say 216 or more, there
are decided advantages in using this type of experiment, as with any
other type the blocks would still be rather large.

The details of setting up and analyzing a three-dimensional experiment may be obtained from Example 38.

**Example 38. Three-Dimensional Quasi-Factorial Experiment with Three Groups
of Sets.** The specifications are:

Varieties (v)	$= p^3$	$=$	27
Sets (s)	$= 3p^2$	$=$	27
Replications of each group (n)		$=$	2
Complete replications (r)	$= 3n$	$=$	6
Total number of blocks (b)	$= 3np^2$	$=$	54
Total number of plots (N)	$= 3np^3$	$=$	162

After forming the $(3 \times 3 \times 3)$ cube we can write out the sets as follows:

Group $X(\cdot vw)$				Group $Y(u \cdot w)$				Group $Z(uv \cdot)$			
Set No.				Set No.				Set No.			
1	111	211	311	1	111	121	131	1	111	112	113
2	112	212	312	2	211	221	231	2	121	122	123
3	113	213	313	3	311	321	331	3	131	132	133
4	121	221	321	4	112	122	132	4	211	212	213
5	122	222	322	5	212	222	232	5	221	222	223
6	123	223	323	6	312	322	332	6	231	232	233
7	131	231	331	7	113	123	133	7	311	312	313
8	132	232	332	8	213	223	233	8	321	322	323
9	133	233	333	9	313	323	333	9	331	332	333

After the distribution of the blocks over the field and the randomization of the varieties within the blocks we have such an arrangement as is shown in Table 53, in which the individual plot yields corresponding to the varieties are given. In this case the blocks are distributed at random over the whole field, but it would have been more convenient to keep them together in complete replications.

The calculations are carried out in tabular form in Table 54. The data are first collected by groups so that the yield of any one variety in one group will be a total of n plots. The marginal totals are obtained as indicated in three directions, and it will be noted that $X_{.vw}$, $Y_{u.w}$, and $Z_{uv.}$ represent the totals for the sets. The complete variety totals represented by T_{uv} are entered next and all the marginal totals of these obtained.

For calculating the corrected variety means (t_{uvw}) the most convenient formula is

$$t_{uvw} = \frac{T_{uvw}}{3n} + C_{.vw} + C_{u.w} + C_{uv.}$$

where

$$C_{.vw} = \frac{1}{6np^2} (pT_{.vw} - 3pX_{.vw} - T_{.v.} + 3Y_{.v.})$$

$$C_{u.w} = \frac{1}{6np^2} (pT_{u.w} - 3pY_{u.w} - T_{..w} + 3Z_{..w})$$

$$C_{uv.} = \frac{1}{6np^2} (pT_{uv.} - 3pZ_{uv.} - T_{u..} + 3X_{u..})$$

Thus

$$C_{.11} = \frac{1}{108} (3 \times 2735 - 9 \times 340 - 9875 + 3 \times 3635) = 57.176$$

$$C_{1.1} = \frac{1}{108} (3 \times 3330 - 9 \times 1385 - 9645 + 3 \times 3105) = -25.972$$

$$C_{11.} = \frac{1}{108} (3 \times 3305 - 9 \times 1185 - 9470 + 3 \times 3180) = - 6.296$$

Having obtained all the correction terms, we check by obtaining the total, which in this case comes to $+0.001$. This is a sufficiently close check.

The corrected means are obtained by adding the corresponding correction terms to the actual means. For example, $t_{111} = 151.667 + 57.176 - 25.972 - 6.296 = 176.575$.

To obtain the sum of squares for varieties we first average the corrected means in three directions to give $t_{.vw}$, $t_{u.w}$, and $t_{uv.}$. To illustrate this:

$$t_{.11} = \tfrac{1}{3} (176.575 + 190.001 + 164.723) = 177.100$$

$$t_{1.1} = \tfrac{1}{3} (176.575 + 192.222 + 224.028) = 197.608$$

$$t_{11.} = \tfrac{1}{3} (176.575 + 180.556 + 197.917) = 185.016$$

The sum of squares for varieties is then given by

$$\text{Varieties } (SS) = \Sigma(t_{uvw} \cdot T_{uvw}) - \Sigma(X_{.vw} \cdot t_{.vw}) - \Sigma(Y_{u.w} \cdot t_{u.w}) - \Sigma(Z_{uv.} \cdot t_{uv.})$$

which in this case is

$$5,847,432.06 - 5,754,971.44 = 92,460.62$$

Then after calculating the total and block sum of squares from Table 53, we can set up the analysis of variance.

TABLE 52

ANALYSIS OF VARIANCE

THREE-DIMENSIONAL QUASI-FACTORIAL EXPERIMENT
WITH THREE GROUPS OF SETS

	SS	DF	MS	F	5% Point
Blocks............	1,154,025	53			
Varieties.........	92,461	26	3556	1.23	1.62
Error.............	236,872	82	2889		
Total........	1,483,358	161			

The variances and standard errors for comparing the varieties are as follows. It will be noted that such comparisons now fall into three groups that can be determined from the variety numbers.

$$V(t_{211}-t_{111}) = \frac{2s^2}{3np^2}(p^2+p+1) \quad = \frac{2\times 2889}{54}\times 13 = 1391 \qquad SE=\sqrt{1391}=37.30$$

$$V(t_{122}-t_{111}) = \frac{s^2}{3np^2}(2p^2+3p+4) = \frac{2889}{54}\times 31 = 1658 \qquad SE=\sqrt{1658}=40.72$$

$$V(t_{222}-t_{111}) = \frac{s^2}{3np^2}(2p^2+3p+6) = \frac{2889}{54}\times 33 = 1766 \qquad SE=\sqrt{1766}=42.02$$

And the mean variance of all comparisons is

$$V_m = \frac{s^2}{3n}\left(\frac{2p^2+5p+11}{p^2+p+1}\right) = \left(\frac{2889}{6}\times\frac{44}{13}\right) = 1630 \qquad SE=\sqrt{1630}=40.37$$

19. Symmetrical Incomplete Block Experiments. It will be remembered from the discussion of Section 15 that, if all the possible groups of degrees of freedom are not confounded, certain of the comparisons are determined with less precision than others. For this reason in using the quasi-factorials we have two or more standard errors depending on the " dimensions " of the experiment. This difficulty can be overcome by confounding all the possible groups of degrees of freedom or in other words by using all the possible groups of sets. We then have a design that is perfectly symmetrical and not only do we have equal precision for all comparisons but also the calculations are considerably simplified.

The chief problem in setting up the design of a symmetrical experiment is in writing out the sets. For this purpose we can conveniently

TABLE 53

POSITION OF VARIETIES IN THE FIELD AND CORRESPONDING PLOT YIELDS THREE-DIMENSIONAL QUASI-FACTORIAL EXPERIMENT WITH THREE GROUPS OF SETS

Set No.	Variety	Yield	Variety	Yield	Variety	Yield	Block Totals	Set No.	Variety	Yield	Variety	Yield	Variety	Yield	Block Totals
2x	212	315	312	370	112	360	1045	4y	122	195	112	310	132	315	820
5y	222	265	232	355	212	345	965	6z	233	215	231	330	232	270	815
6y	322	245	312	185	332	160	590	9y	333	290	313	95	323	140	525
8y	223	285	233	355	213	240	880	7x	231	330	131	410	331	235	975
2y	211	325	221	315	231	300	940	6y	312	255	322	375	332	305	935
5x	122	240	322	220	222	350	810	4x	121	255	321	235	221	230	720
2x	212	360	312	230	112	225	815	5y	232	275	222	245	212	140	660
3y	331	270	311	255	321	170	695	5z	223	270	222	230	221	135	635
6x	323	175	123	290	223	330	795	5z	222	95	221	245	223	330	670
6x	323	180	123	275	223	290	745	9z	332	215	333	300	331	255	770
3y	321	155	331	180	311	160	495	3x	213	185	313	145	113	150	480
9y	323	120	313	70	333	100	290	9x	333	50	133	45	233	105	200
7y	113	100	123	170	133	65	335	8z	322	155	323	125	321	30	310
9x	233	55	333	145	133	40	240	7x	131	65	331	130	231	55	250
1x	111	35	311	45	211	55	135	2z	122	85	123	55	121	110	250
7y	123	140	133	45	113	15	200	9z	331	130	332	40	333	45	215
1x	111	85	211	65	311	55	205	3z	131	45	132	60	133	15	120
1z	112	80	111	115	113	165	360	3x	313	0	213	70	113	65	135
1y	121	180	111	255	131	290	725	8y	223	285	213	270	233	185	740
5x	222	150	122	55	322	50	255	1y	111	210	131	265	121	185	660
8x	332	130	132	215	232	155	500	2y	211	95	221	95	231	155	345
4x	121	210	221	90	321	95	395	4z	213	160	212	140	211	125	425
7z	311	140	312	195	313	310	645	1z	111	210	112	290	113	325	825
4y	132	230	122	220	112	310	760	4z	211	230	213	155	212	195	580
3z	132	245	133	315	131	215	775	8x	132	160	232	285	332	230	675
6z	232	185	233	220	231	175	580	7z	311	275	313	185	312	130	590
2z	121	190	122	160	123	110	460	8z	323	155	321	150	322	240	545

divide such experiments into two types: (1) where the number of varieties $(v) = p^2$; and (2) where $v = p^2 - p + 1$. There are, of course, other types, but the two mentioned are likely to be of the most value in field experiments. Considering the first type, $(v = p^2)$, it is obvious that the variety numbers can be written in the form of a square. Suppose that we have 9 varieties; then the square is

$$
\begin{array}{ccc}
11 & 12 & 13 \\
21 & 22 & 23 \\
31 & 32 & 33
\end{array}
$$

The first two groups of sets are written as for a two-dimensional quasi-factorial, from the rows and columns of the square. Two more groups may then be written from the diagonals of the above square. These are

$$
\begin{array}{ccc}
11 & 22 & 33 \\
21 & 32 & 13 \\
31 & 12 & 23
\end{array}
\qquad\qquad
\begin{array}{ccc}
11 & 32 & 23 \\
21 & 12 & 33 \\
31 & 22 & 13
\end{array}
$$

TABLE 54

Yields of Varieties Collected by Groups and for All Groups and Calculation of Corrected Variety Means. Three-Dimensional Quasi-Factorial Experiment with Three Groups of Sets

$w=$	1				2				3				$X_{uv\cdot}$			
$v\backslash u$	1	2	3	$X_{\cdot vw}$	1	2	3	$X_{\cdot vw}$	1	2	3	$X_{\cdot vw}$	1	2	3	$X_{\cdot v}$
X 1	120	120	100	340	585	675	600	1,860	215	255	145	615	920	1,050	845	2,815
X 2	465	320	330	1,115	295	500	270	1,065	565	620	355	1,540	1,325	1,440	955	3,720
X 3	475	385	365	1,225	375	440	360	1,175	85	160	195	440	935	985	920	2,840
$X_{u\cdot w}$	1,060	825	795	2,680	1,255	1,615	1,230	4,100	865	1,035	695	2,595	3,180	3,475	2,720	9,375
Y 1	465	420	415	1,300	620	485	440	1,545	115	510	165	790	1,200	1,415	1,020	3,635
Y 2	365	410	325	1,100	415	510	620	1,545	310	570	260	1,140	1,090	1,490	1,205	3,785
Y 3	555	455	450	1,460	545	630	465	1,640	110	540	390	1,040	1,210	1,625	1,305	4,140
$Y_{u\cdot w}$	1,385	1,285	1,190	3,860	1,580	1,625	1,525	4,730	535	1,620	815	2,970	3,500	4,530	3,530	11,560
Z 1	325	355	415	1,095	370	335	325	1,030	490	315	495	1,300	1,185	1,005	1,235	3,425
Z 2	300	380	180	860	245	325	395	965	165	600	280	2,345	710	1,305	855	2,870
Z 3	260	505	385	1,150	305	455	255	1,015	330	435	345	1,110	895	1,395	985	3,275
$Z_{u\cdot w}$	885	1,240	980	3,105	920	1,115	975	3,010	985	1,350	1,120	3,455	2,790	3,705	3,075	9,570
X	910	895	930	2,735	1,575	1,495	1,365	4,435	820	1,080	805	2,705	3,305	3,470	3,100	9,875
Y	1,130	1,110	835	3,075	955	1,335	1,285	3,575	1,040	1,790	895	3,725	3,125	4,235	3,015	10,375
Z	1,290	1,345	1,200	3,835	1,225	1,525	1,080	3,830	525	1,135	930	2,590	3,040	4,005	3,210	10,255
$T_{u\cdot w}$	3,330	3,350	2,965	9,645	3,755	4,355	3,730	11,840	2,385	4,005	2,630	9,020	9,470	11,710	9,325	30,505
$T_{uvw}/3n$ 1	151.667	149.167	155.000	+57.176	262.500	249.167	227.500	−22.268	136.667	180.000	134.167	+33.426	−6.296	0.741	−27.592	
$T_{uvw}/3n$ 2	188.333	185.000	139.167	+1.574	159.167	222.500	214.167	+19.630	173.333	298.333	149.167	−15.787	+28.287	−3.009	+1.713	
$T_{uvw}/3n$ 3	215.000	224.167	200.000	+24.491	204.167	254.167	180.000	+28.518	87.500	189.167	155.000	+55.324	+10.509	−16.898	−3.704	
$C_{u\cdot w}$	−25.972	−17.083	−19.861		−53.380	−40.463	−49.491		+34.120	−11.296	+17.592					
t_{uvw} 1	176.575	190.001	164.723	177.100	180.556	187.177	128.149	165.294	197.917	202.871	157.593	186.127	185.016	193.350	150.155	
t_{uvw} 2	192.222	166.482	122.593	160.432	153.704	198.658	186.019	179.460	219.953	268.242	152.685	213.626	188.626	211.127	153.766	
t_{uvw} 3	224.028	214.677	200.926	213.210	189.814	225.324	155.323	190.154	187.453	216.297	224.212	209.321	200.432	218.766	193.487	
$t_{u\cdot w}$	197.608	190.387	162.747		174.691	203.720	156.497		201.774	229.136	178.163					

the second one being written from the diagonals of the first.   This must be all the groups, as we know from a study of the degrees of freedom in a Latin square, and also from the fact that, if we repeat the process on the last square written, the original square is regenerated.   The maximum number of groups that can be written is always $p + 1$.   On examining these sets we note that each variety occurs once and once only in the same set with any other variety.   Taking variety 11 the sets in which it occurs are

$$(11 \quad 12 \quad 13), \quad (11 \quad 21 \quad 31), \quad (11 \quad 22 \quad 33), \quad (11 \quad 32 \quad 23),$$

and in these four sets all the other varieties have occurred once.

If p is a *prime number* the above method of writing out the sets will work for the type $(v = p^2)$.   If p is not a prime number we must make use of a completely orthogonalized square, if such a square can be prepared.   For $p = 6$ the orthogonalized square is impossible, so that we cannot write more than three groups of sets.   This is the same as saying that a Latin square is possible for any number of rows and columns, but Graeco-Latin squares are impossible for certain numbers, Fisher (2). A completely orthogonalized 4×4 square is given below, and further squares are given in R. A. Fisher's "Design of Experiments," 1937.

Completely Orthogonalized 4×4 Square

111	234	342	423
222	143	431	314
333	412	124	241
444	321	213	132

This square may be used to show how the sets for 16 varieties can be made up.

The first two groups of sets are obtained from the rows and columns of the square of variety numbers in the usual way, and the orthogonalized square is used to write out the remaining groups.   Assuming that the square of variety numbers is as follows:

11	12	13	14
21	22	23	24
31	32	33	34
41	42	43	44

and is superimposed on the orthogonalized square, we note, considering the first of the three-digit numbers only, that 1 corresponds with the variety numbers 11, 22, 33, 44; 2 with the numbers 21, 12, 43, 34; 3 with 31, 42, 13, 24; and 4 with 41, 32, 23, 14.   These are the sets for the third group, and we make up two more groups by using the second and third figures of the orthogonalized square.

To write the sets for the type $v = p^2 - p + 1$, it is only necessary to modify the above procedure. Suppose that $v = 13$; then $p = 4$ and $p - 1 = 3$. A convenient method of designating the varieties is as follows:

01	02	03	04
	11	12	13
	21	22	23
	31	32	33,

and if the sets are written for the 9 numbers in the square, the sets for the 13 varieties are obtained by making one set out of 01, 02, 03, 04, and the remaining sets by adding one of these to the sets of each group formed by the other 9 numbers. The sets finally are as follows:

01	02	03	04

01	11	12	13		02	11	21	31		03	11	22	33		04	11	32	23
01	21	22	23		02	12	22	32		03	21	32	13		04	21	12	33
01	31	32	33		02	13	23	33		03	31	12	23		04	31	22	13

If the number of varieties is 21, the numbers would be written out as below:

01	02	03	04	05
	11	12	13	14
	21	22	23	24
	31	32	33	34
	41	42	43	44

and we would have to use a completely orthogonalized 4×4 square in order to make up the 20 sets for the 16 numbers in the square, to which the remaining numbers would be added as described above.

Special mention should be made of the fact that, as the sets are written out by the methods described above for the $v = p^2 - p + 1$ type, the blocks cannot be arranged so that they form complete replications. There is a method of making up the sets (Youden's square) by means of which all the blocks are placed side by side and all the plots in a single row from one end of the field to the other would form a complete replication. This method is likely to be of considerable value in laboratory experiments, but in field plot experiments it is not likely that the long narrow strips one plot wide would be of any value in error control.

Example 39. A Symmetrical Incomplete Block Experiment for 25 Varieties and 6 Replications. The sets have been written out by the method described above, and those for each group have been kept together to form complete replications. This will be obvious from Table 55, and it will be noted also that no attempt has been made to randomize the blocks. All the randomization is of the varieties within blocks. It is convenient to enter on the plan of the field the individual yields and the block totals. The variety totals are obtained by collecting the individual yields as in Table 56. These are denoted by T_{uv}. The figures in the column headed Σ_{uv} are obtained by adding for any one variety the totals for all the blocks in which that variety occurs. Thus from Table 55 for variety 11 we have

$$\Sigma_{11} = 257 + 181 + 177 + 265 + 271 + 303 = 1454$$

The second last column is obtained as indicated, and this can be checked by adding, as the total for all the $(pT_{uv} - \Sigma_{uv})$ values is zero. The last column gives the corrected variety means (t_{uv}) which are given by the formula

$$t_{uv} = \frac{pT_{uv} - \Sigma_{uv}}{v} + m$$

where m is the general mean of the whole experiment and v is the number of varieties. The sum of squares for varieties is given simply by

$$\text{Varieties } (SS) = \frac{\Sigma(pT_{uv} - \Sigma_{uv})^2}{pv}$$

The analysis of variance can then be set up as at the foot of Table 56. The method is also given for calculating the variance of a difference between two corrected means. The general formula is

$$V_m = \frac{2s^2}{r}\left(\frac{p+1}{p}\right)$$

where r is the number of replications.

THE FIELD PLOT TEST

TABLE 55

LOCATION OF THE VARIETIES IN THE FIELD AND CORRESPONDING YIELDS. SYMMETRICAL INCOMPLETE BLOCK EXPERIMENT FOR 31 VARIETIES AND 6 REPLICATIONS

Replicate VI

Plot No.	1	2	3	4	5	6	7	8	9	10	11	12	13	14	15	16	17	18	19	20	21	22	23	24	25
Variety	52	34	25	11	43	12	44	35	21	53	31	13	54	22	45	41	14	32	23	55	33	15	51	42	24
Yields	57	52	38	60	50	31	31	28	32	24	24	40	19	20	30	40	35	32	19	36	36	44	46	57	68
Block totals	257					146					133					162					251				

Replicate total = 949

Replicate V

Plot No.	1	2	3	4	5	6	7	8	9	10	11	12	13	14	15	16	17	18	19	20	21	22	23	24	25
Variety	35	23	42	54	11	33	52	14	21	45	55	12	43	24	31	41	53	15	34	22	25	44	32	13	51
Yields	54	39	28	40	20	14	11	10	24	19	30	42	32	28	30	32	38	26	16	20	19	24	8	12	26
Block totals	181					78					162					132					89				

Replicate total = 642

Replicate IV

Plot No.	1	2	3	4	5	6	7	8	9	10	11	12	13	14	15	16	17	18	19	20	21	22	23	24	25
Variety	32	24	45	53	11	34	13	21	42	55	52	23	15	31	44	54	33	12	41	25	35	22	51	43	14
Yields	57	39	25	32	24	7	23	18	24	24	30	42	16	16	23	25	39	35	18	21	20	23	15	16	27
Block totals	177					96					127					138					101				

Replicate total = 639

Replicate III

Plot No.	1	2	3	4	5	6	7	8	9	10	11	12	13	14	15	16	17	18	19	20	21	22	23	24	25
Variety	33	44	22	55	11	15	32	43	54	21	14	53	31	25	42	13	35	24	52	41	12	23	34	51	45
Yields	74	57	34	49	51	45	43	31	44	40	41	36	28	8	16	19	30	23	22	35	25	31	19	23	27
Block totals	265					203					129					129					125				

Replicate total = 851

Replicate II

Plot No.	1	2	3	4	5	6	7	8	9	10	11	12	13	14	15	16	17	18	19	20	21	22	23	24	25
Variety	11	31	51	21	41	22	12	42	52	32	13	53	43	33	23	14	44	54	24	34	45	55	35	15	25
Yields	52	57	40	79	43	36	33	24	44	32	22	27	11	18	32	37	29	24	37	32	22	19	21	29	26
Block totals	271					169					110					159					117				

Replicate total = 826

Replicate I

Plot No.	1	2	3	4	5	6	7	8	9	10	11	12	13	14	15	16	17	18	19	20	21	22	23	24	25
Variety	12	14	15	13	11	23	22	21	24	25	34	35	32	31	33	43	44	41	45	42	53	51	52	55	54
Yields	74	65	54	66	44	48	57	37	44	55	33	35	37	38	30	46	72	57	62	89	76	54	55	75	84
Block totals	303					241					173					326					344				

Replicate total = 1387
Grand total = 5294

TABLE 56

YIELDS OF SINGLE PLOTS BY VARIETIES, VARIETY TOTALS, VALUES OF Σ_{uv} AND THE CORRECTED MEANS (t_{uv}). SYMMETRICAL INCOMPLETE BLOCK EXPERIMENT FOR 25 VARIETIES AND 6 REPLICATIONS

Vari- ties	VI	V	IV	III	II	I	T_{uv}	Σ_{uv}	$pT_{uv}-\Sigma_{uv}$	$t_{uv}=\dfrac{pT_{uv}-\Sigma_{uv}}{v}+m$
11	60	20	24	51	52	44	251	1,454	−199	27.33
12	31	42	35	25	33	74	240	1,043	157	41.57
13	40	12	23	19	22	66	182	860	50	37.79
14	35	10	27	41	37	65	215	932	143	41.01
15	44	26	16	45	29	54	214	1,133	−63	32.77
21	32	24	18	40	79	37	230	1,035	115	39.89
22	20	20	23	34	36	57	190	1,041	−91	31.65
23	19	39	42	31	32	48	211	946	109	39.65
24	68	28	39	23	37	44	239	1,119	76	38.33
25	38	19	21	8	26	55	167	971	−136	29.85
31	24	30	16	28	57	38	193	995	−30	34.09
32	32	8	57	43	32	37	209	973	72	38.17
33	36	14	39	74	18	30	211	1,015	40	36.89
34	52	16	7	19	32	33	159	942	−147	29.41
35	28	54	20	30	21	35	188	847	93	39.01
41	40	32	18	35	43	57	225	1,158	−33	33.97
42	57	28	24	16	24	89	238	1,152	38	36.81
43	50	32	16	31	11	46	186	1,159	−229	26.13
44	31	24	23	57	29	72	236	1,112	68	38.01
45	30	19	25	27	22	62	185	956	−31	34.05
51	46	11	15	23	40	54	189	1,181	−236	25.85
52	57	26	30	22	44	55	234	1,104	66	37.93
53	24	38	32	36	27	76	233	1,038	127	40.37
54	19	40	25	44	24	84	236	1,158	22	36.17
55	36	30	24	49	19	75	233	1,146	19	36.05
Totals	949	642	639	851	826	1387	5294	26,470	0	

$$\frac{\Sigma(pT_{uv}-\Sigma_{uv})^2}{pv} = \frac{324,354}{125} = 2594.83 \qquad m = \frac{5294}{150} = 35.29$$

Replications $\Sigma(x^2)$

I	83,531
II	32,228
III	34,039
IV	19,029
V	19,568
VI	40,367

Total = 228,762.00
CT = 186,842.91

$\Sigma(x - \bar{x})^2 = $ 41,919.09

$\Sigma(T_b{}^2)/5 = 1,088,496/5 = 217,699.20$
$CT = $ 186,842.91

Blocks = 30,856.29

Analysis of Variance

	SS	DF	MS	F	5% Pt.
Blocks.....	30,856.29	29			
Varieties...	2,594.83	24	108.12	1.22	1.63
Error......	8,467.97	96	88.21		
Total....	41,919.09	149			

$$V_{md} = \frac{2 \times 88.21}{6} \times \left(\frac{6}{5}\right) = 35.28$$

$$SE_{md} = \sqrt{35.28} = 5.94$$

Example 40. A Symmetrical Incomplete Block Experiment for 31 Varieties in 6 Replications. The sets were written out by setting up the variety numbers as follows:

$$
\begin{array}{cccccc}
01 & 02 & 03 & 04 & 05 & 06 \\
 & 11 & 12 & 13 & 14 & 15 \\
 & 21 & 22 & 23 & 24 & 25 \\
 & 31 & 32 & 33 & 34 & 35 \\
 & 41 & 42 & 43 & 44 & 45 \\
 & 51 & 52 & 53 & 54 & 55,
\end{array}
$$

writing out the 6 groups of sets for the 5×5 square and adding, to each, one of the numbers in the first row. An additional set was then made up from the numbers in the first row, giving 31 sets in all. The blocks were arranged as indicated in Table 58, after randomizing the varieties within the blocks. The variety totals are collected as in Table 59, and it is convenient for this purpose and for obtaining the values of Σ_{uv} to make up a table similar to Table 60 giving the sets with their corresponding numbers and block totals. Then, to collect the yields of, say, variety 23, we can locate it in each group, note the numbers of the sets, and then proceed from the table of individual yields to obtain the total. Similarly to obtain Σ_{23} we add the block totals in the same line as 23 throughout the table.

From this point the calculations are exactly as in Example 39 for 25 varieties, except that, since this experiment is of the $v = p^2 - p + 1$ type, the variance for the difference between two corrected variety means is

$$V_m = \frac{2s^2}{r}\left(\frac{p^2}{p^2 - p + 1}\right)$$

The analysis of variance is given in Table 57.

TABLE 57

ANALYSIS OF VARIANCE

INCOMPLETE BLOCK EXPERIMENT FOR 31 VARIETIES IN 6 REPLICATIONS

	SS	DF	MS	F	5% Point
Blocks.........	1,083,491	30	36,116	10.5	1.53
Varieties.......	103,977	30	3,466	1.01	1.53
Error..........	429,756	125	3,438		
Total.........	1,617,224	185			

TABLE 58

LOCATION OF THE VARIETIES IN THE FIELD, CORRESPONDING PLOT YIELDS, AND BLOCK TOTALS. SYMMETRICAL INCOMPLETE BLOCK EXPERIMENT WITH 31 VARIETIES AND 6 REPLICATIONS

Set No.	Variety	Yield	Variety	Yield	Variety	Yield	Variety	Yield	Variety	Yield	Variety	Yield	Block Totals
1	11	315	13	370	01	360	14	265	12	355	15	345	2,010
2	23	245	22	185	21	160	01	285	24	355	25	240	1,470
3	01	325	33	315	32	300	35	240	31	220	34	350	1,750
4	45	360	43	230	42	225	01	270	41	255	44	170	1,510
5	01	175	53	290	51	330	54	220	52	220	55	265	1,500
6	31	195	11	310	21	315	02	215	41	330	51	270	1,635
7	22	290	52	95	02	140	32	330	12	410	42	235	1,500
8	13	255	23	375	43	305	33	255	02	235	53	230	1,655
9	54	275	44	245	34	140	24	270	14	230	02	135	1,295
10	45	95	35	245	02	330	25	235	15	200	55	285	1,390
11	44	180	11	275	33	290	55	155	03	180	22	160	1,240
12	03	120	32	70	21	100	15	100	43	170	54	65	625
13	53	55	42	145	31	40	25	35	03	45	14	55	375
14	24	140	13	45	35	15	03	85	52	65	41	55	405
15	45	80	23	115	34	165	03	85	51	55	12	120	620
16	32	215	11	300	45	255	24	185	04	145	53	150	1,250
17	13	50	34	45	55	105	42	155	21	125	04	30	510
18	23	65	15	130	44	55	31	85	04	55	52	110	500
19	25	130	33	40	41	45	12	45	54	60	04	15	335
20	35	−5	04	70	22	65	43	35	14	255	51	80	500
21	05	180	11	255	23	290	42	285	35	270	54	185	1,465
22	21	150	52	55	14	50	45	210	33	265	05	185	915
23	55	130	24	215	12	155	31	95	05	95	43	155	845
24	15	210	41	90	53	95	22	160	05	140	34	125	820
25	32	140	05	195	13	310	51	195	25	130	44	285	1,255
26	11	210	34	290	43	325	25	230	52	220	06	310	1,585
27	12	230	44	155	35	195	53	245	06	315	21	215	1,355
28	13	160	31	285	54	230	22	185	45	220	06	175	1,255
29	14	275	55	185	06	130	32	190	41	160	23	110	1,050
30	15	155	42	150	24	240	06	130	33	145	51	125	945
31	01	220	05	215	06	195	03	240	02	295	04	230	1,395
													34,960

TABLE 59

YIELDS OF SINGLE PLOTS BY VARIETIES, VARIETY TOTALS, VALUES OF Σ_{uv}, AND THE CORRECTED MEANS t_{uv}. SYMMETRICAL INCOMPLETE BLOCK EXPERIMENT WITH 31 VARIETIES AND 6 REPLICATIONS

Variety No.	Single Plot Yields						T_{uv}	Σ_{uv}	$pT_{uv}-\Sigma_{uv}$	t_{uv}
01	360	285	325	270	175	220	1,635	9,635	175	193.6
02	215	140	235	135	330	295	1,350	8,870	−770	163.2
03	180	120	45	85	85	240	755	4,660	−130	183.8
04	145	30	55	15	70	230	545	4,490	−1220	148.6
05	180	185	95	140	195	215	1,010	6,695	−635	167.5
06	310	315	175	130	130	195	1,255	7,585	−55	186.2
11	315	310	275	300	255	210	1,665	9,185	805	214.0
12	355	410	120	45	155	230	1,315	6,665	1225	227.5
13	370	255	45	50	310	160	1,190	7,090	50	189.6
14	265	230	55	255	50	275	1,130	6,145	635	208.5
15	345	200	100	130	210	155	1,140	6,290	550	205.7
21	160	315	100	125	150	215	1,065	6,510	−120	184.1
22	185	290	160	65	160	185	1,045	6,785	−515	171.4
23	245	375	115	65	290	110	1,200	6,760	440	202.2
24	355	270	140	185	215	240	1,405	6,210	2220	259.6
25	240	235	35	130	130	230	1,000	6,410	−410	174.8
31	220	195	40	85	95	285	920	6,360	−840	160.9
32	300	330	70	215	140	190	1,245	7,430	40	189.3
33	315	255	290	40	265	145	1,310	6,840	1020	220.9
34	350	140	165	45	125	290	1,115	6,580	110	191.9
35	240	245	15	−5	270	195	960	6,865	−1105	152.4
41	255	330	55	45	90	160	935	5,755	−145	183.3
42	225	235	145	155	285	150	1,195	6,305	865	215.9
43	230	305	170	35	155	325	1,220	6,720	600	207.4
44	170	245	180	55	285	155	1,090	7,155	−615	168.2
45	360	95	80	255	210	220	1,220	6,940	380	200.3
51	330	270	55	80	195	125	1,055	6,455	−125	184.0
52	220	95	65	110	55	220	765	6,405	−1815	129.4
53	290	230	55	150	95	245	1,065	6,955	−565	169.8
54	220	275	65	60	185	230	1,035	6,475	−265	179.4
55	265	285	155	105	130	185	1,125	6,535	215	194.9
	8215	7495	3680	3555	5490	6525	34,960	209,760	0	

$$m = \frac{34,960}{186} = 188.0$$

TABLE 60

Sets Arranged in Order of Numbers with Corresponding Block Totals.
Incomplete Randomized Block Experiment

Set No.							Block Totals	Set No.							Block Totals
1	01	11	12	13	14	15	2010	16	04	11	32	53	24	45	1250
2	01	21	22	23	24	25	1470	17	04	21	42	13	34	55	510
3	01	31	32	33	34	35	1750	18	04	31	52	23	44	15	500
4	01	41	42	43	44	45	1510	19	04	41	12	33	54	25	335
5	01	51	52	53	54	55	1500	20	04	51	22	43	14	35	500
6	02	11	21	31	41	51	1635	21	05	11	42	23	54	35	1465
7	02	12	22	32	42	52	1500	22	05	21	52	33	14	45	915
8	02	13	23	33	43	53	1655	23	05	31	12	43	24	55	845
9	02	14	24	34	44	54	1295	24	05	41	22	53	34	15	820
10	02	15	25	35	45	55	1390	25	05	51	32	13	44	25	1255
11	03	11	22	33	44	55	1240	26	06	11	52	43	34	25	1585
12	03	21	32	43	54	15	625	27	06	21	12	53	44	35	1355
13	03	31	42	53	14	25	375	28	06	31	22	13	54	45	1255
14	03	41	52	13	24	35	405	29	06	41	32	23	14	55	1050
15	03	51	12	23	34	45	620	30	06	51	42	33	24	15	945
								31	06	01	02	03	04	05	1395

Grand Total = 34,960

20. Choosing the Best Type of Incomplete Block Experiment for a Given Test. After a study of the various incomplete block experiments it will be noted that each has certain limitations. On account of general simplicity the symmetrical incomplete blocks are to be preferred to the quasi-factorials, and in addition all comparisons are made with equal precision. However, for the symmetrical types we must have, when $v = p^2$, $p + 1$ replications, and when $v = p^2 - p + 1$, p replications. For a test of 121 or 133 varieties we require 12 replications, and if the number of varieties is greater than this it is obvious that in general the test will be more expensive than is usually warranted in such cases. At a certain point, therefore, it would seem that the quasi-factorials should be extremely useful. On account of its relative simplicity the two-dimensional quasi-factorial with two groups of sets is preferable to the three-dimensional type, but the latter will probably be the most efficient if the number of varieties is quite large. These points can now be used as a basis for setting up a general schedule as to the type of experiment best suited to a given number of varieties. For this purpose Table 61 has been prepared, taking as a basis the number of varieties that can be tested by at least one of three types.

In Table 61 the dotted lines indicate the range through which the methods are generally recommended. The two-dimensional quasi-factorial can be used at the point where the number of replications for the symmetrical type becomes too large. For very large numbers the three-dimensional quasi-factorial is probably the most efficient, but, since it can be applied easily only to numbers that are cubes, the two-dimensional type must be extended to include fairly high numbers.

A possible objection to incomplete block experiments in general may be that certain numbers of varieties cannot be tested and hence the experimenter may feel that it is still necessary to use randomized blocks. However, it would seem to be desirable where possible to suit the number of varieties to the experiment even if it involves using "dummy" varieties. Also, for those who wish definitely to use other numbers than those listed here, Yates (20), has developed methods for laying out and analyzing quasi-factorials in which the dimensions are not equal. Thus instead of a 12 × 12 quasi-factorial for 144 varieties we might use a 12 × 11 for 132 varieties. These modifications, however, require additional computations and will be avoided if possible.

TABLE 61

VALUES OF p AND r REQUIRED FOR DIFFERENT NUMBERS OF VARIETIES
AND RANGES THROUGH WHICH THE THREE GENERAL TYPES OF
INCOMPLETE BLOCK EXPERIMENTS ARE RECOMMENDED

No. of Varieties	Symmetrical Incomplete Blocks		Two-Dimensional Quasi-Factorial		Three-Dimensional Quasi-Factorial	
	$p*$	r	p	r	p	r
13	4	4				
16	4	5	4	$2n$	2	$3n$
21	5	5				
25	5	6	5	$2n$		
27					3	$3n$
31	6	6				
36			6	$2n$		
49	7	8	7	$2n$		
57	8	8				
64	8	9	8	$2n$	4	$3n$
73	9	9				
81	9	10†	9	$2n$		
91	10	10				
100	10	11	10	$2n$		
111	11	11				
121	11	12	11	$2n$		
125					5	$3n$
133	12	12				
144	12	13	12	$2n$		
157	13	13				
169	13	14	13	$2n$		
183	14	14				
196	14	15	14	$2n$		
211	15	15				
216					6	$3n$
225	15	16	15	$2n$		
etc.					etc.	

* p = number of plots in one block.
 r = number of replications.
† Completely orthogonalized squares greater than (9×9) have not yet been written, and therefore we cannot if we wished go beyond this point at the present time.

TABLE 62

YIELDS OF OAT VARIETIES IN AN EXPERIMENT ON THE EFFECT
OF SOIL INOCULATION WITH A ROOT ROT ORGANISM

Variety	Soil Treatment	Replicates			
		1	2	3	4
I	I	24.1	16.1	31.6	28.9
	U	65.4	49.3	39.8	48.4
II	I	30.6	51.7	51.7	42.5
	U	51.8	74.8	76.5	56.6
III	I	39.1	47.4	36.9	28.9
	U	68.7	42.0	81.6	57.3
IV	I	120.1	69.5	96.2	69.7
	U	112.2	88.6	102.8	85.0
V	I	118.7	24.1	45.9	10.4
	U	58.5	68.0	77.7	54.7
VI	I	76.2	66.3	77.7	65.3
	U	109.1	91.5	124.1	96.9
VII	I	57.8	45.9	29.7	56.4
	U	112.2	95.9	91.1	77.3
VIII	I	58.0	40.1	47.6	38.4
	U	127.3	66.3	77.0	63.4
IX	I	81.8	23.6	31.6	32.1
	U	100.3	73.8	81.4	52.7
X	I	85.3	78.2	99.4	85.0
	U	81.6	94.3	96.4	77.2

21. Exercises.

1. The results of a randomized block experiment are given in Table 62. Ten varieties of oats were tested for their reaction to root rot. The plots were arranged in pairs of which one plot was inoculated with the root-rotting organism and one plot uninoculated. Analyze the results. State in words the meaning of a significant interaction between varieties and the soil inoculation.

	DF	MS
Replicates	3	2,042.08
Varieties	9	2,654.19
Error (1)	27	270.54
Treatments	1	12,226.51
Varieties × Treatments	9	401.32
Error (2)	30	232.30

2. In a fertilizer experiment conducted in an 8×8 Latin square, the yields of wheat given in Table 63 were obtained. The fertilizer combinations are designated N, P, K, NP, NK, NPK, O. In the table the yields are in the exact position of the plots in the field, and above each yield figure is the fertilizer treatment which the plot received. Work out the analysis of variance for this experiment, and, by means of the standard error, compare:

(a) Yields for plots receiving N with those receiving no N.
(b) Yields for plots receiving K with those receiving no K.
(c) Yields for plots receiving P with those receiving no P.

The results for the sums of squares are given below to provide a check on the work, but the sum of squares for the treatments must be split up to correspond to individual degrees of freedom.

	SS	DF
Rows	102.20	7
Columns	84.24	7
Treatments	513.79	7
Error	91.99	42

3. Complete the analysis of the split plot experiment described in Section 8, above. Assume that the plan of this experiment is to be rearranged so that the most accurate comparison is to be between D and W, and make the plan accordingly.

The sums of squares for the three errors as given below will provide a complete check on the calculations.

Error (1) 647.6   Error (2) 1059.1   Error (3) 931.1

4. Assuming that the following sets of figures represent the response to fertilizer at 4 levels, for each set work out the sums of squares for the total and then for the linear, quadratic, and cubic responses. Graph the actual yield results as given below, and then point out the relation between the shape of these graphs and the results obtained for the sums of squares.

	n_1	n_2	n_3	n_4
(a)	22	65	54	78
(b)	19	61	58	27
(c)	24	58	13	41

The sums of squares are

	(a)	(b)	(c)
Linear..............	1232.45	22.05	1.80
Quadratic..........	90.25	1332.25	9.00
Cubic..............	396.05·	14.45	1155.20

5. Table 64 gives the plan of a field for a $3 \times 3 \times 3$ confounded experiment, with treatment numbers and plot yields. The numbers such as 123 and 321 represent $N_1K_2P_3$ and $N_3K_2P_1$. Cyclic set II was used to confound 2 degrees of the triple interaction $N \times K \times P$ with blocks. Work out the complete analysis of variance for this experiment giving the results for treatment effects by individual degrees of freedom.

The following excerpts from the results for the sums of squares will assist in checking the calculations.

Total for treatments...2,434.93
N_r................... 9.46
$N_r \times K_d$............. 4.73
$K_d \times P_r$............. 438.90
$N \times K \times P$.......... 149.98 (for one pair of DF)
Error................5,770.81

6. Table 65 gives the plan of the field with variety numbers and corresponding plot yields for a two-dimensional quasi-factorial experiment with two groups of sets. Make a complete analysis of the results.

The variety sum of squares is 253,538.

7. Table 66 gives the plan of the field with variety numbers and corresponding plot yields for an incomplete block experiment with 21 varieties. Analyze the results, and make a test of the significance of the mean difference between the varieties 01 and 04.

8. Prepare plans for the layout of:

(a) Two-dimensional quasi-factorial experiment to test 36 varieties.
(b) Symmetrical incomplete block experiment to test 31 varieties.
(c) Three-dimensional quasi-factorial experiment to test 125 varieties.

TABLE 63

Yields of Wheat in an 8 × 8 Latin Square Fertilizer Experiment

P 18.8	N 12.2	NP 18.3	K 15.8	NK 11.4	O 11.5	NPK 19.4	PK 18.9
N 12.9	NK 7.3	PK 17.4	NPK 17.2	P 19.7	K 12.0	NP 19.0	O 15.6
NK 10.7	NP 17.5	N 10.4	P 18.0	O 9.8	NPK 16.6	PK 17.5	K 14.3
PK 18.3	K 12.6	NPK 14.2	O 12.2	N 11.4	NP 14.5	P 16.9	NK 16.1
NP 17.9	O 12.8	NK 13.3	N 11.3	PK 16.5	P 15.6	K 10.9	NPK 16.7
K 14.9	PK 18.2	O 12.8	NP 17.1	NPK 15.8	N 9.5	NK 8.9	P 20.6
NPK 19.0	P 18.9	K 11.2	PK 17.1	NP 17.9	NK 8.6	O 10.2	N 14.5
O 17.5	NPK 20.4	P 20.8	NK 16.4	K 16.8	PK 18.5	N 13.6	NP 23.0

THE FIELD PLOT TEST

TABLE 64

Plan of Field and Plot Yields for a (3 × 3 × 3) Confounded Experiment

Variety	Yield	Variety	Yield	Variety	Yield
111	465	112	364	113	549
123	395	121	348	122	348
132	556	133	421	131	463
213	343	211	455	212	346
222	413	223	374	221	394
231	408	232	507	233	363
312	337	313	421	311	449
321	421	322	374	323	217
333	308	331	334	332	355
333	353	121	381	332	244
312	486	133	403	323	246
213	219	313	75	113	82
321	544	211	325	122	280
123	478	331	141	221	195
231	391	112	259	131	196
222	311	223	254	311	178
111	302	322	259	212	222
132	542	232	398	233	309
222	374	133	299	311	196
321	358	331	273	131	259
213	468	232	437	122	361
231	316	322	485	233	345
111	307	121	311	221	207
333	570	313	343	113	16
312	427	211	353	323	199
123	380	112	454	212	114
132	400	223	251	332	240
132	611	121	403	113	302
123	444	331	338	323	256
312	550	322	405	311	367
333	573	223	331	131	268
213	706	313	522	221	400
111	423	211	319	332	446
321	749	232	383	233	515
231	529	133	292	212	420
222	424	112	554	122	384

TABLE 65

PLAN OF A FIELD WITH VARIETY NUMBERS AND CORRESPONDING PLOT YIELDS FOR A TWO-DIMENSIONAL QUASI-FACTORIAL EXPERIMENT WITH 49 VARIETIES

	Variety	Yield	Variety	Yield	Variety	Yield	Variety	Yield	Variety	Yield	Variety	Yield	Variety	Yield
	12	189	15	284	13	218	14	392	11	211	17	304	16	182
	26	289	25	342	27	345	23	214	21	327	22	270	24	320
Repli-	32	300	34	357	36	298	31	366	37	356	35	283	33	292
cate I	45	132	44	250	46	292	43	384	42	279	41	197	47	214
Group X	56	50	52	42	51	339	54	283	53	126	57	82	55	37
	65	153	66	310	63	306	64	303	61	182	67	121	62	197
	72	214	71	380	77	345	74	363	75	274	76	330	73	242
	71	234	11	283	51	125	41	336	31	233	61	339	21	269
	32	280	62	367	72	305	12	309	52	148	22	252	42	147
Repli-	73	414	23	399	33	381	43	184	13	162	63	191	53	62
cate II	44	217	54	250	24	295	64	277	34	273	14	307	74	287
Group Y	35	144	15	202	25	196	45	375	55	329	65	221	75	141
	26	161	16	204	56	214	46	450	66	165	76	203	36	197
	27	278	47	291	67	214	17	316	57	243	37	134	77	169
	15	263	16	111	12	255	14	201	17	150	11	95	13	259
	22	129	21	156	24	192	26	173	25	133	27	371	23	255
Repli-	31	284	34	240	32	214	35	325	33	149	37	254	36	194
cate III	42	130	47	206	45	234	43	290	44	211	41	225	46	358
Group X	54	165	57	93	52	267	51	242	53	158	55	102	56	339
	65	259	66	11	64	285	62	312	67	165	61	196	63	301
	73	307	74	168	71	245	75	301	76	223	72	265	77	361
	71	139	61	169	31	268	41	173	51	188	11	29	21	79
	72	126	52	142	42	180	12	−16	22	−8	32	−63	62	52
Repli-	63	187	23	254	53	100	43	−29	33	65	73	10	13	199
cate IV	44	257	64	206	74	118	24	209	34	174	14	112	54	108
Group Y	15	254	35	289	65	244	55	191	25	142	75	395	45	265
	36	249	76	201	16	140	26	248	56	235	46	235	66	176
	67	216	27	186	77	209	37	336	57	233	17	105	47	27

· TABLE 66

PLAN OF FIELD WITH VARIETY NUMBERS AND CORRESPONDING PLOT YIELDS FOR
A SYMMETRICAL INCOMPLETE BLOCK EXPERIMENT WITH 21 VARIETIES

Vari-ety	Yield	Vari-ety	Yield	Vari-ety	Yield	Vari-ety	Yield	Vari-ety	Yield	Block Totals
13	465	11	393	14	556	01	343	12	413	2170
22	408	21	337	24	421	23	308	01	353	1827
31	486	01	219	34	544	32	478	33	391	2118
01	311	44	302	43	542	42	374	41	358	1887
41	468	21	316	02	307	11	570	31	427	2088
02	380	32	400	42	611	12	444	22	550	2385
43	573	13	706	23	423	02	749	33	529	2980
44	424	02	638	24	736	14	488	34	758	3044
22	364	11	348	44	421	33	455	03	374	1962
12	507	34	421	43	374	21	334	03	381	2017
24	403	42	75	13	325	31	141	03	259	1203
32	254	23	259	03	398	14	299	41	273	1483
24	437	11	485	32	311	04	343	43	353	1929
14	454	33	251	21	403	42	338	04	405	1851
31	331	04	522	44	319	12	383	23	292	1847
22	554	04	626	41	753	34	505	13	668	3106
42	549	34	348	05	463	11	346	23	394	2100
05	363	21	449	13	217	44	355	32	244	1628
43	246	31	82	14	280	22	195	05	196	999
41	178	05	222	24	309	12	196	33	259	1164
02	361	04	345	01	207	05	16	03	199	1128

REFERENCES

1. L. D. BATCHELOR and H. S. REED. *Jour. Agr. Research*, **12**: 245–283, 1918.
2. R. A. FISHER. The Design of Experiments. Oliver and Boyd, London, 1937. Reading: Chapters V, VI, VII, and VIII.
3. R. A. FISHER. Statistical Methods for Research Workers. Oliver and Boyd, London, 1936. Reading: Chapter VIII, Sections 48 and 49.
4. R. A. FISHER and J. WISHART. The Arrangement of Field Experiments and the Statistical Reduction of the Results. *Imp. Bur. Soil Science, Tech. Com.*, 10.
5. C. H. GOULDEN. *Sci. Agr.*, **11**: 681–701, 1931.
6. C. H. GOULDEN. *Can. Jour. Research*, C, **15**: 231–241, 1937.
7. C. H. GOULDEN. Modern Methods for Testing a Large Number of Varieties. *Dom. of Canada, Tech. Bull.* 9. 1937.
8. F. R. IMMER, H. K. HAYES, and LEROY POWERS. *Jour. Amer. Soc. Agron.*, **26**: 403–419, 1934.
9. W. SAYER, M. VAIDYANATHAN, and S. S. IYER. *Indian Jour. Agr. Sci.*, **6**: 684–714, 1936.
10. O. TEDIN. *Jour. Agr. Sci.*, **21**: 191–208, 1931.
11. G. A. WIEBE. *Jour. Agr. Research*, **50**: 331–357, 1935.
12. J. WISHART. The Analysis of Variance Illustrated in its Application to a Complex Agricultural Experiment on Sugar Beets. *Archiv. Pflanzen*, **5**: 4, 1931.
13. J. WISHART. *Jour. Roy. Stat. Soc.*, **1**: 26–61, 1934.
14. J. WISHART. *Jour. Roy. Stat. Soc.*, **1**: 94–106, 1934.
15. J. WISHART and H. G. SANDERS. Principles and Practices of Field Experimentation. Empire Cotton Growing Corp., London, 1936.
16. F. YATES. The Principles of Orthogonality and Confounding in Replicated Experiments. *Jour. Agri. Sci.*, **23**: 108–145, 1933.
17. F. YATES. Complex Experiments. *Supp. Journ. Roy. Stat. Soc.*, II: 181–247, 1935.
18. F. YATES. Incomplete Randomized Blocks. *Ann. Eugen.*, **7**: 121–140, 1936.
19. F. YATES. The Design and Analysis of Factorial Experiments. *Imp. Bur. Soil Sci., Tech. Comm.* 35, 1937.
20. F. YATES. A New Method of Arranging Variety Trials Involving a Large Number of Varieties. *Jour. Agr. Sci.*, **26**: 424–455, 1936.

CHAPTER XIII

THE ANALYSIS OF VARIANCE APPLIED TO LINEAR REGRESSION FORMULAE

1. Significance of the Regression Function. If, in a series of paired values, y is the dependent and x is the independent variable, the regression of y on x is represented by the linear equation $Y = \bar{y} + b(x - \bar{x})$, where b is the regression coefficient and Y_i is a value of y estimated from the equation for $x = x_i$. Now if the equation is used to estimate each value of y from the corresponding values of x, it can be shown that

$$
\left.
\begin{aligned}
(1 - r^2)\Sigma(y - \bar{y})^2 &= \Sigma(y - Y)^2 \\
r^2\Sigma(y - \bar{y})^2 &= \Sigma(Y - \bar{y})^2
\end{aligned}
\right\}
\tag{1}
$$

And since $\Sigma(y - \bar{y})^2 = (1 - r^2)\Sigma(y - \bar{y})^2 + r^2\Sigma(y - \bar{y})^2$, it is obvious that, if the total sum of squares for the dependent variable is broken up into two parts, one part $\Sigma(y - Y)^2$, representing deviations from the regression function, and another part $\Sigma(Y - \bar{y})^2$, representing that portion of the total variability that is accounted for by the regression function, these two parts are proportional to $(1 - r^2)$ and r^2, respectively. It should be clear that $\Sigma(y - Y)^2$ represents deviations from the regression function because for each value of y we are taking the square of the deviation of that value from the corresponding Y value on the regression line. Similarly $\Sigma(Y - \bar{y})^2$ represents the regression function itself because for each value of y we take the square of the difference between $\bar{y}$ and the corresponding point on the regression line. As the slope of the regression line increases, $\Sigma(Y - \bar{y})^2$ must increase also, and as the y values approach more closely to the regression line the value of $\Sigma(y - Y)^2$ decreases correspondingly.

The direct relation between $\Sigma(Y - \bar{y})^2$ and the regression equation may be shown by equating it to

$$
\Sigma(Y - \bar{y})^2 = \Sigma\{\bar{y} + b(x - \bar{x}) - \bar{y}\}^2 = b^2\Sigma(x - \bar{x})^2
\tag{2}
$$

In the expression on the right $\Sigma(x - \bar{x})^2$ is obviously independent of the correlation so that any variations in $\Sigma(Y - \bar{y})^2$ are due entirely to b. This is an important concept as it shows that, since the value of

$\Sigma(Y - \bar{y})^2$ for any given distribution of y is dependent on a single statistic b, it must represent only 1 degree of freedom. Hence the analysis of variance corresponding to equation (1) will be:

	Sum of Squares	$D\,F$	Mean Square
Regression function......	$b^2\Sigma(x - \bar{x})^2$	1	$b^2\Sigma(x - \bar{x})^2$
Deviations from regression function.............	$\Sigma(y - Y)^2$	$n' - 2$	$\Sigma(y - Y)^2/n' - 2$
Total...........	$\Sigma(y - \bar{y})^2$	$n' - 1$	

where n' is the number of pairs of values of x and y.

In calculating the sum of squares $b^2\,\Sigma(x - x)^2$ it is frequently convenient to make use of the equality

$$b^2\Sigma(x - \bar{x})^2 = \frac{[\Sigma y(x - \bar{x})]^2}{\Sigma(x - \bar{x})^2} \tag{3}$$

If b has already been obtained it is of course just as convenient to multiply $\Sigma(x - \bar{x})^2$ by b^2.

If the correlation coefficient has been determined, a short method of determining the significance of r_{xy} which is exactly comparable to determining the significance of b_{yx} arises from the substitution of $(1 - r^2)\,\Sigma(y - \bar{y})^2$ for $\Sigma(y - Y)^2$, and $r^2\Sigma(y - \bar{y})^2$ for $b^2\Sigma(x - \bar{x})^2$, in the sum of squares column of the analysis of variance. Then F works out to $r^2\,(n' - 2)/1 - r^2$, and this is all the calculation necessary. In other words, for a total correlation or a regression coefficient, $F = t^2$, and tables either of F or of t may be used to test their significance. Refer here to Chapter VII, equation (11), and note that $F = v_b/v_e$.

2. Test for Non-Linearity. When correlation data are set up in the form of a correlation table the total sum of squares may be split up into two portions, one part representing differences between the means of arrays and the other representing differences between values within arrays. The equation is

$$\Sigma(y - \bar{y})^2 = \Sigma n_p(\bar{y}_p - \bar{y})^2 + \Sigma\Sigma(y - \bar{y}_p)^2 \tag{4}$$
$$\quad\quad\quad\quad\text{Between}\quad\quad\quad\text{Within}$$

where n_p is the number in an array and $\bar{y}_p$ is the mean of an array. The second summation in the term on the right means that the sums of squares are first computed for each array and these are summed.

The equation for the corresponding degrees of freedom is as follows:

$$n' - 1 = (q - 1) + (n' - q) \tag{5}$$

where q is the number of arrays in the table.

If we picture the sum of squares for between arrays as being due to a set of means running diagonally across the table following in general the regression straight line, it is obvious that the sum of squares for between arrays includes the sum of squares $b^2\Sigma(x - \bar{x})^2$, worked out above for deviations due to the regression function, and that the remainder will be due to deviations of the *means* of arrays *from* the regression line. The equation is

$$\underset{\substack{\text{Between}}}{\Sigma n_p(\bar{y}_p - \bar{y})^2} = \underset{\substack{\text{Deviations}\\\text{of means of}\\\text{arrays from}\\\text{regression line}}}{\Sigma n_p(\bar{y}_p - Y)^2} + \underset{\substack{\text{Due to linear}\\\text{regression}}}{b^2\Sigma(x - \bar{x})^2} \tag{6}$$

If the means of arrays fall directly on the regression line, $\Sigma n_p(\bar{y}_p - Y)^2$ will be zero, and correspondingly its value will increase as the trend of the mean values gets farther away from the trend of the straight regression line. Then since the sum of squares for within arrays measures the random variability in the values of y a comparison of the estimates of variance obtained from $\Sigma n_p(\bar{y}_p - Y)^2$ and $\Sigma\Sigma(y - \bar{y}_p)^2$ should provide a measure of the linearity of regression, or the goodness of fit of the regression straight line to the data in question.

The equation for the degrees of freedom corresponding to equation (6) will be $(q - 1) = (q - 2) + 1$.

The complete analysis of variance may be represented as follows:

	Sum of Squares	D F		Sum of Squares	D F
Between arrays	$\Sigma n_p(\bar{y}_p - \bar{y})^2$	$q - 1$	Linear regression	$b^2\Sigma(x - \bar{x})^2$	1
			Deviations, means of arrays from regression line	$\Sigma n_p(\bar{y}_p - Y)^2$	$q - 2$
Within arrays	$\Sigma\Sigma(y - \bar{y}_p)^2$	$n' - q$			
Total.....	$\Sigma(y - \bar{y})^2$	$n' - 1$			

For the purpose of testing linearity, however, it suffices to set up:

	Sum of Squares	$D\,F$	Variance
Deviations, means of arrays from regression line......	$\Sigma n_p(\bar{y}_p - Y)^2$	$q - 2$	$\Sigma n_p(\bar{y}_p - Y)^2/q - 2$
Within arrays.............	$\Sigma\Sigma(y - \bar{y}_p)^2$	$n' - q$	$\Sigma\Sigma(y - \bar{y}_p)^2/n' - q$
Total...............	$\Sigma(y - Y)^2$	$n' - 2$	

There are various methods of obtaining the sums of squares for the above analysis, but one of the most convenient and direct is first to calculate $\Sigma n_p(\bar{y}_p - \bar{y})^2$, making use of the identity

$$\Sigma n_p(\bar{y}_p - \bar{y})^2 = \Sigma\left(\frac{T_p^2}{n_p}\right) - \frac{T_y^2}{n'} \tag{7}$$

We square the total of each array and divide by the number in the array. These are summated, and from the sum we subtract the square of the y total divided by the number of paired values. Then we calculate $b^2\Sigma(x - \bar{x})^2$ and, $\Sigma(y - \bar{y})^2$ being known, the two sums of squares required can be obtained by subtraction. The procedure is obvious by reference to the outline of the analysis of variance above.

Example 41. Significance of a Regression Function. In Chapter VII, Example 13, we determined the correlation coefficient for the yields of adjacent barley plots and in Chapter VI, Example 11, we determined the regression line. Using the same data and the analysis of variance to test the significance of the regression function we should get a similar result. The sums of squares are

$$\Sigma(x - \bar{x})^2 = 3952 - 850^2/200 = 339.50$$
$$b^2\Sigma(x - \bar{x})^2 = 0.4492^2 \times 339.50 = 68.50$$
$$\Sigma(y - \bar{y})^2 = 8180 - 1246^2/200 = 417.42$$
$$\Sigma(y - Y)^2 = 417.42 - 68.50 = 348.92$$

Then the analysis of variance is as follows:

	Sum of Squares	$D\,F$	Variance	F	1% Point
Regression function.......	68.50	1	68.50	38.9	6.76
Deviations from regression	348.92	198	1.762		
Total..............	417.42	199			

The F value is well beyond its 5% point, indicating a high degree of significance.

Example 42. The Test for Non-Linearity. We shall again use the data of Chapter VI, Table 12, for this test. Since we already have $\Sigma(y - \bar{y})^2$ (Example 41, above) the first step is to calculate $\Sigma n_p(\bar{y}_p - \bar{y})^2$. In Chapter VI, Table 13, the totals for the y arrays are given, so we proceed as follows:

Between arrays.......	$20^2/4 + 60^2/13 + \cdots + 42^2/6 - 1246^2/60 =$	78.70
Linear regression.....	$b^2\Sigma(x - \bar{x})^2 = 0.4492^2 \times 339.50$	= 68.50
Deviations from regression..............	$\Sigma n_p(\bar{y}_p - Y)^2 = $ Difference	= 10.20
Total.......	$\Sigma(y - \bar{y})^2$	= 417.42
Between arrays.......	$\Sigma n_p(\bar{y}_p - \bar{y})^2$	= 78.70
Within arrays........	$\Sigma\Sigma(y - \bar{y}_p)^2 = $ Difference	= 338.72

Setting up the analysis of variance, we have:

	Sum of Squares	D F	Variance	F	5% Point
Deviation means of arrays from regression line.....	10.20	5	2.040	1.16	2.26
Within arrays............	338.72	193	1.755		

The F value does not approach its 5% point, so we conclude that there is no evidence of non-linear regression.

3. Significance of Multiple Correlations.

In multiple correlation where x_1 represents the dependent variable and x_2 and x_3 two independent variables the regression equation is

$$x_1 = \bar{x}_1 + b_{12}(x_2 - \bar{x}_2) + b_{13}(x_3 - \bar{x}_3) \tag{8}$$

and this may of course be extended for any number of variates. The normal equations corresponding to (8) are

$$\left.\begin{aligned}
\Sigma x_1(x_2 - \bar{x}_2) &= b_{12}\Sigma(x_2 - \bar{x}_2)^2 + b_{13}\Sigma x_2(x_3 - \bar{x}_3) \\
\Sigma x_1(x_3 - \bar{x}_3) &= b_{12}\Sigma x_2(x_3 - \bar{x}_3) + b_{13}\Sigma(x_3 - \bar{x}_3)^2
\end{aligned}\right\} \tag{9}$$

and from these we can derive the solution

$$\Sigma(x_1 - \bar{x}_1)^2 = \Sigma(x_1 - X_1)^2 + b_{12}\Sigma x_1(x_2 - \bar{x}_2) + b_{13}\Sigma x_1(x_3 - \bar{x}_3) \tag{10}$$

This equation corresponds to (1) above where the first term on the right represents the portion of the sum of squares for x_1 that is independent of x_2 and x_3. The other two terms on the right represent the portion of the sum of squares for x_1 that is dependent on x_2 and x_3. These terms may of course be written $b_{12}^2\Sigma(x_2 - \bar{x}_2)^2$ and $b_{13}^2\Sigma(x_3 - \bar{x}_3)^2$, in which form they correspond to $b^2\Sigma(x - \bar{x})^2$ as above in equation (2). Equation (10) may also be written

$$\Sigma(x_1 - \bar{x}_1)^2 = (1 - R^2)\Sigma(x_1 - \bar{x}_1)^2 + R^2\Sigma(x_1 - \bar{x}_1)^2 \quad (11)$$

where R is the multiple correlation coefficient. Also

$$(1 - R^2)\,\Sigma(x_1 - \bar{x}_1)^2 = \Sigma(x_1 - X_1)^2, \quad \text{and} \quad R^2\Sigma(x_1 - \bar{x}_1)^2$$
$$= b_{12}\Sigma x_1(x_2 - \bar{x}_2) + b_{13}\Sigma x_1(x_3 - \bar{x}_3).$$

It follows from (10) and (11) that a multiple regression can be expressed as an analysis of variance as follows:

	Sum of Squares	D F	Variance	F
Regression function	$R^2\Sigma(x_1 - \bar{x}_1)^2$	p	$R^2\Sigma(x_1 - \bar{x}_1)^2/p$	$\left(\dfrac{R^2}{1 - R^2}\right)\left(\dfrac{n' - p - 1}{p}\right)$
Deviations from regression function	$(1 - R^2)\Sigma(x_1 - \bar{x}_1)^2$	$n' - p - 1$	$\dfrac{(1 - R^2)\Sigma(x_1 - \bar{x}_1)^2}{n' - p - 1}$	
Total	$\Sigma(x_1 - \bar{x}_1)^2$	$n' - 1$		

where p is the number of independent variables. To test the significance of a multiple correlation therefore it is only necessary to find

$$F = \left(\frac{R^2}{1 - R^2}\right)\left(\frac{n' - p - 1}{p}\right) \quad (12)$$

and look up the 5% point of F corresponding to $n_1 = p$ and $n_2 = n' - p - 1$.

Example 43. The Significance of a Multiple Correlation. Let $R_{1.2345} = 0.6457$, and it has been obtained from a series of 84 values of $x_1, x_2, x_3, x_4,$ and x_5. We have

$$F = \left(\frac{0.416928}{0.583072}\right)\left(\frac{79}{4}\right) = 14.1$$

For $p = 4$ and $n' - p - 1 = 79$, the 1% point of F is 3.56, so that the multiple correlation is highly significant.

4. Special Applications. The analysis of variance can be used to determine the significance of the additional information obtained in calculating multiple correlation coefficients. This method was used by Geddes and Goulden (2) in a practical problem in cereal chemistry. Correlations were first determined between loaf volume of wheat flour and the percentage of protein. In later studies the protein was separated into two portions, peptized and non-peptized, and using these two portions as variables the multiple correlation for their combined effect on loaf volume was calculated. If the proportions of the two kinds of protein have an important effect on loaf volume the multiple correlation should be significantly higher than the simple correlation for total protein and loaf volume. A method of comparing the two correlations would determine therefore the practical significance, for purposes of predicting flour quality, of knowing the amounts of peptized and non-peptized protein in addition to the total protein.

If we let x_1 represent loaf volume, x_2 the peptized protein, x_3 the non-peptized protein, and x_p the total protein, the corresponding simple and multiple correlation coefficients are r_{1p} and $R_{1.23}$. The total protein is of course $(x_2 + x_3)$, the sum of the two fractions.

Assuming these correlations to be determined from 20 pairs of values, the sums of squares representing deviations from the regression function are proportional to $(1 - r_{1p}^2)$ and $(1 - R_{1.23}^2)$, respectively, and the corresponding degrees of freedom are 18 and 17. The effect of using more variables to estimate x_1 as in the case of multiple regression is to decrease the sum of squares due to deviations from the regression function, but for each additional variable introduced 1 degree of freedom is lost and unless the reduction of the sum of squares is more than proportional to the loss in degrees of freedom there is no gain in precision. An analysis may therefore be set up as follows:

	Sum of Squares	D F	Variance
Deviations from regression of x_p on x_1.................	$1 - r_{1p}^2$	18	
Deviations from regression of x_2 and x_3 on x_1...........	$1 - R_{1.23}^2$	17	(1)
Additional degree of freedom	$(1 - r_{1p}^2) - (1 - R_{1.23}^2)$	1	(2)

Applying the z test to the mean squares (1) and (2), using (1) as an error, we can determine the significance of the gain in information due to the addition of another variable.

In one actual experiment for a series of 20 flours from No. 2 Northern wheat $r_{1p} = 0.511$ and $R_{1.23} = 0.732$. The analysis gives:

Sum of Squares		D F	Variance	F	1% Point
$1 - r_{1p}^2$	0.738879	18			
$1 - R_{1.23}^2$	0.464176	17	0.02730		
Difference	0.274703	1	0.2747	10.06	8.40

In this case there was a decided gain in information owing to the separation of the protein into two components.

In the general case to which this method may be applied note that $(1 - r^2)$ represents $(n' - 2)$ degrees of freedom and $(1 - R^2)$, $(n' - p - 1)$ degrees of freedom. The difference between the two sums of squares will be represented therefore by $(n' - 2) - (n' - p - 1) = (p - 1)$ degrees of freedom.

5. Exercises.

1. For the data in Chapter VI, Table 15, determine the significance of the regression function by means of the analysis of variance, where the flour carotene is taken as the dependent variable. $F = 159.5$.

2. For the same data as in Exercise 1 above, test for linearity of regression. $F = 3.21$.

3. Apply the test for non-linearity to the data in Table 67 for the relation between loaf volume according to a standard baking formula and the percentage protein of wheat flour. If there is evidence of non-linearity calculate the regression equation and make a graph showing the regression line and the means of the arrays.

TABLE 67

CORRELATION SURFACE FOR RELATION BETWEEN PROTEIN AND LOAF VOLUME

Protein in Percentage

Loaf volume in cc.	11.0	11.5	12.0	12.5	13.0	13.5	14.0	14.5	15.0	15.5	
950							1				1
900						2	5				7
850				5	2	5	6	3	1		22
800				6	15	7	3	12	2		45
750			9	12	14	5	6	2	1	1	50
700		1	7	3	1	1					13
650		4	5	2							11
600	4	6	2								12
550		2									2
500	1										1
	5	13	23	23	35	15	16	26	6	2	164

4. For $n' = 40$, determine the multiple correlation $R_{1.234}$ that is just significant.

5. Determine the significance of the gain in information through the calculation of multiple correlations in the examples given below.   For each comparison, state your conclusion in words.

$n' = 40$	$r_{12} = 0.7643$	$R_{1.234}\ \ = 0.8031$
$n' = 62$	$r_{12} = 0.8744$	$R_{1.2345} = 0.9664$
$n' = 20$	$r_{12} = 0.7621$	$R_{1.23}\ \ = 0.7635$
$n' = 20$	$r_{12} = 0.7316$	$R_{1.23456} = 0.7329$

REFERENCES

1. R. A. FISHER.   Statistical Methods for Research Workers.   Oliver and Boyd, London, 1936.   Reading: Chapter VIII, Sections 44, 46, 47.
2. W. F. GEDDES and C. H. GOULDEN.   *Cereal Chem.*, **7**: 527–556, 1930.
3. L. H. C. TIPPETT.   The Methods of Statistics.   Williams and Norgate, London, 1931.   Reading: Chapter VII, Sections 7.23, 7.33; Chapter IX, Sections 9.3; Chapter XI, Sections 11.6, 11.72, 11.63.

CHAPTER XIV

NON-LINEAR REGRESSION

1. An Example of Non-Linear Regression. In Chapter XIII, Section 5, Exercise 3, a test for non-linearity was applied to a correlation surface for the relation between protein and loaf volume of wheat flour in a baking experiment. The non-linearity is significant, and on plotting the means of the arrays we find that with increasing protein there is at first a very rapid increase in the loaf volume, but with higher protein flours the increase in loaf volume is slower and finally there are indications that the loaf volume is actually decreasing. Here we have a typical example of non-linearity, and it is obvious that, in such cases, methods for the prediction of values of the dependent variable from specific values of the independent variable cannot be based on a straight-line equation.

2. The Correlation Ratio. In cases of non-linear regression the correlation ratio (1) is sometimes used to represent the relation between the two variables. The correlation ratio is defined by

$$\eta_{yx}^2 = \frac{\Sigma n_p(\bar{y}_p - \bar{y})^2}{\Sigma(y - \bar{y})^2} \tag{1}$$

and its relation to the correlation coefficient will be obvious from the outline of the analysis of variance of Chapter XIII, Section 2. The correlation coefficient may be defined as follows if we take into account its numerical value only:

$$r_{yx}^2 = \frac{\Sigma(Y - \bar{y})^2}{\Sigma(y - \bar{y})^2} \tag{2}$$

and it is clear that in the correlation ratio the numerator contains the sum of squares $\Sigma(Y - \bar{y})^2$ plus the sum of squares due to deviations of means of arrays from the regression line. Hence η^2 is always greater than r^2 unless the means of the arrays fall exactly on the regression line. The correlation ratio measures the *total* variability of the means of arrays, and this may be due in part either to a linear relation between the variables or to some other type of relation. It does not, however, represent a relation that can be expressed by a mathematical equation, either

219

linear or curvilinear. The correlation ratio is therefore not a very satisfactory statistic as it cannot be used to predict one variable from another. Its use must be confined to a measurement of the significance of the total variability of the means of the arrays and in this respect must be interpreted in terms of the analysis of variance. Thus in Chapter XIII, Section 2, the analysis of variance test will involve a comparison of the variance between arrays with the variance within arrays.

The popularity of the correlation ratio was occasioned partly by the use of Blakeman's criterion ($\eta^2 - r^2$) as a test for linearity (1). R. A. Fisher (3) has shown that this test is not satisfactory and that the analysis of variance can be used as described in Chapter XIII to provide an accurate test. The correlation ratio as such is therefore not much used at the present time. It may frequently be necessary to apply a test of significance to the variance for the means of arrays in a correlation surface, but this does not necessitate the actual calculation of the correlation ratio. Elaborate methods have been developed for testing the significance of the correlation ratio, but these are now unnecessary as the problem has been completely solved by Fisher's z distribution and the analysis of variance. The test, as we have noted in the previous chapter, is now quite simple.

3. Types of Regression Equations. The procedure in making a critical study of the relation between two variables when this relation is non-linear is to endeavor to find some type of mathematical equation that will give a good fit. This is obviously not always a simple problem as there are a number of types of equations to choose from and in each case the method of making an accurate test of the goodness of fit must be considered. The first step is to examine the trend of the values in the regression graph and from its general characteristics decide as to the type of equation to be used. After the type has been selected the actual equation must be determined by direct methods.

The simple straight-line equation that we have dealt with previously is

$$Y = \bar{y} + b_{yx}(x - \bar{x}) = \bar{y} - b_{yx}\bar{x} + b_{yx}x$$

and since $\bar{y} - b_{yx}\bar{x}$ is a constant we can write this equation in the form

$$Y = c_0 + c_1 x$$

where $c_0 = y - b_{yx}\bar{x}$ and $c_1 = b_{yx}$, the regression coefficient. This is a convenient form with which to represent the various kinds of regression equations, which in general are of two types: (1) polynomials, and (2) logarithmic. Typical examples are as follows:

POLYNOMIALS

$$Y = c_0 + c_1 x$$
$$Y = c_0 + c_1 x + c_2 x^2$$
$$Y = c_0 + c_1 x + c_2 x^2 + c_3 x^3$$
etc.

LOGARITHMIC

$$Y = c_0 + c_1 \log x$$
$$\log Y = c_0 + c_1 x$$
$$\log Y = c_0 + c_1 \log x$$
etc.

Of the polynomials the first is the simple straight-line equation, the second is the simple parabola or quadratic, and the third is the cubic. The simple parabola has only one maximum or minimum point, and there are no points of inflection. The cubic has both a maximum and a minimum point and one point of inflection. Curves of higher degree have more maximum and minimum points and tend to twist oftener and more rapidly. A most interesting characteristic of the polynomial equations is one that has already been noted in Chapter XII, in dealing with the separation of sums of squares corresponding to individual degrees of freedom. The effects represented by the polynomials of different degree are independent, and we refer to them as the *orthogonal polynomials*. This property is of particular value in curve fitting as it simplifies materially the problem of testing the goodness of fit at each stage of fitting.

Logarithmic curves may be regarded as modifications of the other types. Thus the straight-line equation $Y = c_0 + c_1 x$ may be changed to a logarithmic equation by replacing x by $\log x$. The result of this change is a crowding together of the x ordinates farthest away from zero. A straight line with a positive slope is changed therefore to a curved line which has a very decided slope at the origin but changes rapidly as x increases and reaches a point finally where the slope is fairly constant but much less than that of the original straight line. Logarithmic curves, in addition, cannot be used to represent negative values, and in this respect are therefore much more limited in their application than the polynomials.

The characteristics of the different types of equations are most easily learned by working out the Y values for some imaginary equations and plotting the curves on graph paper.

4. A General Method of Fitting Polynomials. With the data such as those of Table 67, Chapter XIII, before us in the form of a correlation surface, we may inquire as to the possibility of expressing the relation between protein and loaf volume by some simple mathematical equation, the end result of our inquiry being to obtain the best method available for predicting the loaf volume that will be obtained from the flours of a given protein content. The selection of the best type of equation is fairly easy in this case. First we prepare a graph of the means of the y arrays as in Fig. 12, connecting the points with a dotted line. The general trend of the points seems to follow fairly closely the first half of the second degree parabola, or of the portion of a third-degree curve up to the maximum point. There is very little resemblance to a logarithmic curve as the first portion of it is nearly straight and with

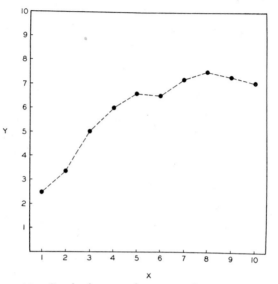

Fig. 12.—Graph of means of y arrays; data of Table 67.

a greater curvature towards the end. Of course polynomials of higher degree may give a better fit than those of the second degree or third degree, and the problem resolves itself therefore into the selection of a polynomial that will give the greatest degree of precision in predicting y from particular values of x.

SELECTION OF EQUATION GIVING THE BEST FIT

The problem of selecting an equation of the degree that gives the greatest precision for prediction purposes is of paramount importance in curve fitting and one which may easily be overlooked in a maze of technical details leading to the fitting of curves of a high order. Unless we can be sure that a curve fits better than a straight line it would be better not to use the curve. In certain cases the improvement in fit due to one equation over another is clearly visible by inspection, but this is certainly not generally true. For example, in comparing second and third-degree curves, the latter often appear to fit better than the former, but a critical test may show that the situation is definitely otherwise.

In the methods of curve fitting described below, particular attention is given to the problem of determining goodness of fit. We begin by fitting a straight line or a curve of low degree and follow up with additional stages of fitting. At each stage one degree of freedom is utilized in fitting, and the variance represented by this degree of freedom is tested against the error of regression. As a general rule, when a curve has been obtained that passes reasonably well through the points, and if in making use of an additional degree of freedom there is no gain in precision, the curve of lower degree fitted previously is taken as giving the best fit.

METHOD

The fitting of polynomials is an application of the method of least squares. Where Y represents the values of y estimated from the regression equation for given values of x, the type regression equation is as follows:

$$Y = c_0 + c_1 x + c_2 x^2 + \cdots + c_m x^m \tag{3}$$

and consequently the error of estimation is given by

$$\Sigma(y - Y) = \Sigma(y - c_0 - c_1 x - c_2 x^2 - \cdots - c_m x^m)^2 \tag{4}$$

The best values for substitution in the equation for c_0, c_1, c_2, $\cdots c_m$ are taken as those that give a minimum value to $\Sigma(y - Y)^2$. Minimizing the expression on the right in (4) we obtain a set of $m + 1$ simultaneous equations, where $m + 1$ is the number of unknowns and m is the highest power of x in the polynomial equation to be derived. These simultaneous equations are known as the *normal equations*, owing to the symmetrical nature of the coefficients. For the general case they are as follows, where x and y are measured from their means:

$$
\begin{aligned}
n'c_0 + \Sigma(x)c_1 &+ \Sigma(x^2)c_2 + \cdots + \Sigma(x^m)c_m = \Sigma(y) \\
\Sigma(x)c_0 + \Sigma(x^2)c_1 &+ \Sigma(x^3)c_2 + \cdots + \Sigma(x^{m+1})c_m = \Sigma(xy) \\
\Sigma(x^2)c_0 + \Sigma(x^3)c_1 &+ \Sigma(x^4)c_2 + \cdots + \Sigma(x^{m+2})c_m = \Sigma(x^2 y)
\end{aligned}
\tag{5}
$$

$$\Sigma(x^m)c_0 + \Sigma(x^{m+1})c_1 + \Sigma(x^{m+2})c_2 + \cdots + \Sigma(x^{2m})c_m = \Sigma(x^m y)$$

The symmetrical nature of the coefficients allows for a method of solution commonly known as the Doolittle method wherein the total amount of calculation involved is very considerably reduced as compared with the ordinary method of solving a set of simultaneous equations. After c_0, c_1, c_2, $\cdots c_m$ have been solved for, the setting up of the regression equation is merely a matter of substituting the values of these statistics in equation (3)

TESTING THE GOODNESS OF FIT

The method of testing the significance of the variance corresponding to each degree of freedom used in fitting is merely an extension of the method described in Chapter XIII for testing the significance of a straight-line regression function.

Let $R_0 = \Sigma(y - \bar{y})^2$, $R_1 = \Sigma(y - Y_1)^2$, and $\Sigma(Y_1 - \bar{y})^2$ is the sum of squares due to the regression function for one degree of fitting. The analysis is of the form:

	SS	DF
Regression function.........	$\Sigma(Y_1 - \bar{y})^2$	1
First residual...............	$R_1 = \Sigma(y - Y_1)^2$	$n' - 2$
Total...........	$R_0 = \Sigma(y - \bar{y})^2$	$n' - 1$

If a second statistic is fitted the residual R_1 will be reduced by an amount equal to the difference between the sums of squares for the two regression functions, i.e., by $\Sigma(Y_2 - \bar{y})^2 - \Sigma(Y_1 - \bar{y})^2$, which for convenience we will put equal to $\Sigma(Y_1 - Y_2)^2$. The new residual may be represented by R_2, and the analysis will be:

	SS	DF
Difference, regression functions....................	$\Sigma(Y_1 - Y_2)^2$	1
Residual..................	R_2	$n' - 3$
First residual.....	R_1	$n' - 2$

Obviously this process can be continued indefinitely, providing at each stage a test of the significance of the additional statistic fitted in the regression equation. Isserliss has shown how the sums of squares for each regression coefficient can be obtained simultaneously with the solution of the equations for the unknowns. His method involves solving for the regression coefficients c_0, c_1, $\cdots$ c_m, by means of algebraical formulae, and since this method appears to be somewhat laborious, the work in the following examples is performed in tables by a technique similar to that used in solving the equations for partial regression and correlation coefficients. It is shown also how the sums of squares required for the tests of significance may be obtained directly from these tables.

The analysis of variance test as used here should not be confused with the test for non-linearity as described in Chapter XIII. The regression straight line may not be a good fit, but, if it is a better fit than the horizontal line representing the mean of y, the test we use here will show it to be significant. At the same time, the test for non-linearity will indicate significant deviations of the means of the y arrays from the regression line. As a matter of fact, after fitting a straight line it is desirable to apply the test for linearity. If there is no evidence of non-linearity there is no object in proceeding to the fitting of a curve of higher degree.

Example 44. For this example we shall use the data of Table 67 and fit polynomials by successive stages up to the third degree.

The first step in the procedure of fitting regression lines is to obtain the values of the coefficients for the normal equations. These are best obtained as in Table 68, which is divided into sections, each section representing the data necessary for calculating one additional constant. Thus Section A is necessary for fitting a straight line; if we wish to fit a second-degree curve we proceed with Section B, and so forth. This is continued until it is obvious that further fitting is unnecessary. In actual practice we will probably not have to go beyond fitting to the third degree.

Note that the actual classes for both y and x are replaced by 1, 2, 3,...9. This reduces the labor a great deal, and, when the Y values have finally been calculated for drawing the curve, they may be converted to actual values by the method described in Chapter II, Section 8, for converting means; or the whole equation may be converted to actual values by methods similar to those described in Chapter VI, Section 5.

The easiest method for calculating the sum of the powers of x is by continuous multiplication. First, $N_{xy}x$ is calculated for each array, and to obtain the figures in $N_{xy}x^2$ we simply multiply each of the $N_{xy}x$ values by x. When we reach the last column of one section it is good practice to check this column using a table of powers of x. This checks all the previous calculations of the powers of x.

Having carried out the calculations as in Table 68, Section A, we write the normal equations for fitting a straight line. For the general case these are

$$n'c_0 + \Sigma(x)c_1 = \Sigma(y)$$
$$\Sigma(x)c_0 + \Sigma(x^2)c_1 = \Sigma(xy)$$

(6)

and substituting the actual coefficients we have

$$164c_0 + 851c_1 = 1014$$
$$851c_0 + 5181c_1 = 5695$$

TABLE 68

Calculation of Coefficients for Fitting a Polynomial up to the Third Degree

Section A

y	Frequency of y for x Arrays N_{yx}	Totals for y Arrays T_{yx}	Means for y Arrays $\bar{y}_x$	x	Frequency of x for y Arrays N_{xy}	$N_{xy}x$	$N_{xy}x^2$	$xT_{yx}=$ $N_{xy}x\bar{y}_x$	T_{yx}^2/N_{yx}
1	1	13	2.6000	1	5	5	5	13	33.8000
2	2	43	3.3077	2	13	26	52	86	142.2308
3	12	115	5.0000	3	23	69	207	345	575.0000
4	11	137	5.9565	4	23	92	368	548	816.0435
5	13	234	6.6857	5	35	175	875	1170	1564.4571
6	50	100	6.6667	6	15	90	540	600	666.6667
7	45	115	7.1875	7	16	112	784	805	826.5625
8	22	199	7.6538	8	26	208	1664	1592	1523.1154
9	7	44	7.3333	9	6	54	486	396	322.6667
10	1	14	7.0000	10	2	20	200	140	98.0000
	164	1014			164	851	5181	5695	6568.5427

	Section B			Section C	
$N_{xy}x^3$	$N_{xy}x^4$	$x^2T_{yx}=$ $N_{xy}x^2\bar{y}_x$	$N_{xy}x^5$	$N_{xy}x^6$	$x^3T_{yx}=$ $N_{xy}x^3\bar{y}_x$
5	5	13	5	5	13
104	208	172	416	832	344
621	1,863	1,035	5,589	16,767	3,105
1,472	5,888	2,192	23,552	94,208	8,768
4,375	21,875	5,850	109,375	546,875	29,250
3,240	19,440	3,600	116,640	699,840	21,600
5,488	38,416	5,635	268,912	1,882,384	39,445
13,312	106,496	12,736	851,968	6,815,744	101,888
4,374	39,366	3,564	354,294	3,188,646	32,076
2,000	20,000	1,400	200,000	2,000,000	14,000
34,991	253,557	36,197	1,930,751	15,245,301	250,489

SUMMARY OF COEFFICIENTS

Section A	Section B	Section C
$n' = 164$	$\Sigma(x^3) = 34{,}991$	$\Sigma(x^5) = 1{,}930{,}751$
$\Sigma(x) = 851$	$\Sigma(x^4) = 253{,}557$	$\Sigma(x^6) = 15{,}245{,}301$
$\Sigma(y) = 1{,}014$	$\Sigma(x^2y) = 36{,}197$	$\Sigma(x^3y) = 250{,}489$
$\Sigma(x^2) = 5{,}181$		
$\Sigma(xy) = 5{,}695$		
$\Sigma(T^2_{yx}/N_{xy}) = 6{,}568.54$		
$\Sigma(y - \bar{y})^2 = 428.512$		

The solution of these equations is carried out as in Table 69, the method being identical with that described in Chapter VIII for partial regression and correlation coefficients.   Note the "check sum" column, which is used for checking the calculations as you proceed, and in addition the "check line" just below the "reverse," that gives a complete check on all the calculations including those in the reverse.   In Table 69 the check line is obtained as follows:

$$164 \times 3.244{,}175 + 851 \times 0.566{,}340 = 1014$$

It is merely a substitution of the statistics c_0 and c_1 in the first equation of (6).

At the foot of Table 69 we have the analysis of variance for testing the significance of the degree of freedom due to the regression straight line. $R_0 = \Sigma(y - \bar{y})^2$ is obtained from Table 68, using the equality

$$\Sigma(y - \bar{y})^2 = \Sigma(y^2) - \frac{T^2_y}{n'}$$

$\Sigma(Y_1 - \bar{y})^2$ is then obtained from the solution of the normal equations by multiplying the figure in line 5, column 1 (5,1), by the square of the figure in line 6, column $K(6,K)^2$.   The difference is the sum of squares $\Sigma(y - Y_1)^2 = R_1$, and may be taken to represent the error of regression and is therefore appropriate for testing the significance of the variance due to the regression line.   In the example, we find that the regression is decidedly significant but we proceed to the second stage in order to determine whether or not greater accuracy can be obtained.

Proceeding to the fitting of a polynomial of the form $Y = c_0 + c_1x + c_2x^2$, we write the normal equations

$$n'c_0 + \Sigma(x)c_1 + \Sigma(x^2)c_2 = \Sigma(y)$$

$$\Sigma(x)c_0 + \Sigma(x^2)c_1 + \Sigma(x^3)c_2 = \Sigma(xy) \tag{7}$$

$$\Sigma(x^2)c_0 + \Sigma(x^3)c_1 + \Sigma(x^4)c_2 = \Sigma(x^2y)$$

and the necessary data for solving the equations are obtained as in section B of Table 68. The solution of the equations is performed according to Table 70, and note that in this table columns (0) and (1) can be copied directly from Table 69, and column K can be copied as far as line 6.   The reverse and the check line are calculated in the usual way.   For the analysis of variance R_1 is brought forward from Table 69, and $\Sigma(Y_1 - Y_2)^2$ is calculated by multiplying (10,2) by $(11,K)^2$, where the numbers in

TABLE 69

SOLUTION OF NORMAL EQUATIONS FOR FITTING A STRAIGHT LINE

Line		0	1	K	Sum
	1	164	851	1014	2029
	2	−1.0000	−5.189,024	−6.182,927	−12.37,195
	3		5181	5695	11,727
	4		−4415.8594	5261.6703	−10,528.530
	5		765.1406	433.3297	1,198.470
	6		−1.0000	−0.566,340	−1.566,340
$c_1 = +0.566,340$	1		+0.566,340	+0.566,340	
$c_0 = +3.244,175$	2	+3.244,175	−2.938,752	+6.182,927	
Check		532.0447	+481.9553	=1014	

(Reverse — label in left margin for lines 1 and 2 of the c block)

	S (sq.)	$D F$	Variance	F	5% Point of F
$R_0 = \Sigma(y - \bar{y})^2$	428.512	163			
$(5,1) \times (6,K)^2$	245.412	1	245.4	225	3.90
$R_1 = \Sigma(y - Y_1)^2$	183.100	162	1.130		

the brackets correspond to line and column respectively. The difference between the two sums of squares is R_2, which can now be taken to represent the error of regression. In the example we find that the variance due to the additional degree of freedom used in calculating the second-degree curve is quite significant, so we can conclude that a real gain in precision has been made.

If the method of procedure up to this point has been thoroughly understood it will be found that the fitting of additional statistics can be carried forward without difficulty. The work involved in fitting to the third degree in the present example has been performed in Table 71. Note that the columns 0, 1, and 2, can be copied directly from previous calculations and that column K can be copied as far as line 11.

The analysis of variance indicates that the variance due to the additional degree of freedom used in fitting a polynomial of the third degree is insignificant. It is, in fact, less than the variance due to error of regression. The conclusion is that the third-degree curve, although it fits the data satisfactorily, is less useful for predicting loaf volume from protein than the second-degree curve. In making use of another degree of freedom to determine a new regression function, precision has actually been lost.

TABLE 70

SOLUTION OF NORMAL EQUATIONS FOR FITTING A SECOND-DEGREE POLYNOMIAL

Line	0	1	2	K	Sum
1	164	851	5,181	1,014	7,210
2	-1.0000	-5.189,024	-31.591,46	-6.182,927	-43.96341
3		5181	34,991	5,695	46,718
4		-4415.8594	-26,884.333	-5,261.6703	37,412.86
5		765.1406	8,106.667	433.3297	9,035.14
6		-1.0000	-10.595	-0.566,340	-12.16135
7			253,557	36,197	329,926
8			-163,675.35	-32,033.740	-227,774.43
9			-85,890.14	-4,591.128	-98,587.96
10			3,991.51	-427.868	3,563.61
11			-1.000	0.107,194	
Reverse 1			-0.107,194	-0.107,194	
Reverse 2		+1.702,060	+1.135,720	+0.566,340	
Reverse 3	+0.737,312	-8.832,030	+3.386,415	+6.182,927	
Check	120.9192	+1448.4531	-555.3721	=1014.0002	

$c_2 = -0.107,194$
$c_1 = +1.702,060$
$c_0 = +0.737,312$

	S(sq.)	DF	Variance	F	5% Point
R_1	183.100	162	45.86	53.8	3.90
$(10,2) \times (11,K)^2$	45.865	1	0.8524		
R_2	137.235	161			

TABLE 71

SOLUTION OF NORMAL EQUATIONS FOR FITTING A THIRD-DEGREE POLYNOMIAL

Line	0	1	2	3	K	Sum
1	164	851	5,181	34,991	1,014	42,201
2	−1.0000	−5.189024	−31.59146	−213.3598	−6.182927	−257.3232
3		5181	34,991	253,557	5,695	300,275
4		−4415.8594	−26,884.333	−181,569.14	−5,261.6703	−218,982.00
5		765.1406	8,106.667	71,987.86	433.3297	81,293
6		1.0000	−10.59500	−94.08448	−0.566340	−106.2458
7			253,557	1,930,751	36,197	2,260,677
8			−163,675.35	−1,105,416.78	−32,033.740	−1,333,191.2
9			−85,890.14	−762,711.38	−4,591.128	−861,299.3
10			3,991.51	62,622.84	−427.868	66,186.5
11			1.0000	−15.68901	0.107194	16.58182
12				15,245,301	250,489	17,715,089
13				−7,465,672.8	−216,346.84	−9,003,996.9
14				−6,772,940.4	−40,769.60	−7,648,409.6
15				−982,490.4	6,712.82	−1,038,400.7
16				24,197.4	85.38	24,281.8
17				−1.0000	−0.003528	
Reverse $c_3 = +0.003528$				+0.003528	+0.003528	
$c_2 = -0.165,545$			−0.162,545	−0.055,351	−0.107,194	
$c_1 = +1.956,574$		+1.956,574	+1.722,164	−0.331,930	+0.566,340	
$c_0 = +0.412,519$	+0.412,519	−10.152,709	+5.135,034	−0.752,733	+6.182,927	
Check	67.6531	+1665.0445	+842.1456	+123.4482	= 1014.0002	

	S(sq.)	D F	Variance	F	5% Point
R_2	137.235	161			
	0.301	1	0.3010		
R_3	136.934	160	0.8558		

$(16,3) \times (17,K)^2 = 24,197.4 \times (0.003528)^2$

5. Fitting Logarithmic Curves. The procedure is best illustrated by means of an example.

Example 45. The data given in Table 72, and presented graphically in Fig. 13, were obtained in a study by Geddes (4), of the effect of time of heating on the baking quality of wheat flour.

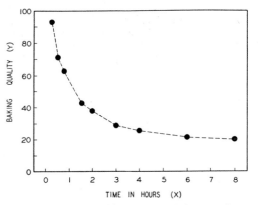

Fɪɢ. 13.—Relation between time of heating and baking quality of wheat flour.

From an examination of Fig. 13 it is obvious that a straight line cannot give a good fit to the results. It is also obvious by inspection that a polynomial cannot be expected to give a good fit as the curve tends to flatten out and run parallel to the

TABLE 72

Iɴꜰʟᴜᴇɴᴄᴇ ᴏꜰ ᴛʜᴇ Tɪᴍᴇ ᴏꜰ Hᴇᴀᴛɪɴɢ ᴀᴛ 170° F. ᴏɴ ᴛʜᴇ Bᴀᴋɪɴɢ Qᴜᴀʟɪᴛʏ ᴏꜰ
Sᴛʀᴀɪɢʜᴛ Gʀᴀᴅᴇ Fʟᴏᴜʀ

Time in Hours	Baking Quality Single Feature Estimate
0.25	93
0.50	71
0.75	63
1.0	54
1.5	43
2.0	38
3.0	29
4.0	26
6.0	22
8.0	20

zero axes at both ends. From $x = 0$ to $x = 4$, the curve might be fitted fairly well by a second-degree polynomial, but as x increases from that point, the curve flattens out and runs almost parallel to the x axis. This is typical of logarithmic curves and decidedly not typical of polynomials. We decide therefore that a logarithmic curve will give the best fit.

The next step is to examine the three principal types of logarithmic curves, as given on page 221, and make a preliminary determination of their goodness of fit to the results by plotting the three pairs of variables, y and log y, log y and x, log y and log x, against each other in a rough graph and noting which of the three give points that fall most nearly in a straight line. As illustrated in Fig. 14, the set of points falling most nearly in a straight line are those given by log y and log x, so we proceed to fit a curve of the type log $Y = c_0 + c_1$ log x.

The calculations, using log y and log x as variables, are exactly the same as in fitting a straight line. These are given in Tables 73 and 74, together with the analysis of variance to determine the significance of the fit of the regression line.

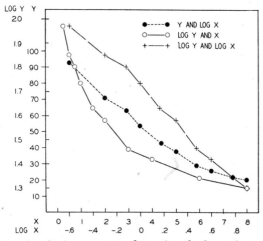

Fig. 14.—Result of preliminary test to determine the logarithmic equation giving the best fit to the data of Table 72.

Note that the goodness of fit is determined on the basis of the logarithms of y and Y, and not on the basis of the actual values. Thus the error of regression is given by $\Sigma(\log y - \log Y)^2$. This can be taken as a general rule, i. e., that when the regression equation gives logarithmic values, the test of goodness of fit must be in terms of the logarithms estimated. It arises from the fact that logarithms express the relative differences between numbers and not their absolute differences. With two numbers such as a and b, their absolute difference is $a - b$, but log $a -$ log b is log a/b, and if a and b are variables and a given percentage increase in a results in a similar percentage increase in b, log a/b is constant and the relation between the logarithms can be expressed by a straight-line equation. To test this fact it is essential that we deal with logarithms throughout and not with actual values.

For graphical purposes it is suitable to express the results of fitting a logarithmic equation as in Fig. 15, where the actual values of x are plotted against the anti-logarithms of log Y, and a smooth curve drawn through the points. The small circles in Fig. 15 represent the original values of y and x.

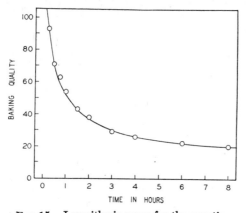

FIG. 15.—Logarithmic curve for the equation

$$\log Y = c_0 + c_1 \log x,$$

fitted to the data of Table 72.

TABLE 73

CALCULATION OF COEFFICIENTS FOR THE CURVE $\log Y = c_0 + c_1 \log x$

x Time in Hours	y Baking Quality	x_1 = Log x	y_1 = Log y	Log Y	Y
0.25	93	−0.6021	1.9685	1.9937	98.6
0.50	71	−0.3010	1.8513	1.8528	71.2
0.75	63	−0.1249	1.7993	1.7704	58.9
1.0	54	0.0000	1.7324	1.7120	51.5
1.5	43	0.1761	1.6355	1.6296	42.6
2.0	38	0.3010	1.5798	1.5711	37.2
3.0	29	0.4771	1.4624	1.4887	30.8
4.0	26	0.6021	1.4150	1.4302	26.9
6.0	22	0.7782	1.3424	1.3478	22.3
8.0	20	0.9031	1.3010	1.2893	19.5

$\Sigma(x_1)$ = 2.209,600
$\Sigma(x_1^2)$ = 2.601,671
$\Sigma(y_1)$* = 6.085,600
$\Sigma(x_1 y_1)$ = 0.355,642,8

$\Sigma(y_1)^2$ = 4.169,362
$[\Sigma(y_1)]^2/10$ = 3.703,453

$\Sigma(y - \bar{y})^2$ = 0.465,909 = R_0

* y_1 coded by subtracting 1.

TABLE 74

CALCULATION OF STATISTICS AND TEST OF GOODNESS OF FIT FOR THE CURVE
$\text{Log } Y = c_0 + c_1 \log x$

	Line	0	1	K	S
	1	10	2.2096	6.0856	18.2952
	2	−1.0	−0.22096	−0.60856	−1.82952
	3		2.60167	0.355,643	5.16691
	4		−0.48823	−1.344,674	−4.04251
	5		2.11344	−0.989,031	1.12440
	6		−1.0000	0.46797	
$c_1 = -0.46797$	1		−0.46797	−0.46797	
$c_0 = +0.71196$	2	+0.71196	+0.10340	+0.60856	
Check Line		7.1196	−1.0340	=6.0856	

	S(sq.)	D F	Variance	F	1% Point
$R_0 =$	0.465,909	9			
$(5,1) \times (6,K)^2 =$	0.462,835	1	0.4628	1205	11.26
$R_1 =$	0.003,074	8	0.000384		

Equation $\log Y = 1.71196 - 0.46797 \log x$.

6. Fisher's Summation Method of Fitting Polynomials.

When the y values are, or can be assumed to be, of equal weight and are given for equal intervals[1] of x, the method of fitting polynomials developed by R. A. Fisher provides a very decided short cut from the actual to the theoretical polynomial values. The arithmetical labor is likewise easy as it consists largely of a process of continuous summation. The procedure will be illustrated by an example.

A summary of formulae for fitting polynomials is given below, and in Tables 79, 80, and 81 the constant factors in the formulae have been calculated for $n = 5$ to 20 and $r = 0$ to 6, where r represents the degree of fitting.

[1] Professor Fisher has now developed this method for application to the case wherein the y values are of unequal weight. See the references at the end of this chapter.

SUMMARY OF FORMULAE FOR FITTING POLYNOMIALS BY THE SUMMATION METHOD

1. S_1, S_2, S_3, S_4, S_5, S_6, $\cdots S_{r+1}$ (by summation)

2. $a = \dfrac{1}{n} S_1$ $\qquad\qquad\qquad a' = a$

$b = \dfrac{2}{n(n+1)} S_2$ $\qquad\qquad b' = a - b$

$c = \dfrac{6}{n(n+1)(n+2)} S_3$ $\qquad c' = a - 3b + 2c$

$d = \dfrac{24}{n(n+1)\cdots(n+3)} S_4$ $\qquad d' = a - 6b + 10c - 5d$

$e = \dfrac{120}{n(n+1)\cdots(n+4)} S_5$ $\qquad e' = a - 10b + 30c - 35d + 14e$

$f = \dfrac{720}{n(n+1)\cdots(n+5)} S_6$ $\qquad f' = a - 15b + 70c - 140d + 126e - 42f,$

$\vdots$

$= \dfrac{1.2.3\cdots(r+1)}{n(n+1)\cdots(n+r)} S_{r+1}$

where the rule for the formation of the coefficients is to multiply successively by

$$\dfrac{r(r+1)}{1.2}, \quad \dfrac{(r-1)(r+2)}{2.3}, \quad \dfrac{(r-2)(r+3)}{3.4},$$

and so on, until the series terminates.

3. $\qquad\qquad\qquad\qquad\qquad\qquad\qquad\qquad\qquad$ Coefficients

$Y_1 = +1 \times (a' + 3b' + 5c' + 7d' + 9e' + 11f')$ $\quad$ 1 $\quad$ 3 $\quad$ 5 $\quad$ 7 $\quad$ 9 $\quad$ 11

$D^1 Y_1 = -\dfrac{6}{(n-1)} (b' + 5c' + 14d' + 30e' + 55f')$ $\qquad$ 1 $\quad$ 5 $\quad$ 14 $\quad$ 30 $\quad$ 55

$D^2 Y_1 = +\dfrac{60}{(n-1)(n-2)} (c' + 7d' + 27e' + 77f')$ $\qquad\quad$ 1 $\quad$ 7 $\quad$ 27 $\quad$ 77

$D^3 Y_1 = -\dfrac{840}{(n-1)(n-2)(n-3)} (d' + 9e' + 44f')$ $\qquad\qquad$ 1 $\quad$ 9 $\quad$ 44

$D^4 Y_1 = +\dfrac{15,120}{(n-1)(n-2)\cdots(n-4)} (e' + 11f')$ $\qquad\qquad\qquad$ 1 $\quad$ 11

$D^5 Y_1 = -\dfrac{332,640}{(n-1)(n-2)\cdots(n-5)} (f')$ $\qquad\qquad\qquad\qquad\qquad$ 1

Each formula is seen to be composed of two parts that are best calculated separately. For the component on the right Fisher gives the coefficients for fitting curves to the tenth degree. They are reproduced here for fitting up to the fifth degree. The factors on the left are of alternate positive and negative signs and in generalized form are as follows:

$$\frac{-2.3}{n-1}, \frac{3.4.5}{(n-1)(n-2)}, \frac{-4.5.6.7}{(n-1)(n-2)(n-3)}, \cdots + \frac{(r+1)(r+2)\cdots(2r+1)}{(n-1)(n-2)\cdots(n-4)}$$

4. Polynomial values Y_1 Y_2 Y_3, etc., by process of summation.[1]

Example 46. The y values in Table 75 represent the percentages of cars of smutty wheat graded at Winnipeg, Manitoba, for the years 1925 to 1933 (6). The x values are therefore years and can be replaced by the numerals 1 to 9. We shall use these data in order to show the procedure of fitting a curve of the fifth degree. Such a curve would probably be of very little practical value for analyzing data of this kind but it is quite suitable as a numerical example. Summing the y values from top to bottom we write down the sum showing on the machine after each value is added. This process is repeated in succeeding columns, the sums of the columns being designated S_1, S_2, etc., and if we are fitting a curve to the fifth degree we must go as far as S_6. At this point the summations must be very carefully checked. This is accomplished simply by adding all the columns and noting that the last figure in any one column must correspond with the sum of the column on the left.

The second step is to calculate values that are denoted by the letters a, b, c, d, e, f, and from these obtain a', b', c', d', e', and f'. The formulae for these calculations are given on page 235. In our example we have

$$a = \quad 53.1/9 \quad = 5.900{,}000 \qquad a' = \quad 5.900{,}000$$
$$b = \quad 253.3/45 \quad = 5.628{,}889 \qquad b' = \quad 0.271{,}111$$
$$c = \quad 790.8/165 \quad = 4.792{,}727 \qquad c' = -\,1.401{,}213$$
$$d = 2020.8/495 \quad = 4.082{,}424 \qquad d' = -\,0.358{,}184$$
$$e = 4577.5/1287 = 3.556{,}721 \qquad e' = \quad 0.302{,}174$$
$$f = 9543.6/3003 = 3.178{,}022 \qquad f' = \quad 0.088{,}117$$

The third step is the calculation of Y_1 the polynomial value of y corresponding to $x = 9$, and five other values known as the first, second, third, fourth, and fifth differences. From Y_1 and the differences represented by the symbols

$$D^1Y_1, \; D^2Y_1, \; D^3Y_1, \; D^4Y_1, \; D^5Y_1$$

the polynomial values are built up by a process of summation as illustrated in Table 76. For Y and the differences we get

$$Y_1 = \quad 1.000{,}000 \times 0.888{,}833 = \quad 0.888{,}833$$
$$D^1Y_1 = -\,0.750{,}000 \times 2.162{,}125 = -\,1.621{,}594$$
$$D^2Y_1 = \quad 1.071{,}428 \times 11.035{,}206 = \quad 11.823{,}429$$
$$D^3Y_1 = -\,2.500{,}000 \times 6.238{,}530 = -\,15.596{,}325$$
$$D^4Y_1 = \quad 9.000{,}000 \times 1.271{,}461 = \quad 11.443{,}149$$
$$D^5Y_1 = -49.500{,}000 \times 0.088{,}117 = -\,4.361{,}792$$

[1] If necessary the actual equation may be written. Details of the calculations are given by Snedecor in "Statistical Methods."

The summation process as illustrated in Table 76 is started in the lower right-hand corner. Beginning with D^4Y_1 we add successively the value of D^5Y_1. The other columns are then built up merely by starting with the first figure at the bottom and adding the figures in the same row in the column to the *right*. The values in the last column on the left are the calculated polynomial values of y. Note that in the second column only five values are required but we require one more in each column as we proceed to the left and also that if only two decimal places are required for the polynomial values the number of decimal places are reduced by one for each column after the second. A final check on all the work following the calculation of S_1, S_2, $\cdots S_6$ is to add the last column. This should give us S, the total for all the values of y.

The summation method is particularly well adapted to fitting by successive stages and to the application of the analysis of variance at each stage. Assuming at the outset that fitting will probably be carried to the fifth degree we first calculate S_1, $S_2 \cdots S_6$ as in Table 75 and the constants a', b', c', d', e', f'. For each stage of fitting we require only Y_1 and the corresponding differences. If desirable we can determine the significance of each degree of freedom used in fitting before we go to the trouble of actually calculating the polynomial values and in this way save ourselves the labor of calculations that are not going to be of any value. The formulae for the sums of squares represented by each additional degree of freedom used in fitting are as follows:

Degree of Fitting (r)	Sum of Squares	
0	S_1^2/n	na'^2 (Represents fitting of the mean)
1	$\Sigma(y - Y_1)^2$	$3\dfrac{n(n+1)}{(n-1)}b'^2$
2	$\Sigma(Y_1 - Y_2)^2$	$5\dfrac{n(n+1)(n+2)}{(n-1)(n-2)}c'^2$
3	$\Sigma(Y_2 - Y_3)^2$	$7\dfrac{n(n+1)\cdots(n+3)}{(n-1)(n-2)(n-3)}d'^2$
4	$\Sigma(Y_3 - Y_4)^2$	$9\dfrac{n(n+1)\cdots(n+4)}{(n-1)(n-2)\cdots(n-4)}e'^2$
5	$\Sigma(Y_4 - Y_5)^2$	$11\dfrac{n(n+1)\cdots(n+5)}{(n-1)(n-2)\cdots(n-5)}f'^2$
.	.	.
.	.	.
.	.	.
r	$\Sigma(Y_{r-1}-Y_r)^2$	$(2r+1)\dfrac{n(n+1)\cdots(n+r)}{(n-1)(n-2)\cdots(n-r)}$ (constant)^2

For the example that has already been fitted to the fifth degree the sums of squares and corresponding analyses of variance are given in Table 77. After fitting to the second degree there is no further gain in precision, consequently in actual practise we would proceed direct to the calculation of the polynomial values for a second-degree curve. This calculation is given at the foot of Table 77.

TABLE 75

CALCULATION OF S_1, S_2, S_3, S_4, S_5, AND S_6 FOR FITTING A POLYNOMIAL OF THE FIFTH DEGREE BY THE SUMMATION METHOD

x	y					
1	2.2	2.2	2.2	2.2	2.2	2.2
2	1.2	3.4	5.6	7.8	10.0	12.2
3	2.6	6.0	11.6	19.4	29.4	41.6
4	5.5	11.5	23.1	42.5	71.9	113.5
5	16.5	28.0	51.1	93.6	165.5	279.0
6	17.0	45.0	96.1	189.7	355.2	634.2
7	6.5	51.5	147.6	337.3	692.5	1326.7
8	1.1	52.6	200.2	537.5	1230.0	2556.7
9	0.5	53.1	253.3	790.8	2020.8	4577.5
	53.1	253.3	790.8	2020.8	4577.5	9543.6
	$= S_1$	$= S_2$	$= S_3$	$= S_4$	$= S_5$	$= S_6$

TABLE 76

CALCULATION OF POLYNOMIAL VALUES

1	2.34					
2	0.87	1.467				
3	2.06	− 1.190	2.265,7			
4	7.91	− 5.845	4.655,4	− 1.998,50		
5	14.40	− 6.495	0.649,9	4.005,52	− 6.004,019	
6	15.90	− 1.497	− 4.997,9	5.647,75	− 1.642,227	
7	9.47	6.429	− 7.926,1	2.928,18	2.719,565	
8	−0.73	10.202	− 3.772,9	− 4.153,18	7.081,357	
9	0.889	− 1.6216	11.823,43	−15.596,325	11.443,149	−4.361,792

Example 47. The whole process of fitting by successive stages may be carried out in tabular form as in Table 78. The data are for the relation between pH and the activity of the enzyme asparaginase (5). Note that three columns are required for fitting to the first degree and thereafter each additional column provides the data for fitting one additional constant. Lines 14 and 15 determine the degree to which the curve should be fitted. In the example it is obvious that the fitting should be carried to the fourth degree; consequently, the remainder of the work applies to a fourth-degree curve only.

TABLE 77

Degree of Fitting		Sums of Squares	Degrees of Freedom	Variance	F	5% Point
1	Total	334.96	8			
	Regression	2.48	1	2.48		
	Error	332.48	7	47.50		
2	Regression	173.55	1	173.6	6.55	5.99
	Error	158.93	6	26.49		
3	Regression	31.75	1	31.75	1.25	6.61
	Error	127.18	5	25.44		
4	Regression	75.54	1	75.54	5.85	7.71
	Error	51.64	4	12.91		
5	Regression	27.48	1	27.48	3.41	10.13
	Error	24.16	3	8.053		

$$Y_1 = 1 \times (5.900,000 + 3 \times 0.271,111 - 5 \times 1.401,213) = -0.292,732$$

$$D^1Y_1 = -0.75 \times (0.271,111 - 5 \times 1.401,213) \qquad = 5.051,216$$

$$D^2Y_1 = 1.071,428 \times -1.401,213 \qquad\qquad = -1.501,299$$

x		Polynomial Values
1		− 1.92
2	−5.458	3.54
3	−3.957	7.50
4	−2.455	9.95
5	−0.954	10.90
6	0.547	10.36
7	2.049	8.31
8	3.550	4.76
9	−1.501,30	5.0512	− 0.293
	Total =	53.1

TABLE 78—COMPLETE TABULAR METHOD FOR FITTING BY THE SUMMATION METHOD IN SUCCESSIVE STAGES

x	y	Degree of Fitting (r)				
		1	2	3	4	5
1	0.2	0.2	0.2	0.2	0.2	0.2
2	0.4	0.6	0.8	1.0	1.2	1.4
3	1.4	2.0	2.8	3.8	5.0	6.4
4	4.1	6.1	8.9	12.7	17.7	24.1
5	6.6	12.7	21.6	34.3	52.0	76.1
6	8.7	21.4	43.0	77.3	129.3	205.4
7	9.8	31.2	74.2	151.5	280.8	486.2
8	9.9	41.1	115.3	266.8	547.6	1,033.8
9	9.5	50.6	165.9	432.7	980.3	2,014.1
10	8.2	58.8	224.7	657.4	1637.7	3,651.8
11	6.4	65.2	289.9	947.3	2585.0	6,236.8
12	3.3	68.5	358.4	1305.7	3890.7	10,127.5
13	0.3	68.8	427.2	1732.9	5623.6	15,751.1
14	0.1	68.9	496.1	2229.0	7852.6	23,603.7
1 S_1, S_2	68.9	496.1	2229.0	7852.6	23603.7	63,218.6
2 Divisor (Table 79)	14	105	560	2380	8568	27,132
3 $a, b, c, \cdots$	4.921,428	4.724,762	3.980,357	3.299,412	2.754,867	2.330,038
4 $a', b', c', \cdots$	+4.921,428	+0.196,666	−1.292,144	−0.120,634	+0.173,236	+0.008,954
5 Squares	24.220,454	0.038,677,5	1.669,636	0.014,552,6	0.030,010,7	0.000,080,17
6 Factor (Table 80)	14.0	48.4615	107.6923	233.007	539.245	1,391.38
7 $S(\text{sq.})$	339.0864	1.8744	179.8069	3.3909	16.1831	0.1115
8 $\Sigma(y)^2$	541.7100					
9 $\Sigma(Y_{r,-1} - Y_r)^2$	339.0864	1.8744	179.8069	3.3909	16.1831	0.1115
10 $\Sigma(y - Y_r)^2$ (error)	202.6236	200.7492	20.9423	17.5514	1.3683	1.2568
11 DF (error)		12	11	10	9	8
12 v_1		1.874	179.8	3.391	16.18	0.1115
13 v_2		16.73	1.904	1.755	0.1520	0.1571
14 F			94.4	1.93	10.6	
15 5% point			4.84	4.96	5.12	
16 $a' + 3b'$, etc.	ǀ0.234,608	−2.755,850	+2.540,790	+1.438,490	+0.173,236	
17 Factor (Table 81)	+1.0	−0.461,538	+0.384,615	−0.489,510	+0.881,119	
18 Y_1, D_1Y_1, etc.	−0.234,608	+1.271,929	+0.977,226	−0.704,155	+0.152,642	

(1) S_{r+1} values entered as columns are summated.

(2) Divisor for S_{r+1} values, taken from Table 79.

(3) Division of line 1 by line 2 gives the constants $a, b, c, d, \ldots$

(4) The constants $a', b', c', d', \ldots$ are calculated from $a, b, c, d, \ldots$ as indicated in summary on page 235.

(5) Squares of $a', b', c', d', \ldots$

(6) Factor taken from Table 80.

(7) Line 5 multiplied by line 6 gives the sum of squares $\Sigma(Y_{r-1} - Y_r)^2$ represented by 1 DF. For each DF utilized in fitting this is the reduction in the sum of squares due to error of regression.

(8) Enter $\Sigma(y)^2$ in first column.

(9) Repeat $\Sigma(Y_{r-1} - Y_r)^2$ values.

(10) Subtracting 9 from 8 in the first column gives the remainder in line 10. Then subtract the values in line 9 successively, putting down the remainders in line 10.

(11) The DF for error of regression are entered here. The DF for the sums of squares in line 9 is 1 in each case so that they do not need to be entered.

(12) Line 9 repeated, reducing to 4-figure accuracy.

(13) Line 10 divided by line 11.

(14) $F = v_1/v_2$.

(15) Enter 5% points from Table 96

(16) Calculate as in section 3 of summary of formulae.

(17) Enter factors from Table 81.

(18) Line 16 multiplied by line 17.

CALCULATION OF POLYNOMIAL VALUES FOR FOURTH-DEGREE CURVE

1	0.2748				
2	0.1691	0.105,651			
3	1.6903	−1.521,180	1.626,831		
4	4.0161	−2.325,746	0.804,566	0.822,265	
5	6.4768	−2.460,689	0.134,943	0.669,623	
6	8.5554	−2.078,651	−0.382,038	0.516,981	
7	9.8877	−1.332,274	−0.746,377	0.364,339	
8	10.2619	−0.374,200	−0.958,074	0.211,697	
9	9.6190	0.642,929	−1.017,129	0.059,055	
10	8.0525	1.566,471	−0.923,542	−0.093,587	
11	5.8087	2.243,784	−0.677,313	−0.246,229	
12	3.2865	2.522,226	−0.278,442	−0.398,871	
13	1.0373	2.249,155	0.273,071	−0.551,513	
14	−0.234,608	1.271,929	0.977,226	−0.704,155	0.152,642

7. Exercises.

1. Calculate the correlation ratio for the data of Table 67, Chapter XIII, and by means of the analysis of variance test the significance of the variance for the means of the arrays.

TABLE 79

$$\frac{n(n+1)\cdots(n+r)}{1\cdot2\cdot3\cdots(r+1)} \text{ FOR USE IN CALCULATION OF } a, b, c, d, e, f\cdots$$

Degree of Fitting (r)

n	0	1	2	3	4	5	6
5	5	15	35	70	126	210	330
6	6	21	56	126	252	462	792
7	7	28	84	210	462	924	1,716
8	8	36	120	330	792	1,716	3,432
9	9	45	165	495	1,287	3,003	6,435
10	10	55	220	715	2,002	5,005	11,440
11	11	66	286	1001	3,003	8,008	19,448
12	12	78	364	1365	4,368	12,376	31,824
13	13	91	455	1820	6,188	18,564	50,388
14	14	105	560	2380	8,568	27,132	77,520
15	15	120	680	3060	11,628	38,760	116,280
16	16	136	816	3876	15,504	54,264	170,544
17	17	153	969	4845	20,349	74,613	245,157
18	18	171	1140	5985	26,334	100,947	346,104
19	19	190	1330	7315	33,649	134,596	480,700
20	20	210	1540	8855	42,504	177,100	657,800

TABLE 80

$$(2r+1)\left[\frac{n(n+1)(n+2)\cdots(n+r)}{(n-1)(n-2)\cdots(n-r)}\right] \text{ FOR CALCULATION OF SUMS OF SQUARES}$$

Degree of Fitting (r)

n	0	1	2	3	4	5	6
5	5.0	22.5000	87.5000	490.000	5670.000		
6	6.0	25.2000	84.0000	352.800	2268.000	30,492.00	
7	7.0	28.0000	84.0000	294.000	1386.000	10,164.00	156,156.00
8	8.0	30.8571	85.7143	264.000	1018.286	5,393.14	44,616.00
9	9.0	33.7500	88.3928	247.500	827.357	3,539.25	20,913.75
10	10.0	36.6667	91.6667	238.333	715.000	2,621.67	12,393.33
11	11.0	39.6000	95.3333	233.567	643.500	2,097.33	8,427.47
12	12.0	42.5454	99.2727	231.636	595.636	1,768.00	6,268.36
13	13.0	45.5000	103.4091	231.636	562.545	1,547.00	4,962.45
14	14.0	48.4615	107.6923	233.007	539.245	1,391.38	4,110.91
15	15.0	51.4286	112.0879	235.385	522.737	1,277.80	3,523.64
16	16.0	54.4000	116.5714	238.523	511.121	1,192.62	3,100.80
17	17.0	57.3750	121.1250	242.250	503.135	1,127.39	2,785.88
18	18.0	60.3529	125.7353	246.441	497.912	1,076.68	2,544.88
19	19.0	63.3333	130.3922	251.005	494.838	1,036.80	2,356.37
20	20.0	66.3158	135.0877	255.872	493.467	1,005.21	2,206.24

TABLE 81

$$\frac{\pm(r+1)\,(r+2)\cdots(2r+1)}{(n-1)\,(n-2)\cdots(n-r)}$$ FOR CALCULATION OF Y_1 AND "DIFFERENCES"

Degree of Fitting (r)

n	0	1	2	3	4	5	6
	+	−	+	−	+	−	+
5	1	1.5	5.0	35.0	630.0		
6	1	1.2	3.0	14.0	126.0	2772.0	
7	1	1.0	2.0	7.0	42.0	462.0	12,012.0
8	1	0.8571,4286	1.4285,7143	4.0	18.0	132.0	1,716.0
9	1	0.75	1.0714,2857	2.5	9.0	49.5	429.0
10	1	0.6666,6667	0.8333,3333	1.6666,6667	5.0	22.0	143.0
11	1	0.60	0.6666,6667	1.1666,6667	3.0	11.0	57.2
12	1	0.5454,5454	0.5454,5454	0.8484,8485	1.9090,9091	6.0	26.0
13	1	0.50	0.4545,4545	0.6363,6364	1.2727,2727	3.5	13.0
14	1	0.4615,3846	0.3846,1538	0.4895,1049	0.8811,1888	2.1538,4615	7.0
15	1	0.4285,7143	0.3296,7033	0.3846,1538	0.6293,7063	1.3846,1538	4.0
16	1	0.40	0.2857,1428	0.3076,9231	0.4615,3846	0.9230,7692	2.4
17	1	0.375	0.25	0.25	0.3461,5385	0.6346,1538	1.5
18	1	0.3529,4118	0.2205,8824	0.2058,8235	0.2647,0588	0.4479,6380	0.9705,8824
19	1	0.3333,3333	0.1960,7843	0.1715,6863	0.2058,8235	0.3235,2941	0.6470,5882
20	1	0.3157,8947	0.1754,3860	0.1444,7884	0.1625,3870	0.2383,9009	0.4427,2446

2. For the following equations, calculate the values of Y for $x = 1$ to $x = 20$, and plot the curves on graph paper.

(a) $$Y = 2.58 + 0.84\,x$$

(b) $$Y = 2.58 + 8.4 \log x$$

(c) $$\text{Log } Y = 0.258 + 0.058\,x$$

(d) $$\text{Log } Y = 0.213 + 0.662 \log x$$

Describe the effect of the logarithmic transformation of equation (a) into equations (b) and (c).

3. Using the data given in Table 85, determine the type of logarithmic curve that should be fitted to the data. Having selected the type of curve proceed with the fitting as in Tables 73 and 74. Prepare two graphs, one showing the fit of the straight-line logarithmic equation to the logarithms of y, and another showing the curve for the actual values of Y estimated from the regression equation. Table 82 may be used for a similar exercise.

4. Table 83 gives the values of y, N_{yx}, and T_{yx} from a correlation surface for the area and head length of 500 bull spermatozoa, Isa (7). The three columns are similar to the first three columns of Table 68 and provide all the data necessary for calculating polynomial regression equations. Find the regression equation that gives the best fit to the data. Then calculate the Y values and construct a graph similar to Fig. 15, showing the means of the arrays and the regression line.

5. Using the data for x and y given below, determine the goodness of fit of curves up to the sixth degree. Select the curve to which the data should be fitted, and proceed accordingly to the calculation of the polynomial values. Graph your results.

x	1	2	3	4	5	6	7	8	9	10	11	12	13	14
y	12.6	13.8	14.1	13.9	12.3	7.2	4.8	2.8	2.4	2.1	3.7	5.3	7.8	8.3

6. In economic analysis, methods of curve fitting are very frequently utilized in order to study *secular trend* in a time series. Secular trend means the smooth long-term movement of a series of statistical values and is entirely distinct from *seasonal* and *cyclical* fluctuations. Cyclical fluctuations are not as periodical as the seasonal ones but as a general rule have sufficient regularity to show definite swings above and below the normal through periods of depression and prosperity. Curve fitting may, on the one hand, be used to measure the secular trend of a statistical series, and, on the other hand, using the fitted curve as a normal, we can plot the deviations from the normal in such a way as to bring out the characteristics of cyclical fluctuations.

Take the data given in Table 84 of the bank clearings in New York City for the years 1860 to 1923 and combining them in 4 year groups obtain 16 points to which a curve may be fitted. Determine the best-fitting polynomial and graph your results on a large sheet of graph paper giving the 16 calculated values and the actual bank clearings for *individual* years. Measure off the deviations of the values for individual years from a smooth curve drawn through the 16 calculated points, and graph these deviations on another sheet showing them as deviations from a straight horizontal line.

TABLE 82

HEAT OF HYDRATION IN CALORIES AND WATER IMBIBED PER GRAM OF FLOUR

Cc. Water Imbibed	Heat of Hydration
0.012	2.3
0.025	5.7
0.039	7.4
0.049	9.2
0.064	10.7
0.073	12.4
0.091	14.6
0.099	15.1
0.123	16.8
0.146	17.8

TABLE 83

DATA FROM CORRELATION SURFACE FOR AREA (y) AND HEAD LENGTH (x) OF
500 BULL SPERMS

y	Frequency of y for x Arrays N_{yx}	Totals for y Arrays T_{yx}
1	2	6
2	0	24
3	7	63
4	7	247
5	14	618
6	12	939
7	22	1038
8	36	897
9	70	557
10	112	311
11	133	82
12	69	29
13	2	41
14	2	29
15	1	7

Total = 500

TABLE 84

BANK CLEARINGS IN NEW YORK CITY (1860–1923)
Figures in thousands of millions

1860	7.2	1876	21.6	1892	36.7	1908	79.3
61	5.9	77	23.3	93	31.2	09	103.6
62	6.9	78	19.9	94	24.4	10	97.3
63	14.9	79	29.2	95	29.9	11	92.4
64	24.1	80	38.6	96	28.8	12	100.7
65	26.0	81	49.4	97	33.4	13	94.6
66	28.7	82	46.9	98	42.0	14	83.0
67	28.7	83	37.4	99	60.8	15	110.6
68	28.5	84	31.0	1900	52.7	16	159.6
69	37.4	85	28.2	01	79.4	17	177.4
70	27.8	86	33.7	02	76.3	18	178.6
71	29.3	87	33.4	03	66.0	19	235.8
72	33.8	88	31.1	04	68.6	20	243.2
73	35.5	89	35.9	05	93.8	21	194.4
74	22.9	90	37.4	06	104.7	22	217.9
75	25.1	91	33.7	07	87.2	23	214.0

TABLE 85

MOISTURE CONTENT AND HEAT OF HYDRATION OF FIFTH MIDDLINGS FLOUR (6)

Per Cent Moisture (y)	Heat of Hydration in Calories (x)
1.7	18.3
2.9	16.0
4.2	12.6
5.6	10.9
6.6	9.1
8.1	7.6
9.0	5.9
10.8	3.7
11.6	3.2
14.0	1.5
16.3	0.5

REFERENCES

1. J. BLAKEMAN, Biometrika, 4: 332. 1905.
2. MORDECAI EZEKIEL. Methods of Correlation Analysis. John Wiley & Sons, Inc., New York, 1930. Reading: Chapter VI.
3. R. A. FISHER. Statistical Methods for Research Workers. Oliver and Boyd, London, 1936. Reading: Chapter V, Sections 27, 28, 28.1, 29.2.
4. W. F. GEDDES, Can. Jour. Research, 1: 528–558. 1929.
5. W. F. GEDDES and A. HUNTER, Jour. Biol. Chem., 77: 1928.
6. W. F. HANNA and W. POPP, Sci. Agric., 11: 200–207, 1930.
7. J. ISA. Unpublished data from master's degree thesis, University of Manitoba.
8. G. W. SNEDECOR. Statistical Methods. Collegiate Press Inc., Ames, Iowa, 1937. Reading: Chapter XIV.
9. L. H. C. TIPPETT. The Methods of Statistics. Williams and Norgate, Ltd., London, 1931. Reading: Chapter IX.
10. C. A. WINKLER and W. F. GEDDES. Cereal Chem., 8: 455–475, 1931.

CHAPTER XV

THE ANALYSIS OF COVARIANCE

1. The Heterogeneity of Covariation and the Principle of Covariance Analysis. We have noted from our study of the analysis of variance that for a single variable the variation is frequently heterogeneous and may be sorted out into components determined largely by the way in which the data are taken. The same is true for the correlated variability or covariation of two variables, and the mechanism for sorting out the covariance effects is known as the *analysis of covariance.* In order to think in terms of actual values, we may suppose that the two variables are yields of grain and straw from cereal plots. The total covariance for grain and straw yields is made up in part by the covariance for the means of the treatments and in part by the covariance within the plots of the same variety. The degree of correlation may be different for the two components and hence the total correlation is heterogeneous. In the same way we may consider the covariance for the replicate means as another component. In fact the components may be taken as exactly equivalent to those according to which the data may be classified for an analysis of variance of either variable.

2. Division of Sums of Products and Degrees of Freedom. Just as the analysis of variance arises from the fact that the sums of squares and degrees of freedom may be subdivided according to the way in which the data are classified, the analysis of covariance arises from the fact that the sums of products of the deviations and corresponding degrees of freedom can be subdivided in the same manner.

Representing a set of data for two variables as follows:

$$k \text{ groups} \begin{cases} x_{11}y_{11} \; x_{12}y_{12} \; \cdots \; x_{1n}y_{1n} \\ x_{21}y_{21} \; x_{22}y_{22} \; \cdots \; x_{2n}y_{2n} \\ \quad \vdots \qquad \vdots \qquad \quad \vdots \\ x_{k1}y_{k1} \; x_{k2}y_{k2} \; \cdots \; x_{kn}y_{kn} \end{cases}$$

in which there are k groups of n pairs of variates of x and y. Then

$$(x_{11} - \bar{x}) = (x_{11} - \bar{x}_1) + (\bar{x}_1 - \bar{x})$$

and
$$(y_{11} - \bar{y}) = (y_{11} - \bar{y}_1) + (\bar{y}_1 - \bar{y})$$

247

Multiplying to obtain a single product of the deviations:

$$(x_{11} - \bar{x})(y_{11} - \bar{y}) = (x_{11} - \bar{x}_1)(y_{11} - \bar{y}_1) + (\bar{x}_1 - \bar{x})(\bar{y}_1 - \bar{y})$$
$$+ (x_{11} - \bar{x}_1)(\bar{y}_1 - \bar{y}) + (\bar{x}_1 - \bar{x})(y_{11} - \bar{y}_1)$$

On summating for all the pairs in the first group the last two terms disappear and we have:

$$\overset{n}{\Sigma}(x - \bar{x})(y - \bar{y}) = \overset{n}{\Sigma}(x - \bar{x}_1)(y - \bar{y}_1) + n(\bar{x}_1 - \bar{x})(\bar{y}_1 - \bar{y})$$

Then summating over the k groups:

$$\overset{nk}{\Sigma}(x - \bar{x})(y - \bar{y}) = \overset{k}{\Sigma}\left[\overset{n}{\Sigma}(x - \bar{x}_g)(y - \bar{y}_g)\right] + n\overset{k}{\Sigma}(\bar{x}_g - \bar{x})(\bar{y}_g - \bar{y}) \quad (1)$$

where $\bar{x}_g$ and $\bar{y}_g$ are group means for x and y. This is the fundamental equation for the sums of products on which the analysis of covariance is based. If the same data are divided into n classes as well as k groups, the equations for sums of products and degrees of freedom are:

$$\overset{nk}{\Sigma}(x - \bar{x})(y - \bar{y}) = \overset{nk}{\Sigma}(x - \bar{x}_g - \bar{x}_c + \bar{x})(y - \bar{y}_g - \bar{y}_c + \bar{y})$$
$$(nk - 1) \qquad = \qquad (n - 1)(k - 1)$$

$$+ n\overset{k}{\Sigma}(\bar{x}_g - \bar{x})(\bar{y}_g - \bar{y}) + k\overset{n}{\Sigma}(\bar{x}_c - \bar{x})(\bar{y}_c - \bar{y}) \quad (2)$$
$$+ \qquad (k - 1) \qquad + \qquad (n - 1) \qquad (3)$$

The method of calculating the sums of products is not according to these formulae but by means of equalities similar to those used for calculating sums of squares. These equalities are described below under Example 48.

3. Coefficients of Correlation Corresponding to Sums of Products and Squares.

Considering the simple classification of the pairs of variates into k groups of n pairs, we have the sums of products and corresponding sums of squares of x and y as follows:

$$\overset{nk}{\Sigma}(x - \bar{x})(y - \bar{y}) = \overset{nk}{\Sigma}(x - \bar{x}_g)(y - \bar{y}_g) + n\overset{k}{\Sigma}(\bar{x}_g - \bar{x})(\bar{y}_g - \bar{y})$$

$$\overset{nk}{\Sigma}(x - \bar{x})^2 \qquad = \overset{nk}{\Sigma}(x - \bar{x}_g)^2 \qquad + n\overset{k}{\Sigma}(\bar{x}_g - \bar{x})^2 \qquad (4)$$

$$\overset{nk}{\Sigma}(y - \bar{y})^2 \qquad = \overset{nk}{\Sigma}(y - \bar{y}_g)^2 \qquad + n\overset{k}{\Sigma}(\bar{y}_g - \bar{y})^2$$

It is now clear that each vertical set represents the factors necessary to calculate correlation or regression coefficients. Hence we can write:

$$r_{xy} \text{ (total)} \quad = \frac{\overset{nk}{\Sigma}(x - \bar{x})(y - \bar{y})}{\sqrt{\overset{nk}{\Sigma}(x - \bar{x})^2 \overset{nk}{\Sigma}(y - \bar{y})^2}}$$

$$b_{yx} = \frac{\overset{nk}{\Sigma}(x - \bar{x})(y - \bar{y})}{\overset{nk}{\Sigma}(x - \bar{x})^2}$$

$$DF = nk - 2$$

$$r_{xy} \text{ (within)} \quad = \frac{\overset{nk}{\Sigma}(x - \bar{x}_g)(y - \bar{y}_g)}{\sqrt{\overset{nk}{\Sigma}(x - \bar{x}_g)^2 \overset{nk}{\Sigma}(y - \bar{y}_g)^2}}$$

$$b_{yx} = \frac{\overset{nk}{\Sigma}(x - \bar{x}_g)(y - \bar{y}_g)}{\overset{nk}{\Sigma}(x - \bar{x}_g)^2}$$

$$DF = k(n - 1) - 1$$

$$r_{xy} \text{ (between)} \quad = \frac{n\overset{k}{\Sigma}(\bar{x}_g - \bar{x})(\bar{y}_g - \bar{y})}{\sqrt{n\overset{k}{\Sigma}(\bar{x}_g - \bar{x})^2 n\overset{k}{\Sigma}(\bar{y}_g - \bar{y})^2}}$$

$$b_{xy} = \frac{n\overset{k}{\Sigma}(\bar{x}_g - \bar{x})(\bar{y}_g - \bar{y})}{n\overset{k}{\Sigma}(\bar{x}_g - \bar{x})^2}$$

$$DF = k - 2$$

(5)

Note that for each component the degrees of freedom for estimating the coefficients are one less than for the corresponding estimates of the variance.

Since it can be proved that the variances and covariances for between and within groups are unbiassed estimates of the true values for the population sampled, it follows that the corresponding coefficients of correlation and regression are also unbiassed estimates of the correlation and regression parameters of the population. They can be used, therefore, to test the significance of the covariance effects represented by the various components for which they are calculated. One practical application of this principle will be seen at once. Total correlation coefficients are obviously incapable of definite interpretation if they represent heterogeneous covariance effects, and tests of significance applied to them cannot give a clear-cut answer. The coefficients calculated from each component, however, are capable of definite interpretation. In the simple case of covariance within and between groups, if the total covariance is made up largely of the covariance between the means of the groups, the total correlation is often referred to as containing a spurious effect. By the covariance method this effect is taken care of in the calculation of the covariance between the means and is completely removed from the covariance within the groups. Thus the so-called spurious effect is not only removed but completely evaluated as a distinct component of the total.

4. Applications of the Covariance Method to the Control of Error. One of the most important applications of the analysis of covariance is in the control of errors that arise at random throughout the experiment and cannot be taken care of by replication. In the case, for example, of number of plants per plot for such crops as mangels and sugar beets, the variations in number of plants arise at random throughout the experiment and, so far as they affect the yields of single plots, add to the experimental error. Correction of the yields on the basis that yield is directly proportional to the number of plants is a frequent practice, but it is not difficult to demonstrate that yield is rarely if ever proportional to the number of plants per plot, and that such an adjustment is likely to exaggerate the yields of plots in which plants are missing. Correction on the basis of the exact relation between yield and number of plots as indicated by the data is, however, perfectly justifiable, and the method of making such a correction is a natural development of the covariance technique. Numerous applications of the same method will undoubtedly occur to workers in other fields.

In order to demonstrate the control of error by the covariance method, we shall represent a covariance analysis algebraically as follows, in which the experiment is presumed to be a randomized block field plot test.

	DF	$\Sigma(x^2)$	$\Sigma(xy)$	$\Sigma(y^2)$	b_{yx}	$b_{yx}\Sigma(xy)$	$\Sigma(y'^2)$	DF
Blocks..	p	A_0	B_0	C_0				
Treatments	q	A_1	B_1	C_1	$b_1 = B_1/A_1$	b_1B_1	$C_1 - b_1B_1$	$q - 1$
Error...	n	A_2	B_2	C_2	$b_2 = B_2/A_2$	b_2B_2	$C_2 - b_2B_2$	$n - 1$
$T + E..$	$n + q$	A_t	B_t	C_t	$b_t = B_t/A_t$	b_tB_t	$C_t - b_tB_t$	$n + q - 1$

In the column headings, x is written for $(x - \bar{x})$, y for $(y - \bar{y})$, b_{yx} for the regression coefficient of y on x, and $\Sigma(y'^2)$ indicates a sum of squares for y adjusted by the regression coefficient in the same line.

The calculations are complete in each line of the table. The regression coefficient is B/A, and the adjustment in the sum of squares for y is bB or B^2/A. In the last line we are considering only treatments and error so that $A_t = A_1 + A_2$, $B_t = B_1 + B_2$ and $C_t = C_1 + C_2$.

The second step in the procedure is indicated as follows:

	DF	S (sq.)	Variance
$T + E$	$n + q - 1$	$C_t - b_t B_t$	
E	$n - 1$	$C_2 - b_2 B_2$	V_2
T	q	$C_1 + b_2 B_2 - b_t B_t$	V_1
T	$q - 1$	$C_1 - b_1 B_1$	V_3
$(b_1 - b_2)$	1	$b_1 B_1 + b_2 B_2 - b_t B_t$	V_4

The first sum of squares for treatments is obtained by differences and, since it has not been adjusted by the treatment regression coefficient, is still represented by q degrees of freedom. The second treatment sum of squares is written down from the first table and is represented by $q - 1$ degrees of freedom, as it has been adjusted by the treatment coefficient. On subtracting the second treatment sum of squares from the first, we have a sum of squares given by $b_1 B_1 + b_2 B_2 - b_t B_t$, and it is not difficult to prove the following equality:

$$b_1 B_1 + b_2 B_2 - b_t B_t = b_1^2 A_1 + b_2^2 A_2 - b_t^2 A_t = \frac{A_1 A_2}{A_1 + A_2}(b_1 - b_2)^2 \quad (6)$$

It follows that when $b_1 = b_2$ this sum of squares is zero, and that a test of significance of the corresponding variance (V_4) is a test of the significance of the difference between the error and treatment regression coefficients.

The test of significance of the treatment differences after adjustment for the regression of y on x involves a comparison of the variances V_2 and V_1. The fact that V_1 may contain a significant effect due to $(b_1 - b_2)$ does not vitiate the meaning of the test, as such an effect is obviously due to some factor characteristic of the treatments. In the case of yield and number of plants per plot, the variety regression coefficient (b_1) might be higher than (b_2), and this will contribute to the significance of V_1, but b_2 represents the regression of yield on number of plants within varieties, and may be taken as a true measure of the effect of number of plants on yield. If the treatment regression coefficient is higher this probably reflects an additional genetic relationship, and one that should contribute to the significance of the differences between the varieties. A further test may be applied, however, to V_3, and by a comparison of the significance of V_3 and V_4 a complete picture of the variety effects is obtained. The value of such an analysis, if, for example, number of roots has a significant effect on yield, is that the error variance and variety variance will be reduced proportionately with a consequent increase in the significance of the variety differences, if such differences exist. If the analysis of the unadjusted yields shows significant differences when the adjusted yields do not, this simply means that the original differences were due to number of roots and not to the yielding characteristics of the varieties as measured by average yield per root.

R. A. Fisher (4) has pointed out that an appropriate scale for measuring the effectiveness of methods of reducing the error is the inverse of the variance. This is sometimes called the *invariance* and is represented by $1/V$. In measuring the reduction of error by means of the covariance analysis, this scale is particularly useful. Example 48 is a good illustration of this point. The original error variance is about three times as large as the final error variance obtained by adjusting the sums of squares for two associated variables. In other words, in the original form without any adjustment about three times as many replications would be required to give the same accuracy as the adjusted values. One should not reason from this that the significance of the differences between the treatments will be increased accordingly, as it must be remembered that at the same time differences between the treatments *due* to the associated variables are also being removed.

The test of significance having been applied as outlined, the next step is to make an actual correction of the variety means. Since the regression coefficient in the error line may be considered as representing the actual effect of number of roots on yield, this regression coefficient should be used for making corrections. The corrected means should then be the best possible estimates of what the means would have been if they had not been affected by variations in number of roots. The regression equation will be of the form:

$$Y_1 = \bar{y}_1 - b_{yx}(\bar{x}_1 - \bar{x}) \tag{7}$$

where $\bar{x}_1$ is the mean of x for one variety, $\bar{y}_1$ is the mean of y for the same variety, b_{yx} is the regression of y on x in the error line, and Y_1 is the estimated mean of the variety.

To compare two corrected means such as Y_p and Y_q we must use for the standard error of the difference between two means

$$s^2\left\{\frac{2}{r} + \frac{(\bar{x}_p - \bar{x}_q)^2}{A}\right\}$$

where s^2 is the variance in the error line of the analysis of covariance table (for example, in Table 87 it will be $7681.3/35 = 219.5$), A is the sum of squares for x in the same line, r is the number of replications, and $(\bar{x}_p - \bar{x}_q)$ is the difference between the two means used in the two expressions for calculating Y_p and Y_q. Thus

$$Y_p = \bar{y}_p - b_{yx}(\bar{x}_p - \bar{x}) \quad \text{and} \quad Y_q = \bar{y}_q - b_{yx}(\bar{x}_q - \bar{x})$$

In comparing two means corrected for two variables x_1 and x_2 we calculate the standard error of a mean difference as follows

$$s^2\left\{\frac{2}{r} + \frac{u^2 B - 2uvP + v^2 A}{AB - P^2}\right\}$$

where A and B are the sums of squares in the error line for x_1 and x_2.

P is the sum of products for x_1 and x_2 in the error line.

$u = (\bar{x}_{1p} - \bar{x}_{1q})$, difference between x_1 means.

$v = (\bar{x}_{2p} - \bar{x}_{2q})$, difference between x_2 means.

The method of error control by means of two or more associated variables is described in Example 48.

5. A Test of the Heterogeneity of a Series of Regression Coefficients. The analysis of covariance provides a unique technique for testing the significance of the differences between two or more regression coefficients. Using the same symbolism as in the previous section, the procedure is as given below.

Group	DF	$\Sigma(x^2)$	$\Sigma(xy)$	$\Sigma(y^2)$	b_{yx}	$b_{yx}\Sigma(xy)$	$\Sigma(y'^2)$	DF
1	q	A_1	B_1	C_1	$b_1 = B_1/A_1$	b_1B_1	$C_1 - b_1B_1$	$q-1$
2	q	A_2	B_2	C_2	$b_2 = B_2/A_2$	b_2B_2	$C_2 - b_2B_2$	$q-1$
3	q	A_3	B_3	C_3	$b_3 = B_3/A_3$	b_3B_3	$C_3 - b_3B_3$	$q-1$
.	.	.	.	.	.	.	.	.
.	.	.	.	.	.	.	.	.
p	q	A_p	B_p	C_p	$b_p = B_p/A_p$	b_pB_p	$C_p - b_pB_p$	$q-1$
Total	pq	A_t	B_t	C_t	$b_t = B_t/A_t$	b_tB_t	$C_t - b_tB_t$	$pq-1$

	DF	$\Sigma(y'^2)$	Variance	
Total.........	$pq - 1$	$C_t - b_t B_t$		
Within groups..	$p(q - 1)$	$\overset{p}{\Sigma}(C - bB)$	V_1	error variance
Difference.....	$(p - 1)$	$\overset{p}{\Sigma}(bB) - b_t B_t$	V_2	due to differences between regression coefficients

The last sum of squares may be shown to be

$$\overset{p}{\Sigma}(bB) - b_t B_t = \overset{^pC_2}{\Sigma}\left(\frac{A_j A_k (b_j - b_k)^2}{A_1 + A_2 + \cdots + A_p}\right)$$

where b_j and b_k represent all possible pairs of the regression coefficients and A_j and A_k all possible pairs of the corresponding sums of squares for x.

The comparison of V_1 and V_2 by means of the z test furnishes therefore the required test of the heterogeneity of the regression coefficient.

Example 48.   For the sake of brevity this one example will be used to demonstrate most of the important applications of the covariance technique.   Data are given by Crampton and Hopkins (1) on weights, gains, and feed consumption in a comparative feeding trial.   These data are reproduced in Table 86 for initial weight, feed eaten, and final weight.   The analysis is concerned with expressing the results for final weight corrected for variations in initial weight, corrected for variations in feed eaten, and corrected for initial weight and feed eaten.   The last is an application of the method of partial regression which is described in detail in the paper by Crampton and Hopkins.   In addition a test will be illustrated of the significance of the differences between the regression coefficients for each treatment.

(1) *Effect of Initial Weight on Final Weight.*   The analysis of covariance is set up in the form shown in Table 87.   In performing the calculations for such a table, it is recommended that the sums of squares, sums of products, and totals be obtained by treatments, as it is necessary to keep these separate if certain tests are to be employed at a later stage.   In obtaining the sums of products it should be noted that a procedure may be followed exactly analogous to that for obtaining sums of squares.   With k replications of n treatments, the sums of products are given as follows:

Total................... $\overset{nk}{\Sigma}(x - \bar{x})(y - \bar{y}) = \overset{nk}{\Sigma}(xy) - T_x T_y / N$

Between means of treatments $k \overset{n}{\Sigma}(\bar{x}_t - \bar{x})(\bar{y}_t - \bar{y}) = \overset{n}{\Sigma}(T_{tx} T_{ty})/k - T_x T_y / N$

Between means of replicates $n \overset{k}{\Sigma}(\bar{x}_r - \bar{x})(\bar{y}_r - \bar{y}) = \overset{k}{\Sigma}(T_{rx} T_{ry})/n - T_x T_y / N$

Residual or error..........Total—(treatments)—(replicates).

Where T_{tx} and T_{ty} are treatment subtotals for x and y and T_{rx} and T_{ry} are replicate subtotals for x and y.

TABLE 86

WEIGHTS, GAINS, AND FEED CONSUMPTION OF PIGS IN COMPARATIVE FEEDING TRIAL

Repli-cate	Lot I			Lot II			Lot III			Lot IV			Lot V		
	Initial Weight	Feed Eaten	Final Weight	Initial Weight	Feed Eaten	Final Weight	Initial Weight	Feed Eaten	Final Weight	Initial Weight	Feed Eaten	Final Weight	Initial Weight	Feed Eaten	Final Weight
1	30	674	195	26	699	194	39	708	203	41	716	226	41	831	242
2	21	628	177	24	626	204	34	614	190	35	769	230	36	754	225
3	21	661	180	20	668	200	32	733	221	32	733	218	32	722	205
4	33	694	200	35	668	201	35	663	173	34	742	235	35	728	228
5	27	713	197	25	707	195	32	607	185	32	624	197	32	646	196
6	24	585	170	26	651	187	35	745	225	35	710	210	36	678	196
7	20	575	150	20	672	191	30	637	190	30	742	217	30	763	230
8	29	638	180	31	660	200	29	662	201	28	648	205	28	625	170
9	28	632	192	29	769	208	32	609	174	34	628	200	32	710	216
10	26	637	184	27	666	218	25	596	180	26	601	191	26	651	175

TABLE 87

Analysis of Covariance—Final Weight and Initial Weight

x_3 = initial weight　　　　　　　　　　x_1 = final weight

	(1) DF	(2) $\Sigma(x_3^2)$	(3) $\Sigma(x_1 x_3)$	(4) $\Sigma(x_1^2)$	(5) b_{13}	(6) $b_{13}\Sigma(x_1 x_3)$	(7) $\Sigma(y'^2)$	(8) DF	(9) r_{13}
Replicates	9	454.4	752.0	2,487.2	1.6549	1,244.5	1,242.7	8	0.7075
Treatments	4	509.2	1,172.2	5,741.7	2.3016	2,697.9	3,043.8	3	0.6854
Error	36	368.4	1,001.8	10,405.5	2.7193	2,724.2	7,681.3	35	0.5117
Treatments + Error	40	877.6	2,173.8	16,147.2	2.4770	5,384.5	10,762.7	39	

(1) DF for unadjusted sums of squares.
(5) b_{13} = item in col. (3) divided by item in col. (2).
(6) $b_{13}\Sigma(x_1 x_3)$ = col. (5) × col. (3) or col. (3)^2/col. (2).
(7) $\Sigma(y'^2)$ = adjusted sums of squares = col. (4) − col. (6).
(8) DF for adjusted sums of squares.
(9) Correlation coefficient (unnecessary for tests of significance).

From Table 87 we can proceed to the test of significance of the treatment differences adjusted for initial weight and of the difference between the treatment and error regression coefficients

	DF	S (sq.)	Variance	F	5% Point
Treatments + Error	39	10,762.7			
Error	35	7,681.3	219.5		
Difference = Treatments	4	3,081.4	770.4	3.51	2.64
Treatments	3	3,043.8	1,014.7		
Difference = $b_e - b_t$	1	37.6	37.6		

Since the difference between the error and treatment regression coefficients ($b_e - b_t$) is obviously insignificant the tests of significance are not carried any further.

To adjust the means of the treatment final weights for the initial weights we use the equation given above which in terms of the symbols now being used will be

$$\bar{x}_{t1} = \bar{x}_{t1} - b_{13}(\bar{x}_{t3} - \bar{x}_3)$$

(2) *Effect of Feed Eaten on Final Weight.* The procedure is exactly the same as above so will be given in tabular form only.

TABLE 88

ANALYSIS OF COVARIANCE—FEED EATEN AND FINAL WEIGHT

x_2 = feed eaten x_1 = final weight

	DF	$\Sigma(x_2^2)$	$\Sigma(x_1x_2)$	$\Sigma(x_2^2)$	b_{12}	$b_{12}\Sigma(x_1x_2)$	$\Sigma(y'^2)$	DF	r_{12}
Replicates.	9	35,150.3	8,774.1	2,487.2	0.24962	2,190.19	297.0	8	0.9384
Treatments	4	28,404.9	11,596.5	5,741.7	0.40826	4,734.39	1,007.3	3	0.9080
Error.....	36	90,792.3	24,508.7	10,405.5	0.26994	6,615.88	3,789.6	35	0.7974
Treatments + Error	40	119,197.2	36,105.2	16,147.2	0.30290	10,936.26	5,210.9	39	

	DF	$\Sigma(y'^2)$	Variance	F	5% Point
Treatments + Error......	39	5210.9			
Error......	35	3789.6	108.3		
Difference = Treatments	4	1421.3	355.3	3.28	2.64
Treatments	3	1007.3	335.8	3.10	2.87
Difference = $(b_e - b_t)$...	1	414.0	414.0	3.82	4.12

There is an indication here of a difference between the regression coefficients for treatments and error but it is hardly significant.

(3) *Effect of Initial Weight and Feed Eaten on Final Weight.* After obtaining the separate sums of squares for each variable and the sums of products for the three ways in which the variables can be paired the next step is to determine the partial regression coefficients. For three variables the sums of squares and products give two simultaneous equations as illustrated in Chapter VIII. These equations contain the partial regression coefficients as unknowns and can be most easily solved by the normal equation method, also described in Chapter VIII. The remainder of the calculations are as in Table 89.

TABLE 89

ANALYSIS OF COVARIANCE—EFFECT OF INITIAL WEIGHT AND FEED EATEN
ON FINAL WEIGHT

	$\Sigma(x_1^2)$	DF	$_3b_{12}\Sigma(x_1x_2)$	$_2b_{13}\Sigma(x_1x_3)$	$\Sigma(y'^2)$	DF
Replicates...............	2,487.2	9				
Treatments.............	5,741.7	4	4002.8	960.0	778.9	2
Error...................	10,405.5	36	5910.9	988.7	3505.9	34
Treatments + Error......	16,147.2	40	9411.5	2264.0	4471.7	38

TABLE 89—*Continued*

ANALYSIS OF COVARIANCE—EFFECT OF INITIAL WEIGHT AND FEED EATEN
ON FINAL WEIGHT

	$\Sigma(y'^2)$	DF	Variance	F	5% Point
Treatments + Error......	4,471.7	38			
Error......	3,505.9	34	103.1		
Difference = Treatments	965.8	4	241.4	2.34	2.64
Treatments	778.9	2	389.4	3.78	3.26
Difference..............	186.9	2	93.4		

The final result is rather unusual in that the treatment variance corrected by
its own regression coefficient is significant while the treatment variance as obtained
by differences is insignificant. This seems to be traceable to the relations between
x_1 and x_3 where, as will be noted in Table 87, the difference between the regression
coefficients is much less than would be expected on the basis of random sampling.
The equation for correcting the mean final weights will now be

$$\overline{X}_{t1} = \bar{x}_{t1} - {}_3b_{12}(\bar{x}_{t2} - \bar{x}_2) - {}_2b_{13}(\bar{x}_{t3} - \bar{x}_3)$$

where ${}_3b_{12}$ and ${}_2b_{13}$ are the partial regression coefficients for the error covariance.

(4) *Test of Heterogeneity of Covariation or the Significance of the Differences
between Regression Coefficients Calculated for Each Group.* If for the above example
we have kept our raw sums of squares and products separate for each treatment
we can very quickly set up the results as in Table 90, showing the sums of squares
and products for x_1 and x_3, the regression coefficients for each group, and finally the
adjusted sums of squares for x_1.

TABLE 90

TEST OF HETEROGENEITY OF REGRESSION BETWEEN TREATMENTS

	DF	$\Sigma(x_3^2)$	$\Sigma(x_1x_3)$	$\Sigma(x_1^2)$	b_{13}	$b_{13}\Sigma(x_1x_3)$	$\Sigma(y'^2)$	DF
Lot I	9	168.9	458.5	2,020.5	2.7146	1244.6	775.9	8
Lot II	9	192.1	102.6	715.6	0.53410	54.8	660.8	8
Lot III ...	9	132.1	169.4	2,869.6	1.2824	217.2	2752.4	8
Lot IV....	9	158.1	333.7	1,964.9	2.1107	704.3	1260.6	8
Lot V.....	9	191.6	689.6	5,722.1	3.5992	2482.0	2740.1	8
Total....	45	842.8	1753.8	12,892.7	2.0809	3649.5	9243.2	44

TABLE 90—*Continued*

TEST OF HETEROGENEITY OF REGRESSION BETWEEN TREATMENTS

	DF	$\Sigma(y'^2)$	Variance	F	5% Point
Total................	44	9243.2			
Treatments............	40	8189.8	204.7	1.29	2.61
Difference.............	4	1053.4	263.4		

For the test of significance we summate the adjusted sums of squares for each treatment and subtracting from the total obtain a sum of squares corresponding to 4 degrees of freedom representing differences between the 5 regression coefficients. In this example there is no evidence of significant heterogeneity of regression.

6. Exercises.

1. The data given in Table 91 are grain and straw yields given by Eden and Fisher (2) for 8 manurial treatments and 8 replicates of each. Calculate the correlation and regression coefficients for treatments, replicates, and residual. Test the significance of the grain yield differences for the treatments after correction for straw yield. Test the significance of the difference between the regression coefficients for treatments and residual, and apply the test for heterogeneity to the regression coefficients calculated for each treatment.

REFERENCES

1. E. M. CRAMPTON and J. W. HOPKINS. *J. Nutrition,* **8**: 329–340, 1934.
2. T. EDEN and R. A. FISHER. *Jour. Agri. Sci.,* **17**: 548–562, 1927.
3. R. A. FISHER. Statistical Methods for Research Workers. Sixth Edition. Oliver and Boyd, London, 1936. Reading: Chapter VIII, 49.1.
4. R. A. FISHER. The Design of Experiments. Oliver and Boyd, London and Edinburgh, 1937. Reading: Chapter IX.
5. G. W. SNEDECOR. Statistical Methods. Collegiate Press, Inc., Ames, Iowa. 1937. Reading: Chapter XII.
6. J. WISHART and H. G. SANDERS. Principles and Practices of Yield Trials. Empire Cotton Growing Corporation, London, 1935.
7. J. WISHART. *Suppl. Jour. Roy. Stat. Soc.,* III. 79–82. 1936.

TABLE 91

The Mean Grain and Straw Yields for Each of 64 Plots, There Being 8 Different Manurial Treatments and 8 Replicates of Each (Eden and Fisher, 1927)

Treatments	Block 1		Block 2		Block 3		Block 4		Block 5		Block 6		Block 7		Block 8	
	Straw	Grain	Straw	Grain	Straw	Grain	Straw	Grain	Straw	Grain	Straw	Grain	Straw	Grain	Straw	Grain
A	242	620	321	646	261	681	317	644	255	706	331	615	216	552	295	726
B	267	644	382	745	201	542	316	711	280	705	285	637	200	543	309	646
C	215	523	330	713	298	686	381	688	300	692	294	612	256	635	284	748
D	212	601	292	693	265	685	255	714	238	699	309	697	283	701	324	746
E	322	664	370	693	284	666	323	516	232	656	393	663	351	657	363	683
F	200	514	261	637	259	697	361	710	234	633	258	595	306	697	376	712
G	260	550	318	708	266	663	340	673	362	671	400	626	276	655	385	671
H	203	521	275	661	207	594	331	730	229	625	266	644	276	745	328	747

CHAPTER XVI

MISCELLANEOUS APPLICATIONS

I. THE ESTIMATION OF MISSING VALUES

1. Reasons for Estimating Missing Values and Principles of Estimation. In most experimental work, and especially in field plot studies, the results of one or more observations are occasionally lost or distorted by some disturbing factor in such a way as to make the particular observations useless. In the laboratory it may be possible to repeat a portion of the experiment and obtain new values for those that are missing, but in field experiments repetition is impossible and one has to make the best of the results available. In other biological experiments it is frequently impossible to repeat under the identical conditions of the original experiment, and methods of estimating missing or distorted values are preferable to discarding the whole or a portion of the data.

A method of estimating the yields of missing plots in field experiments on a strictly statistical basis was first developed by Allan and Wishart (1). Their methods were developed for the estimation of one missing yield; but more recently Yates (3) has extended their methods to the estimation of the yields of several missing plots. Since the methods developed by Yates are of general application, we shall use them throughout, although for single missing plots they are identical with those of Allan and Wishart. The mathematical basis of the method of estimating missing values is the substitution of a value for the one missing that will make the sum of the squares of the deviations from the mean a minimum. Equations are written for the sum of squares substituting x for the missing value; and after minimizing, the equations are solved for x.

2. Estimation of Missing Yields in Randomized Block Experiments. The data are first arranged in a table according to treatments and blocks. Table 92 is an example of an experiment with 6 treatments in 4 randomized blocks, and 1 plot of treatment B of block II is missing.

TABLE 92

Treatments

Blocks	A	B	C	D	E	F	Total
I....	18.5	15.7	16.2	14.1	13.0	13.6	91.1
II....	11.7	......	12.9	14.4	16.9	12.5	68.4 = Q
III....	15.4	16.6	15.5	20.3	18.4	21.6	107.8
IV.....	16.5	18.6	12.7	15.7	16.5	18.0	98.0
Total..	62.1	50.9 = P	57.3	64.5	64.8	65.7	365.3 = T

In the generalized formula for x, the yield of the missing plot:

p = number of treatments,

q = number of blocks,

P = total of all the plots receiving the same treatment as the missing plot,

Q = total of all the plots in the same block as the missing plot,

T = total of all plots.

The formula is:

$$x = \frac{pP + qQ - T}{(p - 1)(q - 1)} \tag{1}$$

In Table 93 we have the same data as in Table 92 except that now three plots are missing.

TABLE 93

Treatments

Blocks	A	B	C	D	E	F	Total
I.....	18.5	15.7	16.2	14.1	13.0	13.6	91.1
II.....	11.7	B	12.9	D	16.9	12.5	54.0
III.....	15.4	16.6	15.5	20.3	18.4	21.6	107.8
IV......	A	18.6	12.7	15.7	16.5	18.0	81.5
Total...	45.6	50.9	57.3	50.1	64.8	65.7	334.4

The procedure in such an example where more than one observation is missing is first to substitute approximate values for all the missing values except the one to be estimated. We then apply the missing-plot formula as given above. The same process is in turn applied to all the missing plots. The results given are first approximations, and the whole process is repeated until the estimated values become practically constant.

The methods are illustrated below for the estimation of the missing values in Table 93.

First Approximation

Average yield $= 334.4/11 = 15.9,$
The $T = (334.4 + 2 \times 15.9) = 366.2.$

Here the average yield of the plots is used as an approximation of the yields of two of the three missing plots.

$A.\ P = 45.6$ $\qquad\qquad$ $Q = 81.5$

$\qquad x = (6 \times 45.6 + 4 \times 81.5 - 366.2)/15 = 15.6$

$B.\ P = 50.9$ $\qquad\qquad$ $Q = (54.0 + 15.9) = 59.9$

$\qquad x = (6 \times 50.9 + 4 \times 69.9 - 366.2)/15 = 14.6$

Note that here we have to substitute a value for D and that the mean of all the plots is taken as the best approximation.

$D.\ P = 50.1$ $\qquad\qquad$ $Q = (54.0 + 14.6) = 68.6$

$\qquad x = (6 \times 50.1 + 4 \times 68.6 - 366.2)/15 = 13.9$

Here we have to substitute a value for B, and the previously estimated value is taken as the best approximation.

Second Approximation

$A.\ \ T = 333.4 + 14.6 + 13.9) = 362.9;\quad P = 45.6;\quad Q = 81.5;$

$\qquad x = (6 \times 45.6 + 4 \times 81.5 - 362.9)/15 = 15.8.$

In all the approximations after the first a new value for T is worked out for the estimate of each plot, using the estimates from the previous approximation. To get P and Q it is best to substitute for the missing plot values where necessary, the latest values obtained.

3. Estimation of Missing Yields in a Latin Square. The best arrangement of the data is in a table such that the positions of the figures correspond with the positions of the plots in the field. The treatments should also be indicated on the table in the exact positions that they occur.

The formula for estimating x the yield of a missing plot is:

$$x = \frac{p(P_r + P_c + P_t) - 2T}{(p - 1)(p - 2)} \qquad (2)$$

where P_r = total of row containing the missing plot.

P_c = total of column containing the missing plot.

P_t = total of treatment containing the missing plot.

T = total of all plots.

p = number, of rows, columns, and treatments.

If more than one plot is missing, we proceed exactly as for randomized blocks, substituting approximate values for the plots not being estimated and making continuous applications of formula (2).

4. Correction to Analysis of Variance Due to Estimation of Missing Values. The estimation of missing values for a set of results introduces a complication in the analysis of variance. In the first place, one *DF* must be removed from the total for each missing value; and in the second place a correction must be applied to the sums of squares for treatments or any other component in the analysis, the significance of which is to be tested against the error. An exact mathematical solution of this problem for all cases has been provided by Yates (3), but except for randomized block experiments, and for Latin square experiments with only one missing plot, it is rather complicated for general practice.

In a randomized block experiment as in Table 93, for which three of the missing plot yields were estimated, the following scheme for the analysis of variance shows how the correction is applied to the treatment variance. In this scheme the "original" values refers to those for the 21 plots as given in Table 93, and the "completed" values refers to those in Table 93 with the addition of the three that were estimated.

	DF	Sum of Squares Calculated from
Total..........................	20	Original yields
Error..........................	12	Completed yields
Difference = Blocks + Treatments...	8	
Blocks...............	5	Original yields
Difference = Treatments...........	3	

The procedure for calculation is as follows:

(a) Obtain the sums of squares for blocks, treatments, and error from the completed yields.

(b) Obtain total sum of squares for original yields.

(c) Obtain sum of squares for blocks from original yields, noting that not all the blocks contain 6 plots.

(d) Set up the analysis of variance as above, obtaining the sums of squares first for blocks + treatments and then for treatments by subtraction from the known quantities.

For Latin square experiments with only one plot missing the simplest method of determining the correction to the treatment sum of squares is to use the formula

$$\frac{1}{(p-1)^2(p-2)^2} [(p-1)P_t - P_r - P_c - T]^2$$

which gives the correction directly. The scheme of analysis using a 6 × 6 Latin square would then be as follows:

	DF	Sum of Squares Calculated from
Total	34	Original values
Error.	19	Completed values
Difference = Rows − Columns −		
Treatments.	15	
Treatments − Correction	5	Calculate from complete values and subtract correction

5. Correction of Treatment Means and Standard Errors. The treatment means that contain estimated values for missing plots are in effect corrected means and further corrections are not required. The standard errors of such means, however, require a definite correction, and for methods of doing this accurately the reader should refer to the paper by Yates (3). For general purposes it is probably sufficient to make a correction for the number of plots averaged, i.e., if there are r replications and one plot is missing the standard error of the mean of the treatment containing the missing plot will be

$$s_m = \sqrt{\frac{s^2}{r-1}}$$

II. METHODS OF RANDOMIZATION

Randomization can be effected by tossing coins, drawing cards out of a shuffled deck, throwing dice, etc., but these methods are too slow and in general too inaccurate for actual practice. The problem has been greatly simplified by the preparation of Tippett's "Random Sampling Numbers" (2), and these numbers are now in general use.*

If we have a series of numbers 1, 2, 3, $\cdots$ n, the problem of randomization is to arrange these numbers in such a way that in forming the arrangement any one of the numbers has an equal chance with any other number of being placed in a given position. A procedure that is frequently followed in arranging field plot tests may now be described briefly.

Suppose that the numbers representing the varieties are 1, 2, 3, 4, 5, 6, 7, 8, 9. Turning to page XI of Tippett's "Tables" (the usual practice being to open the book more or less at random), we find that beginning at the upper left-hand corner we can take a series of random two-figure numbers as follows, 40, 81, 89, 58, 87, 74, etc. Assume now that there are 9 places to be filled up by the numbers 1 to 9, and the first one is selected by dividing the first two-figure number by 9 and taking the remainder. Thus for 40/9, the remainder is 4, and number 9 is placed in the fourth place. The second number to be placed is 8 and we divide the second two-figure number by 8; 81/8 gives a remainder of 1, and 8 is placed in the first place. The third number is 7, and dividing it into 89 the remainder is 5, and 7 is placed in the fifth space counting only those that are empty. This procedure is followed until all the numbers have been placed and we get finally the following arrangement:

$$8, \quad 3, \quad 5, \quad 9, \quad 4, \quad 6, \quad 7, \quad 2, \quad 1$$

The same procedure can be modified for application to a Latin square, but in that case it is only necessary, starting with a given Latin square which may be made up systematically, to randomize the rows, columns, and treatments.

REFERENCES

1. F. E. ALLAN and J. WISHART. A Method of Estimating the Yield of a Missing Plot in Field Experimental Work. *Jour. Agr. Sci.* **20**: 399–406, 1930.
2. L. H. C. TIPPETT. Random Sampling Numbers. Cambridge University Press, 1927.
3. F. YATES. The Analysis of Replicated Experiments When the Field Results are Incomplete. *Emp. Jour. Exp. Agr.* **1**: 129–142, 1933.

* More recently, Fisher and Yates in " Statistical Tables for Biological, Agricultural and Medical Research " (Oliver and Boyd, London, 1938) have included an excellent set of random numbers which have been thoroughly tested for randomization work.

TABLES

TABLE 94

TABLE OF t^*

Degrees of Freedom	Probability				
	0.50	0.10	0.05	0.02	0.01
1	1.000	6.34	12.71	31.82	63.66
2	0.816	2.92	4.30	6.96	9.92
3	.765	2.35	3.18	4.54	5.84
4	.741	2.13	2.78	3.75	4.60
5	.727	2.02	2.57	3.36	4.03
6	.718	1.94	2.45	3.14	3.71
7	.711	1.90	2.36	3.00	3.50
8	.706	1.86	2.31	2.90	3.36
9	.703	1.83	2.26	2.82	3.25
10	.700	1.81	2.23	2.76	3.17
11	.697	1.80	2.20	2.72	3.11
12	.695	1.78	2.18	2.68	3.06
13	.694	1.77	2.16	2.65	3.01
14	.692	1.76	2.14	2.62	2.98
15	.691	1.75	2.13	2.60	2.95
16	.690	1.75	2.12	2.58	2.92
17	.689	1.74	2.11	2.57	2.90
18	.688	1.73	2.10	2.55	2.88
19	.688	1.73	2.09	2.54	2.86
20	.687	1.72	2.09	2.53	2.84
21	.686	1.72	2.08	2.52	2.83
22	.686	1.72	2.07	2.51	2.82
23	.685	1.71	2.07	2.50	2.81
24	.685	1.71	2.06	2.49	2.80
25	.684	1.71	2.06	2.48	2.79
26	.684	1.71	2.06	2.48	2.78
27	.684	1.70	2.05	2.47	2.77
28	.683	1.70	2.05	2.47	2.76
29	.683	1.70	2.04	2.46	2.76
30	.683	1.70	2.04	2.46	2.75
35	.682	1.69	2.03	2.44	2.72
40	.681	1.68	2.02	2.42	2.71
45	.680	1.68	2.02	2.41	2.69
50	.679	1.68	2.01	2.40	2.68
60	.678	1.67	2.00	2.39	2.66
70	.678	1.67	2.00	2.38	2.65
80	.677	1.66	1.99	2.38	2.64
90	.677	1.66	1.99	2.37	2.63
100	.677	1.66	1.98	2.36	2.63
125	.676	1.66	1.98	2.36	2.62
150	.676	1.66	1.98	2.35	2.61
200	.675	1.65	1.97	2.35	2.60
300	.675	1.65	1.97	2.34	2.59
400	.675	1.65	1.97	2.34	2.59
500	.674	1.65	1.96	2.33	2.59
1000	.674	1.65	1.96	2.33	2.58
∞	.674	1.64	1.96	2.33	2.58

* The greater portion of this table taken from R. A. Fisher's "Statistical Methods for Research Workers," with the permission of the author and his publishers, Oliver and Boyd, London.

267

TABLE 95

TABLE OF χ^2*

Degrees of Freedom	Probability							
	0.99	0.95	0.50	0.30	0.20	0.10	0.05	0.01
1	0.0002	0.004	0.46	1.07	1.64	2.71	3.84	6.64
2	0.020	0.103	1.39	2.41	3.22	4.60	5.99	9.21
3	0.115	0.35	2.37	3.66	4.64	6.25	7.82	11.34
4	0.30	0.71	3.36	4.88	5.99	7.78	9.49	13.28
5	0.55	1.14	4.35	6.06	7.29	9.24	11.07	15.09
6	0.87	1.64	5.35	7.23	8.56	10.64	12.59	16.81
7	1.24	2.17	6.35	8.38	9.80	12.02	14.07	18.48
8	1.65	2.73	7.34	9.52	11.03	13.36	15.51	20.09
9	2.09	3.32	8.34	10.66	12.24	14.68	16.92	21.67
10	2.56	3.94	9.34	11.78	13.44	15.99	18.31	23.21
11	3.05	4.58	10.34	12.90	14.63	17.28	19.68	24.72
12	3.57	5.23	11.34	14.01	15.81	18.55	21.03	26.22
13	4.11	5.89	12.34	15.12	16.98	19.81	22.36	27.69
14	4.66	6.57	13.34	16.22	18.15	21.06	23.68	29.14
15	5.23	7.26	14.34	17.32	19.31	22.31	25.00	30.58
16	5.81	7.96	15.34	18.42	20.46	23.54	26.30	32.00
17	6.41	8.67	16.34	19.51	21.62	24.77	27.59	33.41
18	7.02	9.39	17.34	20.60	22.76	25.99	28.87	34.80
19	7.63	10.12	18.34	21.69	23.90	27.20	30.14	36.19
20	8.26	10.85	19.34	22.78	25.04	28.41	31.41	37.57
21	8.90	11.59	20.34	23.86	26.17	29.62	32.67	38.93
22	9.54	12.34	21.34	24.94	27.30	30.81	33.92	40.29
23	10.20	13.09	22.34	26.02	28.43	32.01	35.17	41.64
24	10.86	13.85	23.34	27.10	29.55	33.20	36.42	42.98
25	11.52	14.61	24.34	28.17	30.68	34.38	37.65	44.31
26	12.20	15.38	25.34	29.25	31.80	35.56	38.88	45.64
27	12.88	16.15	26.34	30.32	32.91	36.74	40.11	46.96
28	13.56	16.93	27.34	31.39	34.03	37.92	41.34	48.28
29	14.26	17.71	28.34	32.46	35.14	39.09	42.56	49.59
30	14.95	18.49	29.34	33.53	36.25	40.26	43.77	50.89

* Taken from R. A. Fisher's "Statistical Methods for Research Workers," with the permission of the author and the publishers, Oliver and Boyd, London.

TABLE 96

5% (Roman Type) and 1% (Bold-Face Type) Points for the Distribution of F *

n_1 Degrees of Freedom for Greater Mean Square

Each cell shows the 5% point (roman) over the 1% point (bold-face).

n_2	1	2	3	4	5	6	7	8	9	10	11	12	14	16	20	24	30	40	50	75	100	200	500	∞
1	161 **4052**	200 **4999**	216 **5403**	225 **5625**	230 **5764**	234 **5859**	237 **5928**	239 **5981**	241 **6022**	242 **6056**	243 **6082**	244 **6106**	245 **6142**	246 **6169**	248 **6208**	249 **6234**	250 **6258**	251 **6286**	252 **6302**	253 **6323**	253 **6334**	254 **6352**	254 **6361**	254 **6366**
2	18.51 **98.49**	19.00 **99.01**	19.16 **99.17**	19.25 **99.25**	19.30 **99.30**	19.33 **99.33**	19.36 **99.34**	19.37 **99.36**	19.38 **99.38**	19.39 **99.40**	19.40 **99.41**	19.41 **99.42**	19.42 **99.43**	19.43 **99.44**	19.44 **99.45**	19.45 **99.46**	19.46 **99.47**	19.47 **99.48**	19.47 **99.48**	19.48 **99.49**	19.49 **99.49**	19.49 **99.49**	19.50 **99.50**	19.50 **99.50**
3	10.13 **34.12**	9.55 **30.81**	9.28 **29.46**	9.12 **28.71**	9.01 **28.24**	8.94 **27.91**	8.88 **27.67**	8.84 **27.49**	8.81 **27.34**	8.78 **27.23**	8.76 **27.13**	8.74 **27.05**	8.71 **26.92**	8.69 **26.83**	8.66 **26.69**	8.64 **26.60**	8.62 **26.50**	8.60 **26.41**	8.58 **26.35**	8.57 **26.27**	8.56 **26.23**	8.54 **26.18**	8.54 **26.14**	8.53 **26.12**
4	7.71 **21.20**	6.94 **18.00**	6.59 **16.69**	6.39 **15.98**	6.26 **15.52**	6.16 **15.21**	6.09 **14.98**	6.04 **14.80**	6.00 **14.66**	5.96 **14.54**	5.93 **14.45**	5.91 **14.37**	5.87 **14.24**	5.84 **14.15**	5.80 **14.02**	5.77 **13.93**	5.74 **13.83**	5.71 **13.74**	5.70 **13.69**	5.68 **13.61**	5.66 **13.57**	5.65 **13.52**	5.64 **13.48**	5.63 **13.46**
5	6.61 **16.26**	5.79 **13.27**	5.41 **12.06**	5.19 **11.39**	5.05 **10.97**	4.95 **10.67**	4.88 **10.45**	4.82 **10.27**	4.78 **10.15**	4.74 **10.05**	4.70 **9.96**	4.68 **9.89**	4.64 **9.77**	4.60 **9.68**	4.56 **9.55**	4.53 **9.47**	4.50 **9.38**	4.46 **9.29**	4.44 **9.24**	4.42 **9.17**	4.40 **9.13**	4.38 **9.07**	4.37 **9.04**	4.36 **9.02**
6	5.99 **13.74**	5.14 **10.92**	4.76 **9.78**	4.53 **9.15**	4.39 **8.75**	4.28 **8.47**	4.21 **8.26**	4.15 **8.10**	4.10 **7.98**	4.06 **7.87**	4.03 **7.79**	4.00 **7.72**	3.96 **7.60**	3.92 **7.52**	3.87 **7.39**	3.84 **7.31**	3.81 **7.23**	3.77 **7.14**	3.75 **7.09**	3.72 **7.02**	3.71 **6.99**	3.69 **6.94**	3.68 **6.90**	3.67 **6.88**
7	5.59 **12.25**	4.74 **9.55**	4.35 **8.45**	4.12 **7.85**	3.97 **7.46**	3.87 **7.19**	3.79 **7.00**	3.73 **6.84**	3.68 **6.71**	3.63 **6.62**	3.60 **6.54**	3.57 **6.47**	3.52 **6.35**	3.49 **6.27**	3.44 **6.15**	3.41 **6.07**	3.38 **5.98**	3.34 **5.90**	3.32 **5.85**	3.29 **5.78**	3.28 **5.75**	3.25 **5.70**	3.24 **5.67**	3.23 **5.65**
8	5.32 **11.26**	4.46 **8.65**	4.07 **7.59**	3.84 **7.01**	3.69 **6.63**	3.58 **6.37**	3.50 **6.19**	3.44 **6.03**	3.39 **5.91**	3.34 **5.82**	3.31 **5.74**	3.28 **5.67**	3.23 **5.56**	3.20 **5.48**	3.15 **5.36**	3.12 **5.28**	3.08 **5.20**	3.05 **5.11**	3.03 **5.06**	3.00 **5.00**	2.98 **4.96**	2.96 **4.91**	2.94 **4.88**	2.93 **4.86**
9	5.12 **10.56**	4.26 **8.02**	3.86 **6.99**	3.63 **6.42**	3.48 **6.06**	3.37 **5.80**	3.29 **5.62**	3.23 **5.47**	3.18 **5.35**	3.13 **5.26**	3.10 **5.18**	3.07 **5.11**	3.02 **5.00**	2.98 **4.92**	2.93 **4.80**	2.90 **4.73**	2.86 **4.64**	2.82 **4.56**	2.80 **4.51**	2.77 **4.45**	2.76 **4.41**	2.73 **4.36**	2.72 **4.33**	2.71 **4.31**
10	4.96 **10.04**	4.10 **7.56**	3.71 **6.55**	3.48 **5.99**	3.33 **5.64**	3.22 **5.39**	3.14 **5.21**	3.07 **5.06**	3.02 **4.95**	2.97 **4.85**	2.94 **4.78**	2.91 **4.71**	2.86 **4.60**	2.82 **4.52**	2.77 **4.41**	2.74 **4.33**	2.70 **4.25**	2.67 **4.17**	2.64 **4.12**	2.61 **4.05**	2.59 **4.01**	2.56 **3.96**	2.55 **3.93**	2.54 **3.91**
11	4.84 **9.65**	3.98 **7.20**	3.59 **6.22**	3.36 **5.67**	3.20 **5.32**	3.09 **5.07**	3.01 **4.88**	2.95 **4.74**	2.90 **4.63**	2.86 **4.54**	2.82 **4.46**	2.79 **4.40**	2.74 **4.29**	2.70 **4.21**	2.65 **4.10**	2.61 **4.02**	2.57 **3.94**	2.53 **3.86**	2.50 **3.80**	2.47 **3.74**	2.45 **3.70**	2.42 **3.66**	2.41 **3.62**	2.40 **3.60**
12	4.75 **9.33**	3.88 **6.93**	3.49 **5.95**	3.26 **5.41**	3.11 **5.06**	3.00 **4.82**	2.92 **4.65**	2.85 **4.50**	2.80 **4.39**	2.76 **4.30**	2.72 **4.22**	2.69 **4.16**	2.64 **4.05**	2.60 **3.98**	2.54 **3.86**	2.50 **3.78**	2.46 **3.70**	2.42 **3.61**	2.40 **3.56**	2.36 **3.49**	2.35 **3.46**	2.32 **3.41**	2.31 **3.38**	2.30 **3.36**
13	4.67 **9.07**	3.80 **6.70**	3.41 **5.74**	3.18 **5.20**	3.02 **4.86**	2.92 **4.62**	2.84 **4.44**	2.77 **4.30**	2.72 **4.19**	2.67 **4.10**	2.63 **4.02**	2.60 **3.96**	2.55 **3.85**	2.51 **3.78**	2.46 **3.67**	2.42 **3.59**	2.38 **3.51**	2.34 **3.42**	2.32 **3.37**	2.28 **3.30**	2.26 **3.27**	2.24 **3.21**	2.22 **3.18**	2.21 **3.16**

* This table taken from G. W. Snedecor's "Statistical Methods." Reproduced by permission of the author and his publishers. Calculated by G. W. Snedecor from Table VI of R. A. Fisher's "Statistical Methods for Research Workers."

TABLE 96—(Continued)

5% (Roman Type) and 1% (Bold-Face Type) for Distribution of F

n_1 Degrees of Freedom for Greater Mean Square

n_2	1	2	3	4	5	6	7	8	9	10	11	12	14	16	20	24	30	40	50	75	100	200	500	∞
14	4.60 **8.86**	3.74 **6.51**	3.34 **5.56**	3.11 **5.03**	2.96 **4.69**	2.85 **4.46**	2.77 **4.28**	2.70 **4.14**	2.65 **4.03**	2.60 **3.94**	2.56 **3.86**	2.53 **3.80**	2.48 **3.70**	2.44 **3.62**	2.39 **3.51**	2.35 **3.43**	2.31 **3.34**	2.27 **3.26**	2.24 **3.21**	2.21 **3.14**	2.19 **3.11**	2.16 **3.06**	2.14 **3.02**	2.13 **3.00**
15	4.54 **8.68**	3.68 **6.36**	3.29 **5.42**	3.06 **4.89**	2.90 **4.56**	2.79 **4.32**	2.70 **4.14**	2.64 **4.00**	2.59 **3.89**	2.55 **3.80**	2.51 **3.73**	2.48 **3.67**	2.43 **3.56**	2.39 **3.48**	2.33 **3.36**	2.29 **3.29**	2.25 **3.20**	2.21 **3.12**	2.18 **3.07**	2.15 **3.00**	2.12 **2.97**	2.10 **2.92**	2.08 **2.89**	2.07 **2.87**
16	4.49 **8.53**	3.63 **6.23**	3.24 **5.29**	3.01 **4.77**	2.85 **4.44**	2.74 **4.20**	2.66 **4.03**	2.59 **3.89**	2.54 **3.78**	2.49 **3.69**	2.45 **3.61**	2.42 **3.55**	2.37 **3.45**	2.33 **3.37**	2.28 **3.25**	2.24 **3.18**	2.20 **3.10**	2.16 **3.01**	2.13 **2.96**	2.09 **2.89**	2.07 **2.86**	2.04 **2.80**	2.02 **2.77**	2.01 **2.75**
17	4.45 **8.40**	3.59 **6.11**	3.20 **5.18**	2.96 **4.67**	2.81 **4.34**	2.70 **4.10**	2.62 **3.93**	2.55 **3.79**	2.50 **3.68**	2.45 **3.59**	2.41 **3.52**	2.38 **3.45**	2.33 **3.35**	2.29 **3.27**	2.23 **3.16**	2.19 **3.08**	2.15 **3.00**	2.11 **2.92**	2.08 **2.86**	2.04 **2.79**	2.02 **2.76**	1.99 **2.70**	1.97 **2.67**	1.96 **2.65**
18	4.41 **8.28**	3.55 **6.01**	3.16 **5.09**	2.93 **4.58**	2.77 **4.25**	2.66 **4.01**	2.58 **3.85**	2.51 **3.71**	2.46 **3.60**	2.41 **3.51**	2.37 **3.44**	2.34 **3.37**	2.29 **3.27**	2.25 **3.19**	2.19 **3.07**	2.15 **3.00**	2.11 **2.91**	2.07 **2.83**	2.04 **2.78**	2.00 **2.71**	1.98 **2.68**	1.95 **2.62**	1.93 **2.59**	1.92 **2.57**
19	4.38 **8.18**	3.52 **5.93**	3.13 **5.01**	2.90 **4.50**	2.74 **4.17**	2.63 **3.94**	2.55 **3.77**	2.48 **3.63**	2.43 **3.52**	2.38 **3.43**	2.34 **3.36**	2.31 **3.30**	2.26 **3.19**	2.21 **3.12**	2.15 **3.00**	2.11 **2.92**	2.07 **2.84**	2.02 **2.76**	2.00 **2.70**	1.96 **2.63**	1.94 **2.60**	1.91 **2.54**	1.90 **2.51**	1.88 **2.49**
20	4.35 **8.10**	3.49 **5.85**	3.10 **4.94**	2.87 **4.43**	2.71 **4.10**	2.60 **3.87**	2.52 **3.71**	2.45 **3.56**	2.40 **3.45**	2.35 **3.37**	2.31 **3.30**	2.28 **3.23**	2.23 **3.13**	2.18 **3.05**	2.12 **2.94**	2.08 **2.86**	2.04 **2.77**	1.99 **2.69**	1.96 **2.63**	1.92 **2.56**	1.90 **2.53**	1.87 **2.47**	1.85 **2.44**	1.84 **2.42**
21	4.32 **8.02**	3.47 **5.78**	3.07 **4.87**	2.84 **4.37**	2.68 **4.04**	2.57 **3.81**	2.49 **3.65**	2.42 **3.51**	2.37 **3.40**	2.32 **3.31**	2.28 **3.24**	2.25 **3.17**	2.20 **3.07**	2.15 **2.99**	2.09 **2.88**	2.05 **2.80**	2.00 **2.72**	1.96 **2.63**	1.93 **2.58**	1.89 **2.51**	1.87 **2.47**	1.84 **2.42**	1.82 **2.38**	1.81 **2.36**
22	4.30 **7.94**	3.44 **5.72**	3.05 **4.82**	2.82 **4.31**	2.66 **3.99**	2.55 **3.76**	2.47 **3.59**	2.40 **3.45**	2.35 **3.35**	2.30 **3.26**	2.26 **3.18**	2.23 **3.12**	2.18 **3.02**	2.13 **2.94**	2.07 **2.83**	2.03 **2.75**	1.98 **2.67**	1.93 **2.58**	1.91 **2.53**	1.87 **2.46**	1.84 **2.42**	1.81 **2.37**	1.80 **2.33**	1.78 **2.31**
23	4.28 **7.88**	3.42 **5.66**	3.03 **4.76**	2.80 **4.26**	2.64 **3.94**	2.53 **3.71**	2.45 **3.54**	2.38 **3.41**	2.32 **3.30**	2.28 **3.21**	2.24 **3.14**	2.20 **3.07**	2.14 **2.97**	2.10 **2.89**	2.04 **2.78**	2.00 **2.70**	1.96 **2.62**	1.91 **2.53**	1.88 **2.48**	1.84 **2.41**	1.82 **2.37**	1.79 **2.32**	1.77 **2.28**	1.76 **2.26**
24	4.26 **7.82**	3.40 **5.61**	3.01 **4.72**	2.78 **4.22**	2.62 **3.90**	2.51 **3.67**	2.43 **3.50**	2.36 **3.36**	2.30 **3.25**	2.26 **3.17**	2.22 **3.09**	2.18 **3.03**	2.13 **2.93**	2.09 **2.85**	2.02 **2.74**	1.98 **2.66**	1.94 **2.58**	1.89 **2.49**	1.86 **2.44**	1.82 **2.36**	1.80 **2.33**	1.76 **2.27**	1.74 **2.23**	1.73 **2.21**
25	4.24 **7.77**	3.38 **5.57**	2.99 **4.68**	2.76 **4.18**	2.60 **3.86**	2.49 **3.63**	2.41 **3.46**	2.34 **3.32**	2.28 **3.21**	2.24 **3.13**	2.20 **3.05**	2.16 **2.99**	2.11 **2.89**	2.06 **2.81**	2.00 **2.70**	1.96 **2.62**	1.92 **2.54**	1.87 **2.45**	1.84 **2.40**	1.80 **2.32**	1.77 **2.29**	1.74 **2.23**	1.72 **2.19**	1.71 **2.17**
26	4.22 **7.72**	3.37 **5.53**	2.98 **4.64**	2.74 **4.14**	2.59 **3.82**	2.47 **3.59**	2.39 **3.42**	2.32 **3.29**	2.27 **3.17**	2.22 **3.09**	2.18 **3.02**	2.15 **2.96**	2.10 **2.86**	2.05 **2.77**	1.99 **2.66**	1.95 **2.58**	1.90 **2.50**	1.85 **2.41**	1.82 **2.36**	1.78 **2.28**	1.76 **2.25**	1.72 **2.19**	1.70 **2.15**	1.69 **2.13**

TABLE 96—(Continued)

5% (ROMAN TYPE) AND 1% (BOLD-FACE TYPE) FOR DISTRIBUTION OF F

n_1 Degrees of Freedom for Greater Mean Square

n_2	1	2	3	4	5	6	7	8	9	10	11	12	14	16	20	24	30	40	50	75	100	200	500	∞
27	4.21 / **7.68**	3.35 / **5.49**	2.96 / **4.60**	2.73 / **4.11**	2.57 / **3.79**	2.46 / **3.56**	2.37 / **3.39**	2.30 / **3.26**	2.25 / **3.14**	2.20 / **3.06**	2.16 / **2.98**	2.13 / **2.93**	2.08 / **2.83**	2.03 / **2.74**	1.97 / **2.63**	1.93 / **2.55**	1.88 / **2.47**	1.84 / **2.38**	1.80 / **2.33**	1.76 / **2.25**	1.74 / **2.21**	1.71 / **2.16**	1.68 / **2.12**	1.67 / **2.10**
28	4.20 / **7.64**	3.34 / **5.45**	2.95 / **4.57**	2.71 / **4.07**	2.56 / **3.76**	2.44 / **3.53**	2.36 / **3.36**	2.29 / **3.23**	2.24 / **3.11**	2.19 / **3.03**	2.15 / **2.95**	2.12 / **2.90**	2.06 / **2.80**	2.02 / **2.71**	1.96 / **2.60**	1.91 / **2.52**	1.87 / **2.44**	1.81 / **2.35**	1.78 / **2.30**	1.75 / **2.22**	1.72 / **2.18**	1.69 / **2.13**	1.67 / **2.09**	1.65 / **2.06**
29	4.18 / **7.60**	3.33 / **5.42**	2.93 / **4.54**	2.70 / **4.04**	2.54 / **3.73**	2.43 / **3.50**	2.35 / **3.33**	2.28 / **3.20**	2.22 / **3.08**	2.18 / **3.00**	2.14 / **2.92**	2.10 / **2.87**	2.05 / **2.77**	2.00 / **2.68**	1.94 / **2.57**	1.90 / **2.49**	1.85 / **2.41**	1.80 / **2.32**	1.77 / **2.27**	1.73 / **2.19**	1.71 / **2.15**	1.68 / **2.10**	1.65 / **2.06**	1.64 / **2.03**
30	4.17 / **7.56**	3.32 / **5.39**	2.92 / **4.51**	2.69 / **4.02**	2.53 / **3.70**	2.42 / **3.47**	2.34 / **3.30**	2.27 / **3.17**	2.21 / **3.06**	2.16 / **2.98**	2.12 / **2.90**	2.09 / **2.84**	2.04 / **2.74**	1.99 / **2.66**	1.93 / **2.55**	1.89 / **2.47**	1.84 / **2.38**	1.79 / **2.29**	1.76 / **2.24**	1.72 / **2.16**	1.69 / **2.13**	1.66 / **2.07**	1.64 / **2.03**	1.62 / **2.01**
32	4.15 / **7.50**	3.30 / **5.34**	2.90 / **4.46**	2.67 / **3.97**	2.51 / **3.66**	2.40 / **3.42**	2.32 / **3.25**	2.25 / **3.12**	2.19 / **3.01**	2.14 / **2.94**	2.10 / **2.86**	2.07 / **2.80**	2.02 / **2.70**	1.97 / **2.62**	1.91 / **2.51**	1.86 / **2.42**	1.82 / **2.34**	1.76 / **2.25**	1.74 / **2.20**	1.69 / **2.12**	1.67 / **2.08**	1.64 / **2.02**	1.61 / **1.98**	1.59 / **1.96**
34	4.13 / **7.44**	3.28 / **5.29**	2.88 / **4.42**	2.65 / **3.93**	2.49 / **3.61**	2.38 / **3.38**	2.30 / **3.21**	2.23 / **3.08**	2.17 / **2.97**	2.12 / **2.89**	2.08 / **2.82**	2.05 / **2.76**	2.00 / **2.66**	1.95 / **2.58**	1.89 / **2.47**	1.84 / **2.38**	1.80 / **2.30**	1.74 / **2.21**	1.71 / **2.15**	1.67 / **2.08***	1.64 / **2.04**	1.61 / **1.98**	1.59 / **1.94**	1.57 / **1.91**
36	4.11 / **7.39**	3.26 / **5.25**	2.86 / **4.38**	2.63 / **3.89**	2.48 / **3.58**	2.36 / **3.35**	2.28 / **3.18**	2.21 / **3.04**	2.15 / **2.94**	2.10 / **2.86**	2.06 / **2.78**	2.03 / **2.72**	1.98 / **2.62**	1.93 / **2.54**	1.87 / **2.43**	1.82 / **2.35**	1.78 / **2.26**	1.72 / **2.17**	1.69 / **2.12**	1.65 / **2.04**	1.62 / **2.00**	1.59 / **1.94**	1.56 / **1.90**	1.55 / **1.87**
38	4.10 / **7.35**	3.25 / **5.21**	2.85 / **4.34**	2.62 / **3.86**	2.46 / **3.54**	2.35 / **3.32**	2.26 / **3.15**	2.19 / **3.02**	2.14 / **2.91**	2.09 / **2.82**	2.05 / **2.75**	2.02 / **2.69**	1.96 / **2.59**	1.92 / **2.51**	1.85 / **2.40**	1.80 / **2.32**	1.76 / **2.22**	1.71 / **2.14**	1.67 / **2.08**	1.63 / **2.00**	1.60 / **1.97**	1.57 / **1.90**	1.54 / **1.86**	1.53 / **1.84**
40	4.08 / **7.31**	3.23 / **5.18**	2.84 / **4.31**	2.61 / **3.83**	2.45 / **3.51**	2.34 / **3.29**	2.25 / **3.12**	2.18 / **2.99**	2.12 / **2.88**	2.07 / **2.80**	2.04 / **2.73**	2.00 / **2.66**	1.95 / **2.56**	1.90 / **2.49**	1.84 / **2.37**	1.79 / **2.29**	1.74 / **2.20**	1.69 / **2.11**	1.66 / **2.05**	1.61 / **1.97**	1.59 / **1.94**	1.55 / **1.88**	1.53 / **1.84**	1.51 / **1.81**
42	4.07 / **7.27**	3.22 / **5.15**	2.83 / **4.29**	2.59 / **3.80**	2.44 / **3.49**	2.32 / **3.26**	2.24 / **3.10**	2.17 / **2.96**	2.11 / **2.86**	2.06 / **2.77**	2.02 / **2.70**	1.99 / **2.64**	1.94 / **2.54**	1.89 / **2.46**	1.82 / **2.35**	1.78 / **2.26**	1.73 / **2.17**	1.68 / **2.08**	1.64 / **2.02**	1.60 / **1.94**	1.57 / **1.91**	1.54 / **1.85**	1.51 / **1.80**	1.49 / **1.78**
44	4.06 / **7.24**	3.21 / **5.12**	2.82 / **4.26**	2.58 / **3.78**	2.43 / **3.46**	2.31 / **3.24**	2.23 / **3.07**	2.16 / **2.94**	2.10 / **2.84**	2.05 / **2.75**	2.01 / **2.68**	1.98 / **2.62**	1.92 / **2.52**	1.88 / **2.44**	1.81 / **2.32**	1.76 / **2.24**	1.72 / **2.15**	1.66 / **2.06**	1.63 / **2.00**	1.58 / **1.92**	1.56 / **1.88**	1.52 / **1.82**	1.50 / **1.78**	1.48 / **1.75**
46	4.05 / **7.21**	3.20 / **5.10**	2.81 / **4.24**	2.57 / **3.76**	2.42 / **3.44**	2.30 / **3.22**	2.22 / **3.05**	2.14 / **2.92**	2.09 / **2.82**	2.04 / **2.73**	2.00 / **2.66**	1.97 / **2.60**	1.91 / **2.50**	1.87 / **2.42**	1.80 / **2.30**	1.75 / **2.22**	1.71 / **2.13**	1.65 / **2.04**	1.62 / **1.98**	1.57 / **1.90**	1.54 / **1.86**	1.51 / **1.80**	1.48 / **1.76**	1.46 / **1.72**
48	4.04 / **7.19**	3.19 / **5.08**	2.80 / **4.22**	2.56 / **3.74**	2.41 / **3.42**	2.30 / **3.20**	2.21 / **3.04**	2.14 / **2.90**	2.08 / **2.80**	2.03 / **2.71**	1.99 / **2.64**	1.96 / **2.58**	1.90 / **2.48**	1.86 / **2.40**	1.79 / **2.28**	1.74 / **2.20**	1.70 / **2.11**	1.64 / **2.02**	1.61 / **1.96**	1.56 / **1.88**	1.53 / **1.84**	1.50 / **1.78**	1.47 / **1.73**	1.45 / **1.70**

TABLE 96—(Continued)

5% (Roman Type) and 1% (Bold-Face Type) for Distribution of F

n_1 Degrees of Freedom for Greater Mean Square

n_2	1	2	3	4	5	6	7	8	9	10	11	12	14	16	20	24	30	40	50	75	100	200	500	8
50	4.03 **7.17**	3.18 **5.06**	2.79 **4.20**	2.56 **3.72**	2.40 **3.41**	2.29 **3.18**	2.20 **3.02**	2.13 **2.88**	2.07 **2.78**	2.02 **2.70**	1.98 **2.62**	1.95 **2.56**	1.90 **2.46**	1.85 **2.39**	1.78 **2.26**	1.74 **2.18**	1.69 **2.10**	1.63 **2.00**	1.60 **1.94**	1.55 **1.86**	1.52 **1.82**	1.48 **1.76**	1.46 **1.71**	1.44 **1.68**
55	4.02 **7.12**	3.17 **5.01**	2.78 **4.16**	2.54 **3.68**	2.38 **3.37**	2.27 **3.15**	2.18 **2.98**	2.11 **2.85**	2.05 **2.75**	2.00 **2.66**	1.97 **2.59**	1.93 **2.53**	1.88 **2.43**	1.83 **2.35**	1.76 **2.23**	1.72 **2.15**	1.67 **2.06**	1.61 **1.96**	1.58 **1.90**	1.52 **1.82**	1.50 **1.78**	1.46 **1.71**	1.43 **1.66**	1.41 **1.64**
60	4.00 **7.08**	3.15 **4.98**	2.76 **4.13**	2.52 **3.65**	2.37 **3.34**	2.25 **3.12**	2.17 **2.95**	2.10 **2.82**	2.04 **2.72**	1.99 **2.63**	1.95 **2.56**	1.92 **2.50**	1.86 **2.40**	1.81 **2.32**	1.75 **2.20**	1.70 **2.12**	1.65 **2.03**	1.59 **1.93**	1.56 **1.87**	1.50 **1.79**	1.48 **1.74**	1.44 **1.68**	1.41 **1.63**	1.39 **1.60**
65	3.99 **7.04**	3.14 **4.95**	2.75 **4.10**	2.51 **3.62**	2.36 **3.31**	2.24 **3.09**	2.15 **2.93**	2.08 **2.79**	2.02 **2.70**	1.98 **2.61**	1.94 **2.54**	1.90 **2.47**	1.85 **2.37**	1.80 **2.30**	1.73 **2.18**	1.68 **2.09**	1.63 **2.00**	1.57 **1.90**	1.54 **1.84**	1.49 **1.76**	1.46 **1.71**	1.42 **1.64**	1.39 **1.60**	1.37 **1.56**
70	3.98 **7.01**	3.13 **4.92**	2.74 **4.08**	2.50 **3.60**	2.35 **3.29**	2.23 **3.07**	2.14 **2.91**	2.07 **2.77**	2.01 **2.67**	1.97 **2.59**	1.93 **2.51**	1.89 **2.45**	1.84 **2.35**	1.79 **2.28**	1.72 **2.15**	1.67 **2.07**	1.62 **1.98**	1.56 **1.88**	1.53 **1.82**	1.47 **1.74**	1.45 **1.69**	1.40 **1.62**	1.37 **1.56**	1.35 **1.53**
80	3.96 **6.96**	3.11 **4.88**	2.72 **4.04**	2.48 **3.56**	2.33 **3.25**	2.21 **3.04**	2.12 **2.87**	2.05 **2.74**	1.99 **2.64**	1.95 **2.55**	1.91 **2.48**	1.88 **2.41**	1.82 **2.32**	1.77 **2.24**	1.70 **2.11**	1.65 **2.03**	1.60 **1.94**	1.54 **1.84**	1.51 **1.78**	1.45 **1.70**	1.42 **1.65**	1.38 **1.57**	1.35 **1.52**	1.32 **1.49**
100	3.94 **6.90**	3.09 **4.82**	2.70 **3.98**	2.46 **3.51**	2.30 **3.20**	2.19 **2.99**	2.10 **2.82**	2.03 **2.69**	1.97 **2.59**	1.92 **2.51**	1.88 **2.43**	1.85 **2.36**	1.79 **2.26**	1.75 **2.19**	1.68 **2.06**	1.63 **1.98**	1.57 **1.89**	1.51 **1.79**	1.48 **1.73**	1.42 **1.64**	1.39 **1.59**	1.34 **1.51**	1.30 **1.46**	1.28 **1.43**
125	3.92 **6.84**	3.07 **4.78**	2.68 **3.94**	2.44 **3.47**	2.29 **3.17**	2.17 **2.95**	2.08 **2.79**	2.01 **2.65**	1.95 **2.56**	1.90 **2.47**	1.86 **2.40**	1.83 **2.33**	1.77 **2.23**	1.72 **2.15**	1.65 **2.03**	1.60 **1.94**	1.55 **1.85**	1.49 **1.75**	1.45 **1.68**	1.39 **1.59**	1.36 **1.54**	1.31 **1.46**	1.27 **1.40**	1.25 **1.37**
150	3.91 **6.81**	3.06 **4.75**	2.67 **3.91**	2.43 **3.44**	2.27 **3.14**	2.16 **2.92**	2.07 **2.76**	2.00 **2.62**	1.94 **2.53**	1.89 **2.44**	1.85 **2.37**	1.82 **2.30**	1.76 **2.20**	1.71 **2.12**	1.64 **2.00**	1.59 **1.91**	1.54 **1.83**	1.47 **1.72**	1.44 **1.66**	1.37 **1.56**	1.34 **1.51**	1.29 **1.43**	1.25 **1.37**	1.22 **1.33**
200	3.89 **6.76**	3.04 **4.71**	2.65 **3.88**	2.41 **3.41**	2.26 **3.11**	2.14 **2.90**	2.05 **2.73**	1.98 **2.60**	1.92 **2.50**	1.87 **2.41**	1.83 **2.34**	1.80 **2.28**	1.74 **2.17**	1.69 **2.09**	1.62 **1.97**	1.57 **1.88**	1.52 **1.79**	1.45 **1.69**	1.42 **1.62**	1.35 **1.53**	1.32 **1.48**	1.26 **1.39**	1.22 **1.33**	1.19 **1.28**
400	3.86 **6.70**	3.02 **4.66**	2.62 **3.83**	2.39 **3.36**	2.23 **3.06**	2.12 **2.85**	2.03 **2.69**	1.96 **2.55**	1.90 **2.46**	1.85 **2.37**	1.81 **2.29**	1.78 **2.23**	1.72 **2.12**	1.67 **2.04**	1.60 **1.92**	1.54 **1.84**	1.49 **1.74**	1.42 **1.64**	1.38 **1.57**	1.32 **1.47**	1.28 **1.42**	1.22 **1.32**	1.16 **1.24**	1.13 **1.19**
1000	3.85 **6.66**	3.00 **4.62**	2.61 **3.80**	2.38 **3.34**	2.22 **3.04**	2.10 **2.82**	2.02 **2.66**	1.95 **2.53**	1.89 **2.43**	1.84 **2.34**	1.80 **2.26**	1.76 **2.20**	1.70 **2.09**	1.65 **2.01**	1.58 **1.89**	1.53 **1.81**	1.47 **1.71**	1.41 **1.61**	1.36 **1.54**	1.30 **1.44**	1.26 **1.38**	1.19 **1.28**	1.13 **1.19**	1.08 **1.11**
∞	3.84 **6.64**	2.99 **4.60**	2.60 **3.78**	2.37 **3.32**	2.21 **3.02**	2.09 **2.80**	2.01 **2.64**	1.94 **2.51**	1.88 **2.41**	1.83 **2.32**	1.79 **2.24**	1.75 **2.18**	1.69 **2.07**	1.64 **1.99**	1.57 **1.87**	1.52 **1.79**	1.46 **1.69**	1.40 **1.59**	1.35 **1.52**	1.28 **1.41**	1.24 **1.36**	1.17 **1.25**	1.11 **1.15**	1.00 **1.00**

INDEX